Nuclear Auditing Handbook

A Guide for Quality Systems Practitioners

Editors
Charles Moseley
Karen Douglas
Norman Moreau

ASQ Quality Press
Milwaukee, Wisconsin

Nuclear Auditing Handbook: A Guide for Quality Systems Practitioners
1986, 2009, 2021
Copyright © by ASQ Energy and Environment Division
All rights reserved. Published 2021

Printed in the United States of America
23 22 21 20 24 23 22 21   5 4 3 2 1

Publisher's Cataloging-in-Publication Data

Names: Moseley, Charles H., 1943-, editor. | Douglas, Karen M., 1952-, editor. |
Moreau, Norman P., 1952-, editor.
Title: Nuclear auditing handbook : a guide for quality systems professionals /
Editors: Charles Moseley; Karen Douglas; Norman Moreau.
Description: Includes bibliography. | Milwaukee, WI: ASQ Quality Press, 2021
Identifiers: LCCN: 2021942948 | ISBN: 978-1-63694-007-6 (paperback) |
978-1-63694-008-3 (ebook)
Subjects: LCSH Nuclear power plants—Quality control. | Nuclear industry—
United States—Quality control. | Quality assurance. | Electric power-plants—Quality
control | BISAC BUSINESS & ECONOMICS / Auditing | BUSINESS & ECONOMICS /
Industries / Energy | TECHNOLOGY & ENGINEERING / Power Resources /
Nuclear
Classification: LCC TK9023 .N78 2021 | DDC 621.48/35—dc23

ASQ advances individual, organizational, and community excellence worldwide
through learning, quality improvement, and knowledge exchange.

Attention bookstores, wholesalers, schools, and corporations: Quality Press
books are available at quality discounts with bulk purchases for business, trade, or
educational uses. For information, please contact Quality Press at 800-248-1946 or
books@asq.org.

To place orders or browse the selection of Quality Press titles, visit our website at
http://www.asq.org/quality-press.

Quality Press
600 N. Plankinton Ave.
Milwaukee, WI 53203-2914
E-mail: authors@asq.org
ASQ **The Global Voice of Quality**™

Table of Contents

SECTION 4—DEVELOPMENT AND ADMINISTRATION OF AN AUDIT PROGRAM

SECTION 5—MECHANICS OF AN INDIVIDUAL AUDIT

APPENDICES

Preface

This Handbook is published by the American Society for Quality (ASQ) as an auditing guide primarily for nuclear-related industries. It was developed as a tool for training, indoctrination, and qualification of personnel conducting audits on nuclear quality systems. It is directed primarily at the development of the lead auditor or audit team leader. This Handbook may also be used as a reference by quality managers who plan or are subject to quality system audits. It provides detailed material in such aspects as the development, administration, planning, preparation, performance, and reporting of quality system audits in nuclear-related fields.

The third edition of the Handbook has undergone changes to make it timelier and more useful to individuals actively involved in quality system auditing. Requirements and standards, including those in the 2019 editions III of ASME NQA-1 "Quality Assurance Program Requirements for Nuclear Facility Applications" and ASME BPVC Sections I; IV; and VIII, Divisions 1 and 2, have been added.

In Section 2, "Quality Assurance System Requirements," Figure 2.1 previously depicted document relationships and imposing authorities of various regulations and standards that govern only the design and construction of nuclear facilities. Additional figures now consider the operation of a nuclear facility, including procurement of replacement items and services and the complete nuclear life cycle through plant decontamination and decommissioning.

The numerous figures involving forms presented throughout the text have been expanded, improved, and clarified. Each form is now shown as a blank (not completed) form for convenient use by the auditor and also as a completed form for reference in training auditors. The completed forms are placed within the text while the blank forms are located in the Appendices.

Appendix A, "Reference Documents," has been expanded to include ASME NQA-1, NUREG, technical specifications (Appendix to Operating License), and additional ASME sections. Table A.1 includes standards used in international nuclear industry applications.

The Appendices have also been expanded to include new glossary sections of major terms, which are presented for easy reference by the auditor as well as those involved in training auditors.

Six case studies have been added to Appendix B, and the solutions for all 10 case studies now include a relevant nuclear standard section to improve their overall usefulness for and suitability to the training of auditors.

This document has been developed by ASQ's Nuclear Committee of the Energy and Environment Division. The committee members recognize that the preparation of this Handbook was accomplished as a group effort and many people have been involved in the writing, reviewing, and editing processes. Special appreciation must be given to the organizations that supported the participation of the committee personnel and provided the secretarial and other types of assistance needed to assemble such a publication.

Credit is given to the American National Standards Institute, Nuclear Regulatory Commission, American Society of Mechanical Engineers, ASQ, and other organizations and individuals from whose publications information was extracted and modified for the development of the text material shown in this Handbook. Selected passages and figures are quoted from James H. Rusk's "Quality Assurance System Audit," with the permission of General Atomic Company, San Diego, California. References included in this edition direct the reader to further research topics of interest. Selected passages and figures are also quoted from the course material for the ASQ short course "Quality Audit—Development and Administration" with permission.

Special credit is given to those individuals and their organizations who contributed significant effort in the tedious review of the entire text and the subsequent valuable comment of a positive and useful nature. Mr. J. Norris and Mr. J. H. Rusk of Management Analysis Company, in particular, voluntarily gave of their expertise, which was extremely helpful and greatly appreciated by each of the committee members.

The members of the committee who were instrumental in developing the contents of the 2021 Handbook are as follows:

Authors

Charles Moseley
Norman Moreau
Thomas Ehrhorn
Stephen Prevette
James Hill
Abhijit Sengupta
Karen Douglas

Reviewers

Mitch Ivey
Thomas Ehrhorn
Michael Gilman
Benjamin Trujillo
Ronald Post
Stephen Prevette
Karen Douglas
Jeffrey Worthington
Abhijit Sengupta

James Hill
Charles Moseley
Norman Moreau

Editors

Carol Smith
Karen Douglas
Charles Moseley
Norman Moreau

Section 1
Introduction

HANDBOOK OBJECTIVE AND USE

1.1 Objective

This Handbook provides prospective lead auditors and auditors with sufficient formal training to assist in meeting the training and maintenance of proficiency requirements for quality system auditors in nuclear-related industries. Courses utilizing this Handbook should leave students with a knowledge and understanding of auditing methods and techniques. The material includes the development, organization, and administration of an audit program; the mechanics of an individual audit; audit objectives; and auditing techniques, as well as case studies on particular aspects of auditing. Upon completion of such a course, auditors should be examined to measure their comprehension of the material presented.

1.2 Use

This Handbook can be used outside of the classroom situation. It is essentially a reference text that includes auditing techniques and information from many sources. As a textbook, the Handbook can be used by teachers, learners, and practitioners alike either for classroom training, on-the-job training, a self-help training aid or refresher for practicing auditors. The Handbook is comprised of the following:

   a. Quality assurance (QA) systems and reference information
   b. Basic auditing theory and techniques
   c. Case studies to provide practical examples of auditing situations and methods
   d. Examination base

As indicated above, this Handbook is comprehensive, and except for actual auditing experience, provides the QA auditor with the written information required to become a qualified lead auditor. With proper guidance and satisfactory experience, persons aspiring to be fully qualified lead auditors will find in the Handbook answers to their questions on ethics, auditing methods, quality organization, reporting of results, and many other useful items needed for successful auditing.

The instructor should present the information at an undergraduate college level since the student background should be about two or more years of college or equivalent. The Table of Contents provides a course outline and is structured in a topical subject matter to facilitate classroom presentation.

The case studies can be used as work assignments for after-class study or workshop-type sessions during class time. Classroom discussions should be utilized to evaluate student comments and reactions to the case study situations and to practice the techniques presented.

Referenced standards should be made available to explain requirements and to expand upon technical points noted in the Handbook. Students utilizing the Handbook for self-help should do likewise.

This third edition of the Handbook uses the contemporary titles and names of standards, references, and organizations. Care should be taken by the student to ensure that current reference information is utilized. Although these requirements may change because of revision and reorganization of agencies and companies, the philosophy of quality system auditing is basic and generally unchanging.

TYPES OF AUDITS

This section first defines a *quality system audit* and then differentiates it from a *quality system survey*. Other types of audits are also discussed, but the emphasis is on quality system audits.

1.3   Quality System Audit

A quality system audit is a documented activity performed in accordance with written procedures or checklists to verify by examination and evaluation of objective evidence that applicable elements of the QA program have been developed, documented, and effectively implemented in accordance with specified requirements. The results of quality system audits are intended to be used by management to determine the degree to which company organizations meet commitments established by management and how effective the program is in assuring quality.

Generally, nuclear quality system audits are based upon criteria established in either Title 10 of the Code of Federal Regulations, Part 50 (10 CFR 50), Appendix B, with further details specified in American Society of Mechanical Engineers (ASME) Nuclear Quality Assurance-1 (NQA-1); ASME Boiler and Pressure Vessel Code (BPVC) Section III; or ASME BPVC Sections I, IV, and VIII require QA programs that may be the subject of quality system audits. Code revisions applicable will be those specified in the contract.

Utilities with nuclear facilities often combine the quality system audit program with the technical specification audit program. The approach and objectives of the technical specification audit program are basically the same as those for quality system audits.

1.4   Quality System Survey vs. Quality System Audit

For the purposes of this Handbook, a quality system survey is defined as an activity similar to a quality system audit but one with a different purpose. A *quality system survey* takes place with relation to a prospective procurement of a service or an item. Generally, they are conducted prior to contract award and are used to evaluate the overall capability of a prospective supplier/contractor, including the adequacy and implementation of their QA program. Those performing such a survey will point out deficiencies found in the QA program or its implementation. They should also discuss their company's policies relative to requiring correction of deficiencies prior to placing a purchase order or contract.

A *quality system audit* is a detailed evaluation of an existing QA program for its conformance to company policies, contract commitments, regulatory requirements, and performance to additional requirements specified. It includes the preparation of formal plans and checklists based on established requirements, evaluation of the implementation of detailed activities within the QA program, and formal request(s) for corrective action where necessary. The quality system audit may be performed either externally or internally. External audits are conducted by an organization on a QA program not retained under its direct control and not within its organizational structure. Such audits are used to determine whether the audited organization is meeting its obligations for QA, and whether the management controls on the product(s) or service(s) provided meet the requirements of the contract. Internal audits are audits of portions of an organization's QA program retained under its direct control and within its organizational structure. The following summarizes quality system survey vs. quality system audit considerations.

Quality System Audit vs. Quality System Survey

Considerations	Survey	Audit
When does it occur?	Prior to contract award.	During a contract or after a commitment.
Is it planned?	Yes.	Yes.
Is it scheduled?	Yes, up to several months in advance.	Yes, up to one year in advance.
Are checklists used?	Yes.	Yes.
Are qualified people required to perform it?	Yes.	Yes.
What requirements are used?	Regulatory or auditor's standard.	Contract/commitments.
On what organizations is it performed?	External.	External/internal.
Are formal reports required?	Yes.	Yes.
Are follow-up actions required?	Yes, when contract is awarded.	Yes.

1.5   Other Types of Audits

In addition to quality system audits described in this Handbook, the other types of quality audits most frequently referred to are *product audits* and *process audits*.

A *product audit* is the examination, inspection, or test of a product that has been previously accepted for the characteristics being audited. Such an audit is a reinspection and retest of the product that has already been accepted or a review of documented evidence of acceptance. It includes performing operational tests to the same requirements used by manufacturing, using the same production test procedure, methods, and equipment. The audit will measure the level of product conformance to specified standards of workmanship, performance, and quality. It is an indicator of quality going to the customer. The audit frequently includes an evaluation of packaging; examination for cosmetics; and checking for proper documentation and accessories such as proper tags, stamps, shipment preparation, and protection. The audit may involve a check of accuracy of the tests, test equipment, and test procedure.

A *process audit* is a verification by evaluation of a manufacturing or test operation against documented instructions and standards to measure conformance to these standards and the effectiveness of the instructions. Such an audit is a check of conformance of process, personnel, and equipment to defined requirements such as time, temperature, pressure, composition, amperage, component mixture, etc. It may involve special processes such as heat treating, soldering, plating, encapsulation, welding, and nondestructive examination. The audit is a check for adequacy and effectiveness of the process controls over the equipment and operators as established by procedures, work instructions, and process specifications.

AUDITOR ETHICS

To ensure that the audit is conducted in a professional manner, the lead auditor should be guided by the American Society for Quality (ASQ) Code of Ethics (see Figure 6.15) and the ethical conduct described in this Handbook when interfacing with the auditee and audit team.

Section 2
Quality Assurance Program Requirements

Quality control had its formal beginning after World War I. During World War II, rising demands for efficient and reliable weapons caused material specifications to be standardized and inspections to be increased to guarantee that items produced would consistently perform satisfactorily. QA formally began during the period of the first sustained controlled nuclear reaction, the Jet Age, and the Space Age. The need for QA was emphasized when several failures were experienced during attempts to launch satellites.

2.1 Commercial Nuclear Quality Assurance

Formal introduction of QA in commercial applications of nuclear power was met with much resistance by industry because of the anticipated costs. Consequently, the emphasis on QA practices governing commercial applications of nuclear power in the United States was on practices acceptable to industry, while also meeting the essential regulatory requirements of the US Nuclear Regulatory Commission (NRC).

QA requirements established for the design and construction of nuclear power plants were first identified by the Atomic Energy Commission when it published 10 CFR 50. It later enumerated these requirements in detail when it issued Appendix B to 10 CFR 50, which has become the genesis document for nuclear QA.

2.2 Other Energy Sources

A formalized program for QA was first introduced in the fossil power industry in 1972. In the Winter 1972 Addenda to the ASME Code, Sections I—Power Boilers, IV—Heating Boilers, and VIII—Unfired Pressure Vessels, the ASME issued appendices that required a documented quality control program for all manufacturers and assemblers. Each appendix outlined specific elements of a quality system such as document control, material control, and welding; however, it did not impose a system requirement for auditing. In addition, owners have, in many cases, imposed requirements for systems audits in their bid specifications. The US Department of Energy (DOE) imposes nuclear QA requirements for defense nuclear applications initiating with product conception and extending through dismantlement, decommissioning, to final environmental cleanup for site reuse.

Other nuclear-related industries either voluntarily or because of local jurisdictions impose codes, standards, and management controls as part of an organized approach to ensure system and facility quality. These same industries may also impose system audits to assess the effectiveness of the controls.

5

2.3   Reference Documents

QA programs are required to be documented and include methods and procedures that incorporate the guidelines stated in industry codes and standards. The following documents provide guidelines and/or requirements for preparation of QA programs; they are discussed in more detail in Appendix A.

a. NRC 10 CFR 50 Appendix B

b. DOE 10 CFR 830

c. ASME Section III, Articles NCA-3800, NCA-3900, and NCA-4000

d. American National Standards Institute (ANSI) **18.7/ ANS-3.2 Management, Administrative, and Quality Assurance Controls for the Operational Phase of Nuclear Power Plants**

e. Institute of Electrical and Electronics Engineers (IEEE) Std. 336-2020 and IEEE Std. 467-1980

f. ASME Section I, Appendix A-300

g. ASME Section IV, Appendix F

h. ASME Section VIII, Division 1, Appendix 10

i. ASME Section VIII, Division 2, Appendix 18

j. ASME NQA-1 with Addenda

k. Environmental Protection Agency

l. NEMA -National Electrical Manufacturers Association

m. NBIC -National Board Inspection Code

The relationships and imposing authorities of various regulations and standards that govern energy facilities are depicted in Figures 2.1, 2.2, and 2.3.

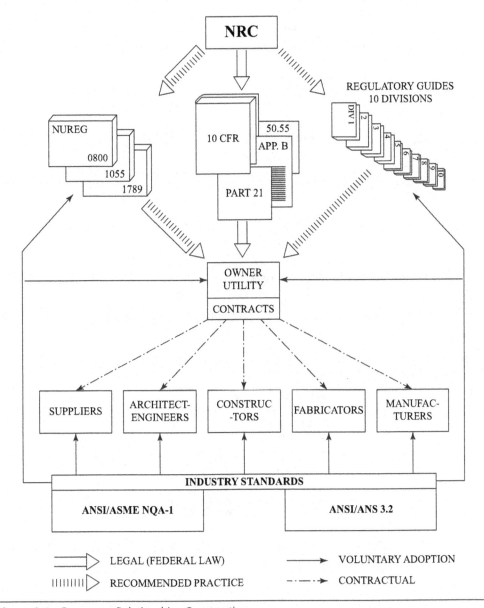

Figure 2.1 Document Relationships Construction

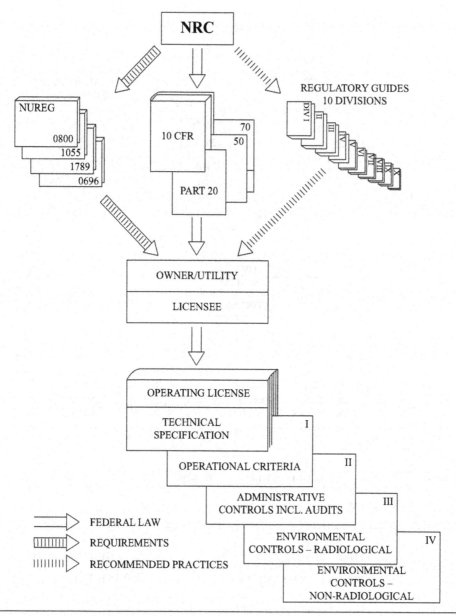

Figure 2.2 Document Relationships Operations

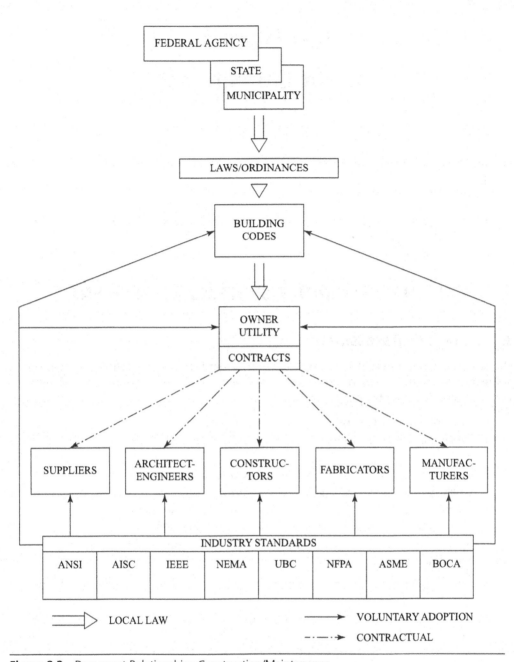

Figure 2.3 Document Relationships Construction/Maintenance

Section 3
Audit Objectives

This section discusses objectives for the assessment of QA systems by the owner/operator and participating organizations.

QUALITY ASSURANCE SYSTEMS ASSESSMENT

3.1   Owner's Assessment

The requirements for overall QA programs for nuclear facilities are delineated in appropriate industry standards and codes as well as governmental regulations. The QA provisions of these documents apply to activities of:

a. The owner, their consultants, and design agents
b. The nuclear steam supply system (NSSS) contractor, defense nuclear facility, and suppliers
c. Manufacturers and material suppliers, construction manager, and/or on-site constructor, subcontractors, and test laboratory services
d. Owner's/operator's designated organizations for pre-operational, in-service inspection, startup activities, and support of operations
e. Spent fuel storage, waste management, fuel fabrication and reprocessing, and additional nuclear cycle programs
f. The licensee of regulated activities, including maintenance, repair, operations, and modification work

Each of these organizations or functions has definitive responsibilities and vested interests in the part it plays on a particular project. Depending on the type of service supplied, their concerns are necessarily limited to the scope of contracted items and services. However, the owner of a nuclear facility has an overriding interest in the entire plant and is duly concerned with the performance of each participating organization. Activities requiring assessment include siting, designing, procuring, fabricating, constructing, handling, receiving, shipping, storage, cleaning, erecting, installing, inspecting, testing, operating, maintaining, repairing, refueling, modifying, and decommissioning.

The owner's/operator's concern stems from two major interests. First, they are required by governmental regulations to provide adequate confidence that the planning, construction, and operation of nuclear facilities are in conformance to the requirements of established standards. In order to provide evidence that work has been done correctly, emphasis has been placed on establishing certain controls with the necessary reports and records to show evidence that these control measures were exercised. These efforts are assessed by the US NRC or DOE on a continuing basis. In order for a plant to be licensed and maintain its license, there must be objective evidence of quality conformance.

The second is purely an economical interest. Am I getting the most effective results for the additional investment of assuring quality? The NRC instituted the Mitigating Systems Performance Index (MSPI) in 2006 to better measure unavailability and record both planned and unplanned unavailability. Recent unavailability and system unreliability data are included among performance indicators measured and reported—a well-documented QA program could facilitate improvement implementation. The costs associated with resolution of nonconformance during the design, construction, and maintenance are not as apparent, but could contribute considerably toward preventing failures and delays during startup of the plant and keeping the plant online.

From the owner's/operator's standpoint, it is vital that all possible measures be taken to minimize the detrimental effects of these two concerns. The imposition of an effective QA program is one measure of control to ensure that the engineering, materials, equipment, and workmanship employed in the construction and maintenance of the nuclear plant or regulated facility meet the safety, operability, and maintainability requirements. Conformance to these controls and assurance that the QA program is functioning as planned can be achieved by meaningful and effective audits.

3.2   Audit Objectives

An owner/operator, by necessity or option, may delegate to other organizations or internal activity some work scope, including pertinent QA actions, but must retain overall administrative responsibility to ensure compliance. To ensure their objectives are met, the owner/operator, either jointly with others within his organizational structure or by contractual requirements, establishes a comprehensive audit program covering all phases of plant design, procurement, construction, and operation. The technical requirements for the various systems, structures, and equipment are specified in appropriate detailed plans and specifications, while the method of assuring adherence to and proper documentation of these requirements is specified in the QA program and procedures. The auditing function is a major element of nuclear QA programs whether they be internal or those of other organizations.

On a given project, any number of interface arrangements may exist as established by the owner/operator. However, the quality system audit objectives in all cases can be summarized as follows:

a. To determine that QA implementing procedures have been developed and documented in accordance with the QA program requirements

b. To verify by examination and objective evidence that the documented program is being implemented

c. To assess the effectiveness of the QA program

d. To identify nonconformance and program deficiencies

e. To verify correction of previously identified program deficiencies

f. To recommend improvements in the QA program, as appropriate

g. To provide management with an assessment of the status and adequacy of the QA program

3.3 Interfaces

The nuclear industry presents various concerns for the auditor depending on the commitments of the audited organization. Their comparative relationships as far as commitments to codes, regulations, contracts, and company standards are shown in Figure 3.1. The area of concern of their QA programs is dependent almost entirely on these comparative relationships with each other and the NRC.

Figure 3.1 shows how typical relationships among organizations vary based on commitments for a project. These commitments provide the baseline for determining specific audit objectives and criteria. A brief description of these relationships follows:

a. **Utility/owner**—In addition to fulfilling the safety analysis report (SAR) and commitments made to various codes, regulations, and in-house procedures, the utility/owner/operator is also concerned with verifying that all their suppliers (equipment, material, services) are fulfilling their contractual requirements.

b. **NSSS supplier, nuclear facility contractor, and architect/engineer**—These groups are concerned with essentially the same problems as a utility/owner/operator; in addition, they are obligated to fulfill other miscellaneous requirements under contract with the utility/owner/operator. Their ultimate responsibility lies in the fulfillment of contractual requirements. However,

ORGANIZATION	COMMITMENTS			
	FEDERAL CODES, REGULATIONS, AND LICENSES	ASME BPVC CODE	CONTRACTUAL REQUIREMENTS (INDUSTRIAL) STANDARDS	INDIVIDUAL COMPANY QUALITY STANDARDS AND PROCEDURES
UTILITY/OWNER	X	X	—	X
NSSS PV SUPPLIER	X NOTE	X NOTE	X	X
ARCHITECT/ ENGINEER	X NOTE	X NOTE	X	X
CONSTRUCTOR	X NOTE	X NOTE	X	X
MATERIAL/ EQUIPMENT SUPPLIER	X NOTE	X NOTE	X	X
SERVICE/SUB- CONTRACTOR ORGANIZATION	X NOTE	X NOTE	X	X

NOTE: Applicable when in contract.

Figure 3.1 Commitments Applicable to Various Organizations

these companies, in the interest of uniform business practice, sometimes exceed the contractual requirements of the customer.

c. **Constructor/supplier**—The constructor is primarily concerned with meeting contractual requirements, which can include ASME codes, ANSI standards, and federal regulations and directives.

d. **Material/equipment suppliers and subcontractor organizations**—These two groups are almost totally interested in the fulfillment of contractual requirements with the utility/owner/operator or the NSSS supplier or the architect/engineer. These requirements can include federal regulations, ASME codes, and ANSI and IEEE standards.

For a specific nuclear project, by necessity or choice, any number of possible arrangements may be entered into by an owner/operator. Figure 3.2 depicts typical audit

ORGANIZATION	FEDERAL CODE REGULATIONS AND OPERATING LICENSE	CONTRACTUAL	
		ASME BPVC CODE SECTION III	QA/QC PROGRAM & PROCEDURES (NQA-1, etc.)
Utility/Owner (1)	Audited by NRC and Subject to Internal Audits	Monitor by ANI	
NSSS Supplier (2)	Audited by NRC and Subject to Internal Audits	Monitor by ANI	Audited by (1) and Subject to Internal Audits
Architect/Engineer (3)	Audited by NRC and Subject to Internal Audits	Monitor by ANI	Audited by (1) and Subject to Internal Audits
Vendor/Suppliers (4)	Selectively Audited by NRC	Monitor by ANI	Audited by (1), (2) or (3) and Subject to Internal Audits Audited by (1)
Construction (5)	As Part of Utility/ Owner Audit by NRC		
Site Constructor (6)	Inspection Audit by NRC	Monitor by ANI	Audited by (1), (2) or (3) and (5); Subject to Internal Audits
Site Installer (7)	Inspection Audit by NRC	Monitor by ANI	
Site Service Subcontractor (8)	Inspection Audit by NRC	Audited by (1), (5), (6) or (7)	
Material MFGs/ Suppliers (9)		Surveyed by ASME or ASME CERT. Holder and Subject to Their Periodic Audits	Audited by (2), (3), (4), (5), (6), (7), or (8) and Subject to Internal Audits

NOTE: An organization may elect by contract to require either internal or external audit commitments in addition to the above.

Figure 3.2 Mandatory Audit Commitments

interfaces of participating organizations and activities involved in a specific nuclear power plant project. It is not intended to indicate a must or ideal arrangement but portrays the possible extent of sub-tier involvement for a particular project.

UTILITY/OWNER

3.4 Responsibilities

The utility/owner is ultimately responsible for every aspect of a nuclear power plant because they are the applicant and licensee of the NRC. They are responsible for the design, procurement, construction, operation, and maintenance of the nuclear plant. They must develop and document a QA program that encompasses every aspect of these activities. The QA program must also provide a method whereby it can be ensured that the utility's/owner's suppliers of safety-related material, equipment, and services have established and implemented effective QA programs. The utility/owner has SAR commitments to numerous federal codes and regulations, the ASME BPVCs (where applicable), and company quality regulations and procedures. In order to ensure compliance to the SAR commitments, the utility/owner must establish and implement both internal and external audit programs. The internal audit program encompasses those portions of the utility's/owner's QA program retained under its direct control and within its organizational structure. The external audit program covers those portions of the QA program not retained under its direct control and not within its organizational structure. The objectives of both the internal and external audit programs are to:

a. Verify by examination and objective evidence that the utility's/owners' and vendors' (material/service/equipment suppliers) QA programs are being adequately implemented
b. Assess the effectiveness of owner's and vendors' QA programs
c. Identify nonconformance and program deficiencies
d. Verify correction of identified nonconformance
e. Recommend, as appropriate, improvements in the utility's/owner's and their suppliers'/vendors' QA programs

3.5 Mandatory Audit Commitments

The possible degree of delegation by the owner for mandatory audit commitments is shown in Figure 3.2. The owner's concern centers on how well these organizations have developed and implemented controls over their internal and external activities. The extent to which the owner elects to conduct audits on sub-tier organizations is at the discretion of the owner. It may be necessary for them to do so if, in their evaluation of the audit efforts of such organization, the owner concludes that their results are inadequate. The owner may consider conducting audits of a sampling of sub-tier organizations to provide assurances that audit reports are indeed factual and audit efforts are effective. The owner may also wish to evaluate particular elements of the program because of the nature or importance of the product supplied or services performed.

Uppermost in the mind of the owner's auditor when assessing controls established by other participating organizations must be such basic questions as:

1. Were the proper requirements and information conveyed to the designated organization to require them to apply the appropriate requirements for their internal operations as well as to their sub-tier suppliers?
2. Did the designated organization's procurement function require surveillance controls including review of associated records during the fabrication and installation of the product or performance of the services as appropriate?
3. Were timely periodic audits conducted to determine the effectiveness of the organization's adherence to approved QA programs and procedures? How effective was the auditing effort?
4. Was the degree of controls established adequate for the operations performed? Were meaningful corrective actions made in a timely manner for serious nonconforming conditions?
5. How effective was the designated organization's performance to the provisions of the approved QA program and procedures?
6. Did the designated organization's management exhibit the proper support and concern for administering an effective QA program as judged by the audit results?

The series of questions employed by the auditor are developed to address these concerns. For example, finding noncompliance to some provisions of a specific procedure may not be indicative of a total breakdown or the inadequacy of established controls that would jeopardize meeting the requirements. Mature judgment is needed to determine if nonconformances are of sufficient importance to require corrective measures. Specific manufacturing or process hold points may be designated when items/processes are procured as Commercial Grade Dedication (CGD) in lieu of acceptance of the supplier's QA program by quality systems audit. Additional acceptance/rejection criteria of nonconformances may also be implemented for CGD procurement applications. Sometimes a series of procedural nonconformances are such that, taken in the overall context, they point to a more serious concern for the adequacy of the established controls. The most meaningful way to handle this situation is to assemble the series of related findings to support a major nonconforming condition. However, this is not always possible or desirable.

One school of thought on the conduct of audits maintains that auditors are not authorized to pass judgment on the *applicability* of an imposed quality system; their function is to observe and analyze previously reviewed and approved systems. However, the owner's broader interests and responsibilities may dictate considering the appropriateness of imposed requirements.

Failure to see the big picture will often diminish the audit function's importance. Too often, the audited organization or activity will gladly acknowledge numerous minor nonconformances that require a minimum fix but will resist any corrective measures. Any audit is recognized as being a degree of sampling to arrive at a reasonable assurance of overall compliance. It is reasonable to expect that the audit function of sub-tier organizations will be sufficiently effective in identifying many of the nonconformances within their own activities. At the next higher tier, the emphasis should be on sampling the program controls to provide adequate assurance that the sub-tier's activities, including their auditing efforts, are effective. For example, an owner is interested in the effectiveness of the QA program of a valve manufacturer who is under contract to the NSSS supplier. Should they schedule a separate owner's audit at the valve manufacturer's facility knowing that the NSSS supplier is responsible for conducting a periodic assessment of the valve manufacturer? A sensible approach may be for the owner's auditor to accompany the NSSS auditor visiting the valve manufacturer, either as an observer or a participant. In the operations phase, audits of several work packages or activity increments may be more effective than audits of an individual function, such as tests. Commitments applicable to various organizations are shown in Figure 3.1, while audit coverage of commitments is shown in Figure 3.2.

OTHER PARTICIPATING ORGANIZATIONS

3.6 Purpose

Because of an owner's responsibilities toward their licensing and contract commitments, and because of their need for a reliable plant, they have an overriding interest in quality activities of other participating organizations. It becomes incumbent on the owner of a nuclear power plant to include applicable QA requirements in contracts for services and hardware.

Because of contractual arrangements with owners, the participating organization's audit concerns, while similar to the generic objectives, are emphasized in areas connected with the scope of contracted services. For instance, their QA programs, while developed to recognize the owner's concern, are also tailored to establish a system to control the activities connected with supplying services and hardware. The audits they conduct will necessarily assess conformance of products or service output, such as design or working documents, as well as program controls. What good is a documented program if its implementation is haphazard or inconsistent and the products or services deviate from established quality requirements?

By no stretch of the imagination can one say that a quality system audit will prevent or eliminate nonconforming equipment from being shipped. Audits are periodic assessments of an operation that provide assurance that activities are being controlled satisfactorily to preclude potential nonconformances. A quality system audit should not be used to determine product acceptance.

3.7 Prime Organizations

Organizations that have been contracted by the owner to provide major activities, such as an architect/engineer, NSSS supplier, and the responsible organization designated as constructor, are sometimes referred to as *prime* contractors, suppliers, etc. Other organizations may be contracted directly by the owner for specific consulting or supporting services and can also be considered prime participating organizations. The primary quality concern of the owner is to ensure development and implementation of effective QA programs by these prime organizations. This includes suitable controls over the prime organizations' sub-tier operations and activities.

Any audit assessment by the owner of the scope of the prime organization's QA program must include an appraisal of the effectiveness of the prime organization's QA controls over their sub-tier operations. Objective questions should cover such areas as:

1. Were the proper QA requirements relayed to the sub-tier organization?

2. Were these requirements reviewed, approved, and monitored by the prime organization?
3. How effective were the prime organization's actions over sub-tier operations?

These owner concerns in the operation of prime organizations provide guidelines to auditing program objectives of the prime organization. The primes' audit functions necessarily conduct an assessment of their established program controls, but they must also consider the adequacy of the program provisions as being responsive to the owner's contracted requirements. Too often the primes' audit actions are confined to their standard program controls without regard to supplementary requirements that may be imposed by the owner.

3.8   Sub-Tier Organizations

This group generally covers those organizations that participate in the construction or supply of individual pieces of equipment for a nuclear power plant or facility via a contract or purchase order placed by either the prime organization or the owner. In some instances, it may include material or other suppliers to a prime organization.

The classification of *sub-tier organization* is employed to define certain actions of the myriad of organizations that are involved in constructing a nuclear power plant. It helps us to understand the degree of delegated authority of the responsible owner's nuclear power plant project. The burden of assuring responsiveness of contracted services and hardware rests with the owner. However, because of the subsequent levels to which the owner contractually delegates the authority to act in their behalf, their authority becomes somewhat diffused because of the contractual requirements with the prime contractors and their subcontractors.

An example of this diffusion occurs when a material supplier is contracted by an equipment manufacturer or fabricator to supply materials that are ultimately incorporated in a piece of hardware the manufacturer has contracted to supply to a prime organization. The supplier's scope is obviously limited to what was requested by the manufacturer, and consequently their program controls are limited to what their scope of supply covers. The owner assumes that the prime organization has exerted sufficient control over the manufacturer, including the control over their material supply sources.

These control measures can be suitably investigated in the following ways: procurement controls, physical surveillance, receipt inspection, and by periodic audits. Procurement of items for safety applications (safety class or safety significant structures, systems, and components) or services impacting these safety items from suppliers/vendors with no nuclear (ASME NQA-1 or 10 CFR 830) compliant QA program requires CGD of the safety items/services. Critical safety item characteristics must be designated by the design organization with specification of allowable tolerances indicating the item will perform its intended function. Interaction with the vendor prior to product fabrication will be essential to determine hold points for measurement/inspection conformance checks during fabrication to schedule audit. Assessment of commercial grade services must determine that service performance does not degrade critical safety item characteristics or capability of performing the intended function. Commercial grade survey of the supplier requires verifying supplier processes and documentation are adequate to ensure critical characteristics compliance with the supplier's certificate of conformance.

Section 4
Development and Administration of an Audit Program

This section acquaints the quality auditor with methods for developing and administering an audit program. To present a logical sequence in the development process, the management baseline is of primary importance and should be addressed before the planning, personnel administration, and records control measures can be established and implemented.

The satisfactory and practical administration of the audit program will depend upon the extent of audit organization development and planning and the related experience of the management and lead auditors in the auditing organization. This section provides guidelines for this development and administrative process covering personnel selection, training and certification, and records maintenance.

DEVELOPMENT OF AUDIT ORGANIZATION

4.1 Company Management Policy and Authority

Management policy is generally established at several levels removed from the lead auditor position. However, it is very important that a lead auditor understand what constitutes a good, viable policy in the auditing area for it is very likely that upper management is going to rely on the input of its lead auditors. When discussing policy, it is important to recognize there are several levels of policy. The highest-level policy relevant to the audit program might consist of an effective QA program commitment in a management policy guide with no specific reference to auditing. A lower-level of policy may be documented in the company QA manual and may consist of a commitment to establish an auditing program consistent with the industry requirements and company needs. The following is an example of such a policy:

> It is Division X's policy to plan and conduct periodic audits to verify that activities affecting the quality of structures, systems, components, and services provided by Division X comply with appropriate regulatory, industry, corporate, and Division X quality assurance requirements. Audits shall also be conducted to assess the overall adequacy and effectiveness of the Division X Quality Assurance Program.

When developing such a policy, the following points should be considered.

4.1.1 Formalization

Policy should be in writing and signed by management at least one level higher than the management level responsible for implementing the policy. Thus, the policy constitutes an endorsement by the organization's management of an independent audit program—a necessary prerequisite for any successful program. The auditing policy may be influenced by many factors. In formulating the policy, management should recognize that an investment is required in terms of money, time, and personnel. The policy will indirectly reflect the degree of commitment of management in these areas. The policy will also be influenced by the requirements to be satisfied, such as the company's own quality requirements and the requirements of the industry and the customer.

4.1.2 Procedures

In order to ensure implementation of an effective audit program on a controlled and consistent basis, the QA auditing policy should require the development of written procedures that describe the mechanics of the audit program. The procedures should also be reviewed, approved, and controlled in accordance with the document control provisions of the QA program.

4.1.3 Responsibilities and Authorities

Having established an audit policy, attention must be given to administering and implementing the audit program. It is important that the responsibilities for carrying out the program at the various levels be clearly defined, and that those responsible be delegated sufficient authority to discharge their responsibilities. The written authority may be contained in company statements of purpose or policy relative to the quality of its product or services, in department charters or organizational charts, or in the QA manual itself.

Specific responsibilities for implementing the program at the grass-roots level are generally found in the implementing procedures. Procedures define who has the responsibility to carry out specific actions. It is imperative that the responsibility for audits be clearly defined.

4.1.4 Implementing Procedures

Other procedures or descriptions that enhance the success of an audit should describe scheduling and notification of the audit, audit plan, audit checklist, pre-audit conference and use of pre-audit conference agenda, conducting the audit, critiquing the findings with the audit team prior to post-audit conference, and writing the report. Examples of these blank and completed forms and procedures are included in Appendix D.

Such procedures or descriptions should include a section devoted to reviewing the response to an audit for adequacy and to following up after the audit to ascertain implementation of corrective and preventive action.

4.2   Organizational Structure

ASME NQA-1 requires that the organizational structure, functional responsibilities, levels of authority, and lines of internal and external communication for management direction of audits be documented. This is generally accomplished through development of an organizational chart and associated written description of position responsibilities.

4.2.1 Quality Assurance Function

When establishing the audit organization, it should be remembered that even though there may be many different organizational structures among NSSS suppliers, architects/engineers, utilities, consultants, and nuclear component suppliers, the audit program can generally be tailored to the existing management system. There are really no blueprints for an auditing organization. In some companies the group responsible for carrying out the auditing policy may be a separate group within the organization, while more commonly it is an added responsibility to an existing group. Regardless of the structure, the group with responsibility for the audit program generally reports within the QA function.

4.2.2 Key Principles

While the organizational structure within which the audit program exists may be influenced by the particular industry and company as well as the quality climate within the company, the following are key principles of an effective audit program regardless of organizational structure:

a. The organizational structure must provide a high level of independence for the group responsible for the audit program to ensure the effectiveness of the program throughout the organization.

b. In order to provide meaningful, credible, unbiased results, the audit group must be independent of the group it audits. Ideally, the auditing organization should have reporting lines of responsibility at the same levels as, or at a higher level than, the organization, function, or groups it audits.

c. The auditing organization must interface with and conduct audits of all functions engaged in activities affecting quality in order to be fully effective.

4.3　Auditor Independence

The individual auditor's ability to report facts as they observe them brings up the question of bias. The qualities contributing to an auditor's performance form a complex whole, and we shall examine the more important ones in this section. However, the best combination of personal attributes is worth nothing unless the auditor has the organizational independence to operate effectively.

4.3.1 Organizational Independence

We indicated earlier that the auditor must not report to a supervisor who is directly responsible for any activity the auditor must examine. We should be aware that accounting auditors have for some time recognized that fact, and that this necessary characteristic is applicable to management audits, operational audits, and system audits. The three terms are used largely interchangeably. A considerable number of the larger corporations now employ internal auditors who conduct continuous programs of system audits. Those auditors are generally assigned such responsibilities from a background of fiscal audit.

Authorities in the financial auditing field, in every publication dealing with the subject, advise that the internal system auditor be so situated in the organization that they deliver their reports and recommendations directly to the president or general manager of the company.

QA system audits differ from general system audits only in that their scope focuses on activities affecting the quality of outputs or industry regulatory requirements and thereby rely on personnel with a QA background. Their audit base consists of the hierarchy of QA requirements, rather than the overall policies directing company activities. Probably because of the limited scope, QA system audit management, for the most part, has considered it logical that the QA audit function remain within the sphere of responsibility of the individual responsible for ensuring its implementation.

Extrapolating the logic of the fiscal auditors, however, the audit function should report to the highest QA authority. Lacking that direct access, the audit function is in the unfortunate position of auditing activities for which the individual to whom it reports is directly responsible. In the long run, the independence of the audit function is evidenced in the quality and effectiveness of the audits, rather than in the lines of the organization chart.

4.3.2 Separation of Responsibilities

The principles of separation of responsibilities appear quite clear. Still, the practice can uncover areas of uncertain interpretation. For example, Department Manager X is directed to audit the document control practices as performed throughout the division to which their department belongs. Does their assignment comply with the requirement for separation independence? Or consider a situation where Lead Auditor Y who, as a secondary duty, maintains the QA division's central file of personnel qualification records. Although the primary files for each type of qualification are maintained by the organizational element responsible for determining whether or not individuals are qualified in particular areas of competence, the auditor in our example is responsible for seeing to it that auditor qualifications are current. Can they legitimately audit the division's qualification record system?

Neither example complies with the essential requirement. Among other things, audit principles are based on avoidance of the necessity for the auditor to place their personal or professional best interests in conflict with their auditing obligations. In neither example should the audit described be assigned to the individual in question.

As a third example, consider Auditor Z who, because of their broad experience, has been on loan to another activity outside the QA division to assist in designing a necessary QA-related control system. A little more than a month after their return to auditing, it is necessary to audit performance to the requirements of the control system they helped design. Is it a good idea, because of their familiarity with that system, for the auditor in question to be assigned to the audit? In this example, the expert should not be disqualified on grounds of potential conflict of interest unless they also were involved in implementing the requirements. The objective is to ensure that an effective QA program is being implemented. Practical considerations related to staffing, allocation of responsibilities, and organization size may often require management decisions based on need rather than on idealization.

4.3.3 Review of Reports

It is important that reports be reviewed by the lead auditor or supervisor of the audit function because they know the impact of a report identified as containing the results of a system audit. During the early life of a QA program, and therefore during the early life of the associated program of system auditing, every audit report needs close scrutiny and mature evaluation before it is released. To the new auditor conscious of the need for integrity of the report, that degree of management concern is likely to take on an appearance of censorship, but he may later change his opinion as he matures on the job.

It should be emphasized here that the actual nature of the surveillance over the audit report will depend on the judgment of the lead auditor/supervisor. If they are highly competent, their close attention to the audit reports (perhaps including a protracted period in which almost every report has to be rewritten repeatedly) may seem no less like censorship, but that period actually constitutes a long period of training for the auditor. The length of time such training lasts will depend primarily on the auditor's capability. As they become truly qualified, revisions will become editorial rather than substantive.

If the management happens not to be competent or suffers from a serious identity (security) problem, the revisions they require in audit reports will be changes of substance. Further, more substantive changes will not diminish unless the auditors succumb to the pressure to suppress the facts. There is no magic solution to that problem; anyone experienced in dealing with industrial and/or corporate management has long since established their own ground rules for such situations.

PLANNING AND SCHEDULING AN AUDIT PROGRAM

4.4   Planning and Scheduling

Planning is the systematic determination of what should be done; scheduling is establishing the detailed timetable to do it. There are many factors involved in the planning and scheduling of an audit program. These include:

   a. Type of audit to be conducted
   b. Availability and experience of audit personnel
   c. Requirements for preparation of checklists and forms
   d. Requirements for frequency of audits

4.5   Type of Audit

As described in Section 1, audits can be divided into two basic groups: *internal audits* and *external audits*. In establishing the planning and scheduling of audits, it is best to treat these two types of audits separately. The reason for this is that the audit planner generally has much more freedom in planning and scheduling internal audits than they do for external audits, since they are not so dependent on the schedule of activities of the auditee. Internal audits generally can be fitted into the schedule more easily. When the audit planner is responsible for both internal and external audits, they should establish the scheduled requirements with available information for external audits and then fit in the requirements for internal audits. The planning of audits is also dependent somewhat on the organization that is to conduct the audits.

The planning and scheduling of an audit program by a utility during the design and construction of their plant will be different from the audit program by a utility whose plant is operating. Likewise, the planning and scheduling of a continuous audit program by a supplier of material or equipment will be different from the audit program planned by a prime contractor, such as an architect/engineer or constructor, or the supplier of the NSSS. In this section are some basic guidelines that should be followed in the planning of an audit program, regardless of the organization or the type of audit.

4.6   Development of an Audit Plan

The first step in establishing an overall audit schedule is to determine the requirements that must be met; that is, what the basic requirements are against which a program or its implementation is going to be evaluated. These requirements may include items such as 10 CFR 50 Appendix B; 10 CFR 830 Subpart A; ASME BPVC; ANSI standards; federal government directives and regulatory guides; and corporation QA implementing procedures or instructions. In establishing the requirements for external audits, it is vital that contractual requirements be reviewed, since these provide the key to all other quality requirements. Once the basic audit requirements have been determined, the audit planner can establish whether the audit is to be for evaluation of a documented QA program or to determine the implementation of the QA system, or both. Frequencies of the audits and tentative dates for conducting the audits may then be charted. In establishing these facts, it may be useful to prepare a master chart identifying the following:

a. Organization to be audited
b. Type of audit—internal/external (including vendor audits of commercial grade items/services)
c. Evaluation or implementation type of audit
d. Location where the audit is to be conducted
e. Frequency of audits (follow-ups, etc.)
f. Required or tentative dates of the audit
g. Reference documents for previous or similar audits (history)
h. Specific requirements for auditing personnel, where applicable
i. Estimated manpower requirements

Before proceeding with how to use this information, let us review items (d), (e), and (g) listed above in a little more detail, and discuss how these will have an effect on the audit planning and scheduling.

Location—The locations where the audits are to be conducted should be tied in very closely with the manpower requirements and the tentative dates for conducting the audit. Where possible, the planner should take advantage of the need for travel and avoid overcommitment of manpower at specific times.

Frequency—If there is a requirement established for frequency of audits, compliance with it is necessary. The possibility that somewhere in the safety analysis report, technical specifications, contracts, or QA manual is a requirement that audits are to be conducted at prescribed frequencies should not be overlooked. The frequency may periodically require revisions due to such circumstances as change in organization, change in program, or changes in requirements. Procurement of commercial grade items/services may require source verification for each fabrication/service performance.

History—Reference documents should include whatever data are available about the past history of the organization that is to be audited. Perhaps audits have been performed on the same organization in the past. Perhaps there are trip reports detailing problem areas, trouble reports, or some other documents that list deficiencies or problems. The data should be examined for the purpose of establishing areas of investigation for the audit. Any history of problems should be evaluated for severity, safety impact, and particularly for trends. The history file may indicate some particular trouble areas, that organizational changes have already been made, or that action has been taken to correct previous problems. In identifying reference documents, do not overlook records of previously conducted audits of a similar scope that may have been conducted on a different organization. This type of data can be very useful in planning audits. Additional acceptable supplier/item performance records from independent sources may also supplement supplier history.

4.7   Scheduling of Audit Activities

If a schedule is available as described in the previous section (Figure 4.1), it may be wise to prepare firm schedules for the forthcoming two or three months. The sequence of activities to be performed during the audit and the scope need not be specified on the schedule. This item is not critically important at this time, since the in-depth details of what will be covered in each audit will be specified in the audit plan. After the overall schedule of the audits has been established, the planning for each of the audits to be conducted during the course of the program can be initiated. Tentative plans for each proposed audit should be prepared, listing the topic and scope of each audit. Scheduling of commercial grade items/services with planned source verification such as witness or hold points will require coordination with the vendor. Characteristics to be verified will include nuclear safety structures, systems, and components.

4.7.1 Notification

The schedule should also provide for the audit notification, listing the dates of the proposed audit, personnel, and the scope of the audit. The notification should be forwarded, preferably in written form, to the organization to be audited. This should be done approximately 30 days before the scheduled external audit or 10 days before an internal audit. It is important to take this initiative so that the auditor establishes the audit activities, not the auditee, and the auditee can ensure availability of necessary personnel (and necessary related documents) from organizations to be audited.

4.7.2 Schedule Review

The auditee's representative should review the suggested date(s) and topic of the audit, as identified in the schedule. They may have some very constructive comments after comparing the suggested dates with his organization's schedule. An audit may have been suggested at a time when the activity to be audited is not taking place, or at a time when the auditee will not have the manpower available to

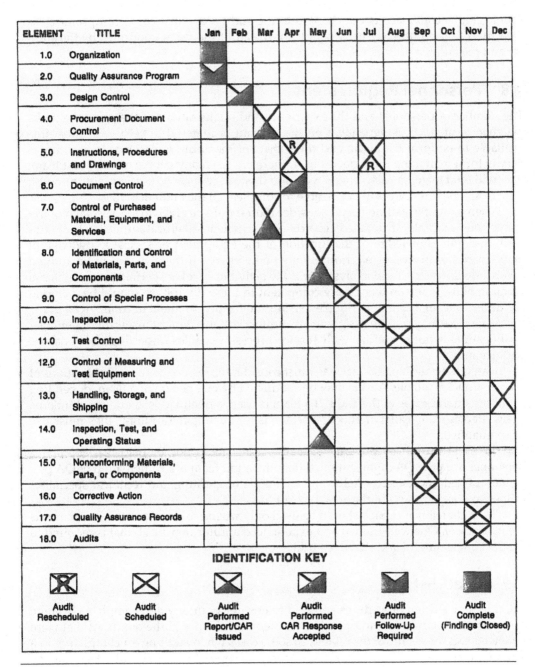

ELEMENT	TITLE	Jan	Feb	Mar	Apr	May	Jun	Jul	Aug	Sep	Oct	Nov	Dec
1.0	Organization	■											
2.0	Quality Assurance Program	▽											
3.0	Design Control		◩										
4.0	Procurement Document Control			◩									
5.0	Instructions, Procedures and Drawings				⊠R				⊠R				
6.0	Document Control				◩								
7.0	Control of Purchased Material, Equipment, and Services			◩									
8.0	Identification and Control of Materials, Parts, and Components					◩							
9.0	Control of Special Processes						⊠						
10.0	Inspection								⊠				
11.0	Test Control								⊠				
12.0	Control of Measuring and Test Equipment										⊠		
13.0	Handling, Storage, and Shipping												⊠
14.0	Inspection, Test, and Operating Status					⊠							
15.0	Nonconforming Materials, Parts, or Components									⊠			
16.0	Corrective Action									⊠			
17.0	Quality Assurance Records											⊠	
18.0	Audits											⊠	

IDENTIFICATION KEY

Audit Rescheduled	Audit Scheduled	Audit Performed Report/CAR Issued	Audit Performed CAR Response Accepted	Audit Performed Follow-Up Required	Audit Complete (Findings Closed)

Figure 4.1   Example of Format of Lead Auditor Qualification Record

accommodate the auditor. This last item is of particular significance when conduct-ing external audits.

Permit the auditee to suggest minor changes to the suggested dates because if an auditor is to conduct a successful audit, sufficient manpower must be available to answer questions, guide the auditor (where required), and locate documents and records that may be needed. Mutually satisfactory schedules are important; however, the auditor should not be convinced about changes to the audit scope that could compromise the objective of the audit. The final schedule for the audit should be confirmed by the auditor and the auditee prior to the actual audit.

4.8 Personnel Requirements

The number of personnel and the experience and qualifications of the personnel to be assigned to an audit is dependent on the amount of material to be covered, the time available to perform the audit, and the subject of the audit. Experience in auditing is very helpful in making these decisions. If there are too many people on the audit team, they will tend to get in each other's way, and this will reduce the efficiency of the audit; if there are too few, they will not be able to complete all the audit activities.

When planning staffing needs, consideration should be given to any special requirements. For example, if detailed records of equipment qualification are to be examined, in-depth knowledge of the function of the equipment or special knowledge of mathematics, statistics, or electronics may be necessary. If the activities to be audited involve detailed structural analyses, or if the activities involve special nuclear material accountability, a person technically competent in these disciplines should be included on the audit team, if possible. Source verification for procurement of commercial grade items/services may require assigning an auditor with mechanical inspector or engineer qualifications who is familiar with service process variables impacting item end-use performance.

In assigning audit personnel, one must consider the experience and qualifications of the personnel available. Audits may be conducted by one person or a team, depending primarily on the scope of the audit. If a team is used, a qualified lead auditor should be designated as team leader. If only one person is conducting the auditing, they must also be so qualified.

The audit team need not, and in many cases should not, be made up entirely of personnel from the QA organization. Often, the audit team is a combination of QA personnel trained and experienced in the technique of auditing and technical specialists trained and experienced in the area to be audited.

The audit team approach should be used only when the scope of the audit warrants the manpower. One well-trained and experienced auditor may be all that is required to conduct a meaningful and effective audit.

4.9 Checklists

Checklists or written procedures are used to ensure continuity and complete coverage of the area of interest, and to provide documented evidence of the questions that were reviewed and the results of the review. In some cases when auditing for compliance to a written procedure, especially on internal audits, a copy of that procedure itself may be utilized, with provisions highlighted that were investigated in lieu of a derived checklist. Checklists should be comprehensive and written prior to conducting the audit. It may be necessary to complete the checklists at the location where the audit is to be conducted if sufficient information is not available prior to arriving at the audit site. Source verification of commercial grade items/services may require checklists specifying critical attribute dimensions or process variables with allowable tolerances/limits. Most supplier audits now utilize the Nuclear Procurement Issues Committee services (see Appendix E).

Even the most experienced auditor should prepare and use a checklist to provide a precise, organized approach to the task of auditing and to assist in documenting the result of their inquiries. The use of a checklist will ensure that the audit, as it is conducted, contains questions designed to probe to an adequate depth, and it will provide a record of the audit that, in a well-planned audit program, will provide continuity between audits. An experienced auditor will use the checklist as a guide, whereas the new auditor should rely heavily on the questions in the checklist to compensate for their lack of experience and to ensure that all areas have been covered. Each auditor should depend on the checklists as a guide to ensure that all of the relevant subjects have been considered and that they do not get diverted from the goal of the audit by taking directions that were not indicated in the agenda. The checklists help keep the audit on target.

An auditor should not let a checklist prevent him from delving into a problem area. Remember, a checklist is a guide; therefore, deviations from the checklist may be necessary due to a change in the scheduled activity or an observation that indicates a possible problem. Experienced auditors are continually alert for potential problem areas and do not limit themselves only to the specific questions or items listed on the checklist. If a potential problem is discovered, investigate further to ascertain the significance. The checklist can be expanded in such a situation, and in this way it will provide objective evidence of the audit.

Audit checklists should be prepared as an extension of the audit scope. The organizations, activities, and subjects to be covered during the audit are identified in the scope. Each area or subject constitutes what will be called an *audit element*. At least one checklist should be prepared for each of these individual elements. After establishing an audit element, the next step is to reduce the element to its essential items. Each item should be looked at in two ways. First, what constraints such as written procedures, instructions, or requirements govern that item? Second, are there applicable portions of regulatory requirements that are not covered by the existing controls? This function is actually an evaluation of the QA program done at its lowest level. Figure 4.2 shows an example of audit report format.

An overall evaluation of the program may have been conducted previously, but that evaluation does not usually provide information at the detailed procedure or instruction level. Procedures and instructions must be checked to ensure that they are in compliance with applicable requirements and can be implemented. Judgment and experience are the most important assets to be exercised in establishing the items on an audit checklist. The checklist should also include provisions for examination of objective evidence.

AUDIT PERSONNEL ADMINISTRATION

4.10 Auditor Attributes

The following is a list of traits that predisposes an individual to function effectively as an auditor:

a. Personal integrity
b. Responsible—willing to act responsibly and be sensitive to what is and what is not reasonable

PART 1
QA AUDIT REPORT

Page 1 of

---

1. General:
    A. This audit report consists of the below listed documents:
        - Part 1: QA-11, Audit Data and Summary Report
        - Part 2: QA-11, Audit Checklist
        - QA-12, Audit Finding Reports   ☒ (X when applicable)
        - QA-13, Corrective Action Reports   ☐ (X when applicable)

    Audit No.   2016

    Date of Audit   July 12-15, 2016

    B. This is a report of a quality audit performed at the facilities listed below:
        Operation (Indicate plant facilities)   Nuclear Valve Div., Chicago, IL.
        Internal audit: ☒   By Corporate audit staff

    Vendor ☐

    Name

Address	City	State	Zip Code	Telephone No.

2. Audit data:
    A. Scope of audit and date performed:

X	Scope	ELEMENTS
	Full — All 18 quality elements	
X	Limited — Indicate quality elements audited in Section 3A on page 2	

    B. Quality program evaluation document: **ASME NQA-1** QA Prog. Requirements   Date 2008/09
    QA Manual with Nuclear Product supplement dated Jan 2016 Revision   Date Jan. 2016
    (Indicates supplements, addendum, etc.)

    Other QA/QC documents used in evaluation: Engineering QA procedures #5, 6, & 7
    (Excluding QA Manual (See also checklist))
    Purchasing control manual, Rev. 3

    C. Audit team members:

	Name	Member status (Auditor, observer, other)	Office, location or title	*Meeting 1	2	3
1.	George B. Jones	Team Lead auditor	QA Mgr, Corporate	X	X	X
2.	Robert T. Smith	Auditor	QA Engineer	X	X	X
3.	John Q. Engineer	Auditor	QA Engineer	X	X	X
4.	Bill O. Day	Observer	Purchasing Agent	X	X	X
5.						
6.						

D. Responsible Personnel Audited or Present: Name	Position		1	2	3
1. Jerry Makit	Prod. Mgr	Valve Assy	⊠		
2. Ray Perfect	QC Mgr	Nuclear Valve Div.	⊠	X	X
3. Joe Bullyboy	Insp. Supv.	Nuclear Valve Div.	⊠		X
4. Roger Livitup	Purch. Mgr.	Nuclear Valve Div.	⊠		X
5.			⊠		

*Meeting attendance at: 1) Pre-audit; 2) Entrance; 3) Exit Ctitique   Entrance meeting not required for internal audit.

Form QA-11

Figure 4.2   Example of Audit Report Form

---

    c. Consistency—an individual whose work and general approach to problems demonstrate their inner consistency but does not necessarily surrender any part of their creativity or imagination

    d. Cooperative

    e. Constructive

    f. Adaptability—the auditor must evaluate the effectiveness and/or adequacy of a system that may differ widely from the one they would have used or had

PART 1
QA AUDIT REPORT   Page   2   of

3. Audit scope and summary						Audit No: 2016	

| A. Scope and findings: | | | | | | Date of Audit:
July 12-15, 2016 | |

In Scope				In Scope			
Yes	No	Quality Element	*Finding	Yes	No	Quality Element	*Finding
X		1. Organization	S	X		10. Inspection	S
X		2. Quality Assurance Program	S		X	11. Test Control	N/A
X		3. Design Control	S		X	12. Control of Measuring and Test Equipment	N/A
X		4. Procurement Document Control	P/O		X	13. Handling, Storage and Shipping	N/A
X		5. Instructions, Procedures and Drawings	X	X		14. Inspection, Testing, and Operating Status	X
X		6. Document Control	X	X		15. Nonconforming items	X
X		7. Control of Purchased Material, Equipment and Services	S	X		16. Corrective Action	P/O
X		8. Identification and Control of Material, Parts and Components	X	X		17. Quality Assurance Records	X
	X	9. Control of Special Processes	N/A		X	18. Audits	N/A

*Audit finding code: S - Satisfactory   N/A - Not applicable
                      X - Program deficiency   P/O - Program omission

B. The elements of the quality program audited were found to be implemented.   ☐ Satisfactorily
   ☐ Program noncompliances, or omissions,   ☐ Comments   ☐ Observations

#4, #16

(4)   Procedures not established for quality evaluation of purchasing documents.

(16) Corrective action plan is not defined in procedures. No evidence of corrective action records or action.

      See audit findings 1 through 12 for deficiencies and omissions.

C. Restrictions or control measures recommended for shipment release or further activities:

   Increase surveillance by corporate staff and timely corrective action by quality manager to resolve deficiencies.

   Expect complete corrective action proposal in 30 days, complete 90 days.

D. Indicate purchase order number, revision and date and description of item or service applicable for vendor audit.
   N/A

Signature of audit team leader: *GB Jones*	Date: *Jul. 20,* 2016

Rev. 1   4/2015   Form QA-11

Figure 4.2   Example of Audit Report Form (Cont'd)

Page __1__ of __1__
Supplements attached
Yes ☐   No ☒

AUDIT FINDING REPORT NO. ___3___ of AUDIT No. __2016__

1. Audited Organization **Zero Defects Corp. – Nuclear Div.**	Location **Chicago**	Activity **QA Program**

2. Audit checklist quality element numbers: **5**

3. Documents used to evaluate quality programs:
(QA manual procedures, spec.) **ASME   NQA-1 & QA Manual Rev. Jan. 2016**

4. Program requirements:
(Quote or paraphrase document by Section, Paragraph)

"Activities affecting quality shall be prescribed by and performed in accordance with documented instr. para. or dwgs."

5. Finding:
(Describe deficiency in detail: i.e., What? Numbers? Where? Impact on quality of activity or equipment?)

Assembly operations for nuclear type 6442 valves were performed with unapproved marked up drawings #63D4567 and 63C6789. Instructions for assembly were by verbal means only. Assembly personnel were unsure of correct procedure. Inspectors indicated high—38% rework rate to correct improper assembly.

Equipment Deficiency ☒   QA Program Deficiency ☒
☒ Significant ☐ Nonsignificant   ☐ Major   ☒ Minor

6. Recommended Corrective Action: (Recommendations are suggestions only. Specific action taken to resolve the finding is at the discretion of the audited organization.)

Use only approved drawings. Develop approved assembly instructions. Provide assembly training to operating personnel.

Auditor(s): **Robert T. Smith**   Date of Audit: **July 13, 2016**

Name/Title
7. Audit finding acknowledged by: **J Makit**   Response required by: **Aug 15, 2016**

8. Signature of auditor: *Robert T. Smith*

FORM QA-12

Disclaimer: These names are fictitious.

Figure 4.3 Example of Audit Finding Report Form

used in the past in fulfillment of any requirement. They must be able to adapt quickly to alien systems and as quickly determine the compliance of evidence.

g. Curiosity—they must respond to the quiet inner sense or doubt or dissatisfaction, so that if it is felt, they are driven to unravel and discover, rather than assuming they would understand the situation.

h. Persistence—more than any other obstacle, the auditor will encounter the experience of being put off. Most of the time that will be the result of the other person's pressing schedule, rather than a deliberate effort to sabotage the audit.

i. Common sense—do not let common sense yield to any other trait. Lack of common sense will inevitably destroy an auditor, regardless of all of their other qualifications.

4.11 Selection

Consideration for selection of auditors should include the following factors.

4.11.1 Qualifications

To effectively establish an audit program of an organization, those responsible for the quality auditing should organize a qualified audit staff. The lead auditor(s) should be trained and certified in accordance with the corporate program and their individual needs. Proposed lead auditors should be qualified according to a rating system, such as that described in ASME NQA-1, Part I, Requirement 2, Section 303.

The selection of audit personnel both for lead auditors and audit team members is important to effective auditing. The best qualified personnel should be a part of the audit team. If the company does not have personnel qualified as lead auditors, it may wish to use an outside consulting firm to perform the audits, hire fully qualified personnel, or train its most qualified people.

The qualifications of personnel in any organization should be evaluated by management to determine those best qualified to perform audits. A lead auditor should be the most experienced person, selected according to the audit program criteria. The audit team members can be less qualified than the lead auditor but must be able to work with the lead auditor to effectively perform audits of those areas or functions for which they are competent. The technical background and education of the individual should be balanced against human factors. Education, experience, and prior training in communications and human relationship should have a direct bearing on selection. The organization responsible for auditing should establish specific qualifications for auditor selection, which ensures that the individuals selected for auditor training meet the necessary requirements.

4.11.2 Personality/Human Relationship

The techniques of auditing can be acquired by training and practice, but the basic aptitude of personal relationships, education, an inquiring mind, and communication skills should be prerequisites for selection. **Not everyone can or should be an auditor**. The evaluation of an auditor's personality is important to the selection of effective auditors. The extrovert salesman may not be auditor material because of their training for excessive control of their clients; likewise, the introverted scientist or engineer may not be effective because they would not be able to associate properly with the auditees and other personnel contacted. This is not to say that their inquiring mind may not be of benefit as an audit team member in a specific area that they are most qualified. These two extremes of personality would not normally be the best lead auditor material.

The auditor, either lead or team member, should have a reasonably balanced personality and be able to converse easily with auditees without antagonism. They should be able to establish a good rapport with the auditee during the early stages of the audit. Personal actions should indicate that the auditor has the initiative and sense of responsibility necessary to satisfactorily complete their duties during the audit.

The auditor must understand the human needs and relationships that can cause error and require corrective action. The big questions of "why" must eventually be answered in order to determine the cause of a deficiency and correct it effectively. The auditor with a balanced personality who can understand the workers' needs and dig out the facts from evidence and conversations with the auditee is an effective member of the audit team.

A person with good personal and human relationship traits can better work with audited personnel to provide accurate information in greater quantities for the audit report than a person who has trouble getting along and communicating. Education and prior training in communication and human relationships should have a direct bearing on selection. These traits, coupled with auditing experience and practice, will produce more effective auditors. Can you communicate effectively with auditees? Can you go into a strange shop and effectively control the audit? Can you conduct interviews and converse easily with operating personnel? These questions should be answered affirmatively if one expects to be an effective auditor.

4.11.3 Technical Specialists

Technical specialists are sometimes utilized on the audit team to provide the special understanding of technical matters needed for the auditors to evaluate the implementation of controls over technical activities. In areas such as station or plant operations, safety item performance, security, nondestructive examination (NDE allowing evaluation of in-service component), chemistry, and health physics, the use of technical specialists is advantageous. Vendor surveys of commercial grade items/services may require technical expertise to assure the item manufactured or process performed does not impact fitness for intended end-use. The technical specialists on the audit team will need a documented indoctrination or orientation, particularly if the audit activities are subject to NRC surveillance. If the specialist is teamed with an experienced auditor, technical knowledge alone may suffice, but they should be familiar with the use of checklists and audit procedures to be utilized during the audit. If the technical specialist indicates a desire to participate in further audits and appears to be competent, they may be given additional training in order to make them a regular member of the audit team.

4.11.4 Communicative Skills

The proposed auditors should be reasonably competent in the use of communicative skills for writing results, reading, and effective oral communication with auditees at all organization levels. The last is most important and can be evaluated during an interview or training session by letting them demonstrate how they would ask questions and obtain and evaluate the results.

Communicating during the audit means judicial and analytical listening, discussion, questioning, and evaluation of facts relating to the subjects on the checklists. It means open discussion of a condition without antagonism. Written communication is as necessary as verbal, and each auditor should be able to write logical remarks and report pertinent facts in a concise and accurate manner. The recording of detailed information is the basis of a good audit. Audit reports must be technically correct and logically written to be effective and provide evidence of compliance or noncompliance. The written findings should be thorough but not padded, and briefly described in clear English in order to be understood.

4.12 Training

It is desirable that auditors be formally trained both in the classroom and in the field before they become lead auditors. Training of auditors can be accomplished either within your company or by outside organizations. However, the training program should be a part of the auditor's organizational QA program. The decision of inside vs. outside training will depend upon number of factors:

a. The qualifications and experience of your present auditor personnel. It is desirable that the personnel who will conduct training of new auditors within your organization be qualified as lead auditors.

b. Your facility and materials. If the responsible organization lacks the facilities and materials to conduct the course in-house, then a logical decision is to send prospective auditors to an outside course that meets your criteria for qualifying auditor personnel. In many cases, the outside training is the way to go for initial training because of the qualification, experience of training personnel, and facilities provided by the teaching organization. After initial training and qualification, adequate experience should be gained to allow your own personnel to conduct such training.

4.12.1 Technical Training

The auditors should be trained and given appropriate orientation in all the governing documents, including 10 CFR 50 Appendix B, 10 CFR 830 Subpart A, ASME NQA-1, ASME BPVC Section ID, QA manuals, specifications, and other appropriate documents. The training program should be designed to provide general and specialized training in audit performance. This should include audit fundamentals, objectives, characteristics, organization, performance, and results of quality auditing. The specialized training should include methods of examining, questioning, evaluating, and documenting specific audit items and methods of closing out audit findings. Inexperienced personnel who are not qualified auditors should receive on-the-job training, guidance, and counseling under the direct supervision of an experienced, qualified auditor. Such training should include planning, performing, reporting, and follow-up action involved in conducting audits.

It is important that auditors selected to be a part of a team are active participants in the audit process and that they periodically review and study codes, standards, procedures, instructions, and other documents related to QA programs and program auditing.

4.12.2 Communication Skill Development

The auditor must be able to communicate effectively with the auditees at all organizational levels. Therefore, they may require additional training either by on-the-job experience for practice and evaluation or by classroom sessions such as workshops, speech making, or management courses that stress public speaking and personal relationships. As stated in Subsection 4.11, if the proposed auditor can get along with people, they can be trained to communicate effectively. Understanding the basic requirements, procedures, and organizational structure of the audited function will go a long way in providing the background for communicating and the ability to discuss the subject intelligently enough to determine compliance.

Writing skills are equally important, but since most audits are conducted by checklists, only the written reports and findings require such skill. These skills should be evaluated during the selection process. Additional training in communication skills should be conducted as necessary if the auditor has other acceptable attributes.

4.12.3 Evaluation

The examination of auditors can be conducted at the end of a course or upon demonstration of experience and competence. The examination may be either oral, written, practical, or a combination thereof to verify the auditor's comprehension of and ability to apply the prescribed body of knowledge and auditing skills. The examination should be administered by authorized personnel and can be either the person conducting the training (an independent certifying organization) or the employer's personnel.

4.13 Certification

Certification of lead auditors is a responsibility of each employer. Certification is the documentation of the auditor's qualifications, signed by an authorized person. An independent organization can certify that the lead auditor has received training, has been examined, and has completed the training program, but the employer must verify the actual certification document. This certificate should contain the following information:

a. Employer's name
b. Lead auditor's name
c. Date of certification or recertification
d. Bases for certification, such as education, experience, skills, training, and examination results
e. Signature of the employer's designated representative who is responsible for certification (see Figure 4.4 for an example of format)

4.13.1 Reevaluation

To remain certified, lead auditors should maintain proficiency by performing satisfactory audits and the review and study of appropriate information and the body of

RECORD OF LEAD AUDITOR QUALIFICATIONS	NAME:		DATE:	
EMPLOYER: **Zero Defects Corp.**	**John Q. Engineer**		**12/2/80**	
2.3.1	QUALIFICATION REQUIREMENTS		CREDITS	
2.3.1.1	EDUCATION - University/Degree/Date	—4 Pts. Max.		
	1. Undergraduate Level **Univ. of Florida/ ME 1976** 2. Graduate Level	**3**		**3**
2.3.1.2	EXPERIENCE - Company/Dates	—9 Pts. Max.		
	Industry (5 pts. max.) and **General Nuclear Corp.** Nuclear Industry (NI). or **1976-1979 (NI, AU, QA)** Quality Assurance (QA), or **Zero Defects Corp.** Auditing (AU), **1979 -date (NI, QA, AU)** Combined NI, QA, AU	**3** **2** **4**		**9**
2.3.1.3	PROFESSIONAL ACCOMPLISHMENT - Certificate/Date	—2 Pts. Max.		
	1. P.E. **Calif. #02345 1980** 2. Society **ASQ - CQE #8910/1979**	**1** **1**		**2**
2.3.1.4	MANAGEMENT - Justification/Evaluator/Date	—2 Pts. Max.		
	Explain: **Mr. Engineer has extensive quality knowledge and works well with customers, vendors, and peers. His audit reports are comprehensive & well written reflecting excellent grasp of audit principles and techniques.**			**2**
	Evaluated by: (Name & Title) *George B. Smith, Dir. QA.*	Date		
		Total Points		**16**
2.3.2	AUDIT COMMUNICATION SKILLS *Satisfactory*			
	Evaluated by: (Name & Title) *Bob Jones Lead Auditor*	Date *11/15/80*		
2.3.3	AUDIT TRAINING COURSES			
	Course Title or Topic **1. ASQ Quality Auditing** **2. Zero Defects Co. - Quality Engineering for Auditors**	Date **July 1978** **Dec. 1979**		
2.3.4	AUDIT PARTICIPATION	Date		
	Location Audit **1. Grand Nuclear Project - Dallas, TX, Dwg. & Documentation Audit** **2. Clinch River Project - Receiving & Mat'l Control Audit** **3. Bestial Engrg. Co. - Quality Program Audit** **4. Quality Widget Co. - New York City, QA Program Audit** **5. Zero Defects Corp. - Internal QA Program Audit**	**5/78** **8/78** **3/79** **4/80** **6/80**		
2.3.5	EXAMINATION Passed Score 93%	Date **11/20/80**		
5.2	AUDITOR QUALIFICATION CERTIFIED BY: (Signature and Title) *GB Smith Dir QA*	Date Certified: *12/12/80*		
3.2	ANNUAL EVALUATION (Signature and Date) *GB 12/10/81*			

Figure 4.4   Example of Format of Lead Auditor Qualification Record

knowledge. The employer should reevaluate the auditor(s) on a periodic basis in order to extend the qualification or determine if retraining or requalification is required. The periodic evaluation should be documented. The easiest way to remain qualified is by performing audits in a satisfactory manner. Participating in the training of other auditors can also be considered as part of maintaining proficiency since training includes a learning process. Auditors should strive to improve their auditing technique and skills so that the employer has no doubt about recertification when the annual evaluation is due.

When evaluating auditors, one should consider their work on audits during the year, the number of audits completed, the accuracy and effectiveness of the audit reports, the additional training they have received, and their initiative in self-improvement. Marginal auditors whose performance has not been satisfactory should be reinstructed, retrained, and reexamined or decertified as appropriate.

MAINTENANCE OF AUDIT RECORDS

Even though audit records may be identified as nonpermanent records, those that serve as significant value in demonstrating capability for safe operation would be considered lifetime records (ASME NQA-1, Part 1, Requirement 17, Section 401). Nonpermanent audit records should be maintained primarily for evidence of evaluation of the QA program and secondarily, that the audits were planned, conducted, and reported according to established audit procedures. Included in the category of quality records of the audit system are audit schedules, audit plans, audit reports, completed audit checklists, auditor qualification records, and audit follow-up records. Specific requirements such as those of ASME NQA-1-2008/09 are self-explanatory and will not be considered in this section except to describe which records must be kept.

4.14 Audit Reports

The final audit reports presented to the auditee's management should be maintained for six years under the present criteria. The field reports should include a copy of each finding or deficiency recorded in the course of the audit. The basic consideration in the maintenance of audit records is to ensure that sufficient data is recorded and kept, which serves as evidence that the audits were conducted as scheduled according to the QA program and license or contractual commitments. The written report is evidence of the evaluation of the QA program and its implementation.

Findings are the evidence of deficiencies and as a record are considered open or incomplete until the condition is resolved and/or corrected to the satisfaction of the applicable requirement, the auditor, and responsible management. See Figures 4.2 and 4.3 for examples of an audit report and audit finding report, respectively.

The organization responsible for conducting audits and the generation of audit reports and data should maintain the original supporting records that were generated during the audit and that were utilized to prepare the final report. These are to be considered nonpermanent or working records that should be maintained for about three years or until the completion of the next audit. Nonpermanent supporting records include the audit system plan, schedule and individual audit plans, and completed checklists.

Assessment of vendor/supplier Commercial Grade Items/Services (including source verification) requires permanent records retention as the supplier has no approved QA program. Checklists can be retained for reference and utilized as the basis of questions for later audits.

4.15 Audit Personnel Records

Records of audit personnel qualification and training are considered to be quality records and should be maintained current and retained for the same period of time as required for the audit report with which the auditors are associated. Personnel records should include the following type of information:

a. Auditor qualification form signed by management (see Figure 4.2)
b. Records of audit training received, such as certificates of satisfactory completion of an accepted auditor training course
c. Testing or examination records that indicate satisfactory knowledge of auditing techniques
d. Records of audits conducted with appropriate critique, if any

4.16 Audit Follow-Up Records

The written response to audit findings that indicate the corrective action proposed or taken are quality records to be retained along with the audit reports. These records are not necessarily collected or generated in the same manner as the audit plans and reports, and therefore are not always filed at the same time as the other records. Often the filing of completed records is delayed pending their satisfactory resolution and corrective action.

A positive program of follow-up activities should be established to ensure that follow-up and corrective actions are completed, and the records are filed in a timely manner. Follow-up records should be correctly completed with legible action or approval signatures, dates, and information prior to filing. These records are only as good as the data thereon that describes in detail the action taken to resolve and correct the deficiency.

4.17 Audit Files

An audit file should be established and may include the following document types:

a. Audit schedule
b. Audit notification
c. Checklists or procedure used audit reports
d. Audit responses and correspondence
e. Follow-up and verification of corrective action auditor qualifications

Since the records may include audits of suppliers, audits of clients or customers, as well as internal audits, appropriate designation of the files should be made and records in files maintained in an orderly manner to ensure irretrievability and adequate control. Completed audit records may be removed from the files and placed in archives or central records after closeout of any findings or corrective action.

Section 5
Mechanics of an Individual Audit

This section gives a detailed description of the mechanics required to successfully perform a typical audit. These include audit preparation, audit performance, audit reporting and follow-up activities. Various techniques that may be applied in the performance of an audit are described in Section 6.

AUDIT PREPARATION

5.1 Key Considerations

The key considerations in preparing for an individual audit are planning, defining the scope of the audit, scheduling the audit, selecting a lead auditor and a competent audit team, and establishing checklists. A typical sequence of events encompassing the audit is as follows:

a. Scheduling and notification of audit
b. Assigning an audit team
c. Pre-audit conference
d. Conducting the audit
e. Recording the objective evidence
f. Critique with audit team of findings prior to post-audit conference
g. Post-audit conference
h. Writing the report
i. Reviewing the audit response
j. Follow-up to evaluate corrective and preventive action

The audit team should always operate in an ethical manner, be well mannered, and ask for (not demand) information. They should work through the assigned contact person and conduct themselves in a manner befitting the company or department they represent.

5.2 Audit Plan

Part of the mechanics involved in the implementation of an audit is preparation. Preparation includes the development of a written audit plan by the auditing organization.

The audit plan should identify the following items as a minimum:

    a. Audit subject, date, and name of auditor
    b. Scope of the audit
    c. Activity to be audited
    d. Organization to be notified
    e. Applicable reference documents
    f. Schedule
    g. Written procedure or checklist

5.3 Defining Scope of Audit

In considering the scope of an individual audit, the following governing criteria must be established.

5.3.1 Scope

The audit must be built around the requirements established by regulatory agencies, codes, and standards, whether they be federal or state, and contractual or company policies and procedures. Nuclear industry QA program requirements originate from the following documents: (1) 10 CFR 50 Appendix B, (2) 10 CFR 830 Subpart A, (3) ASME NQA-1; (4) technical specifications; and (5) company procedures. These documents establish criteria, any one or all of which could be audit considerations.

5.3.2 Personnel Qualifications

The responsible auditing organization should establish the audit personnel qualifications and the requirements for the use of technical specialists to accomplish the auditing of the QA programs. Personnel are selected for specific QA auditing assignments on the basis of experience or training that establishes that their qualifications are commensurate with the complexity or special nature of the activities to be audited.

5.3.3 Orientation

The lead auditor should familiarize the team with the scope of the audit. They should develop and follow a pre-audit conference agenda to prevent straying from the scope of the audit. The ground rules for the audit should be made known to the team, such as the areas that can be audited, auditing in security areas, knowing right of access, the right to talk with individual workers, and safety responsibilities, including Occupational Safety and Health Administration requirements. The assigned auditors should be given appropriate orientation in the governing documents, such as 10 CFR 50, ASME NQA-1, ASME BPVC Section III, QA manuals, procedures, specifications, or other documents appropriate to the specific audit.

5.3.4 Lead Auditor

The audit team leader should be an individual whose experience and training qualify them to organize and direct an audit, report findings, and evaluate corrective action. In order to retain the position of lead auditor, they should take an active part in the auditing process as an audit team leader.

5.4 Audit Scheduling and Notification

An individual audit should be scheduled, and notification should be made to auditees in a timely manner within the audit schedule.

5.4.1 Scheduling Factors

There are many factors that affect the scheduling of audits and therefore the auditing organization should consider the following:

a. Number of audits to be performed
b. Frequency of audits
c. Types of audits
d. Number of people conducting the audits
e. Special facility access and auditor training to use personal protective equipment
f. Complexity of audits
g. Time needed to plan audits
h. Time needed to perform audits
i. Number of days required to issue reports
j. Time required to analyze audit response and to verify corrective action
k. Consideration of other activities such as vacations, holidays, training, etc.
l. Availability of auditees

5.4.2 Control of Scheduling

If many audits are being performed, a computer list may be helpful in scheduling audits. The auditor should prepare a schedule that fits the needs of the auditing organization and satisfies the requirements of the governing activity such as NRC, ASME, contract requirements, standards imposed, or a combination of governing criteria. This might require schedule planning six months to a year in advance, depending on complexity and how long it takes to obtain company approval.

5.4.3 Flexibility

Audit schedules should be flexible enough to permit the addition of one or more audits during the year without diminishing the overall efficiency of the auditing organization.

5.4.4 Notification

In most cases, it is recommended that the auditor notify the auditee in advance of a planned audit. The type of audit affects more than anything else the time frame for notification. Common sense dictates that an external audit would require notifying the supplier 30, 60, or even 90 days prior to auditing, whereas a one week to one month may be enough notification for an announced internal audit.

5.5   Team Selection

The responsible auditing organization should select and assign qualified auditors and the audit team leader. It is most important that they be independent of any direct responsibility for performance of the activities that they will audit.

5.6   Identification of Documents Required to Conduct the Audit

This subsection describes some of the elements needed to identify the documentation requirements of both internal and external audits. The auditors should review pertinent regulations, standards, codes, procedures, and policies related to the subject or activity to be covered by an audit. The following are examples of such documents:

a. NRC regulatory guides
b. Auditee's QA program manual industry/federal codes industry/federal standards Preliminary safety analysis report (PSAR) and final safety analysis report (FSAR)
c. NRC license commitments
d. Technical specifications
e. Contracts/purchase orders

Other information should also be identified and reviewed where applicable, such as:

a. Historical data of previous contracts with auditee or similar types of services. Acceptable item/supplier performance record available from other customers with similar end-use applications to reinforce CGD.
b. Testing and special processes including identification of specified hold points where source verification of CGD item/service may be performed.
c. List of special requirements such as sample preservation, identification, storage, and shipment.
d. Applicable regulatory documents, such as NRC I&E Bulletins, NRC inspection reports, DOE standards and directives imposed, etc.).
e. System or equipment design criteria including capability to maintain acceptable manufacturing tolerances.
f. Detailed requirements for review and approval of reports such as SAR, environmental report, meteorological survey report, and demographic survey reports.
g. Detailed description of testing and measuring equipment that the auditee will use in performing engineering services, including process variables for CGD. Calibration records may also be examined.
h. Detailed description of the test to be performed by the auditee. Some typical questions would be as follows: Who will be responsible for developing test procedures? What phases of test programs are to be performed by others? Are there any special environmental conditions under which tests will be performed?
i. Detailed description of what documentation and procedures the auditee is required to submit for review and approval, when submittal is required, and if

the existence of the approved procedures must be verified by the auditor prior to start or at the completion of the work.

j. Requirement for evaluation of auditee's capabilities and facilities, including review of the experience resumes of key personnel, request for descriptions of auditee's facilities, and request for evidence of similar work.

5.7   Development of the Audit Checklists

Checklists or procedures should be developed as required and used to ensure the depth and continuity of the audit. The audit checklist is intended for use as a guide and should not restrict the audit investigation when findings raise further questions that are not specifically included in the checklist. The checklist should be formatted to allow it to be identified with the audit in which it is being used. Space should be provided specifically for noting the requirement sources against which the audit is being performed, the auditor, the audited activity, the date, the individuals contacted during the audit, identification of items examined, and the audit results—compliance or noncompliance. CGD of vendor items/services may require manufacturing control drawings or vendor process descriptions in lieu of extensive checklist.

AUDIT PERFORMANCE

5.8   Pre-Audit Conference Agenda

The objective of the pre-audit conference is to establish the best climate for developing rapport and to set the ground rules for conducting the audit.

5.8.1 Formality

Formality of the pre-audit conference should be flexible and may be dependent on the audit scope, size of the audit team, and whether the audit is internal or external. The external audit conference generally will be more formal. It will generally be held in a conference room and be conducted by the audit team leader. The audit team leader should prepare a conference agenda to ensure coverage of all key points.

Due to established working relationships, internal audit conferences may be less formal. However, management of the audited organization must be made aware of the auditor's presence and objectives. The conference for either internal or external audits that are narrow in scope or conducted by one auditor may be held in an office with minimum attendance by the auditee's organization.

5.8.2 Attendees and Introductions

Desired attendees are the audit team and appropriate members of auditee's staff with at least one representative of management. Other responsible and interested parties may attend. These are usually supervisory or management personnel of the departments to be audited, as described in the audit scope. The minimum attendance from the auditee's organization may be requested, but not limited, by the audit team leader. Introductions are made of the audit team by the team leader and of the auditee's personnel by their representative.

5.8.3 Scope

The audit team leader explains the areas of interest to include the purpose and scope of the audit. Reference may be made to a previous audit of the facility and any previously required corrective action.

5.8.4 Basis

The audit team leader should also describe the source documents used to develop the audit plan. Examples of source documents are as follows:

a. Company QA program
b. Regulatory requirements
c. Codes or standards
d. Specification or purchase order
e. Implementing procedures
f. Past performance history

5.8.5 Methods

The audit team leader should generally describe how the audit will be conducted and explain the use of checklists as guidelines to ensure depth and continuity of the audit. They should identify those in-progress activities that are to be reviewed to verify adherence to approved implementing procedures. The determination of these activities may be made at this time from current information of activities in progress. A description should also be given of the types of documentation that will be reviewed, such as travelers, inspection records, etc., for in-progress activities and documentation on file.

5.8.6 Schedules

A mutual understanding should be reached for the schedule of the audit. This will include the following key points:

a. Approximate timing for each portion of the audit
b. How the schedule or scope may be changed due to unexpected developments
c. Time for post-audit conference
d. Auditee personnel expected at the post-audit conference
e. Stress that auditors will strive for minimum disruption of operations and establish daily starting time, lunch break and other considerations. Agreement should be reached on scheduling auditee personnel times for their participation in the audit.

5.8.7 Interface Personnel

The particular personnel responsible for interfacing with the audit team for each area to be audited should be established/determined. The auditee personnel should determine availability of interface personnel and whom to contact if the responsible person is not available.

5.9 Conduct of Audit

The audit team members should establish contact at the beginning of each day with their interface for the audit. They should maintain close coordination throughout the audit. Each auditor should ensure circumstances surrounding any observations are understood by his interface. It is not necessary for the auditee to agree with your interpretation of a finding, but they must understand the circumstances surrounding it. The auditor should alert auditees as to records required sufficiently in advance to prevent wasted time.

5.9.1 Data Taking

The audit checklist should be utilized both to include areas of interest and to document observations. The checklist will ensure continuity and complete coverage of the area of interest. It will provide documented evidence of the question that was reviewed and the corresponding findings. A checklist is provided as a guide and may not necessarily be used in its entirety, but any omission should be identified as not applicable or not addressed. The specific item observed should be documented on your checklist (e.g., the revision of a drawing, serial number of an inspection ticket, heat/lot number of materials being worked) along with the location of the observation.

5.9.2 Examination of Evidence

Evidence must be examined to evaluate compliance with criteria described in the checklist. Objective evidence is considered as "any statement of fact, information or record, either quantitative or qualitative, pertaining to the quality of an item or service based on observation, measurements or tests which can be verified." An auditor must use the "Show Me" approach; findings should not be based solely on a verbal explanation. Evidence may be qualitative, such as observations of activities in progress that demonstrate a person's knowledge of program requirements and the degree to which the program is implemented.

The auditor's function is to audit to established criteria and obtain objective evidence. They should not volunteer stories concerning a similar situation that was in the auditor's opinion handled better or differently. The auditor should avoid giving advice, as this may put the auditor into the position of preempting management of the audited organization. During an external audit, another possible consequence could be the application of back charges to the auditor's company as a result of recommendations made that are beyond the scope of the contract.

5.10 Adjustment of Audit Progress

The auditor must be on the alert for unexpected or unplanned situations that may require further investigation. Objectivity must be maintained to ensure the findings are written in an impersonal sense with no reference to personnel competence or capability.

The auditor should be alert for diversionary tactics during the audit, such as prolonged lunch breaks or long discussions. They should strive for random sampling and avoid allowing the auditee to direct them.

5.11 Findings

Findings should be related to established criteria and not influenced by personal opinions or bias, thus minimizing arguments. The written findings must be clearly identified to established criteria. Personal feelings or opinions have no place in the findings but may be a part of the audit report if the report form used has a section appropriate for these remarks. Agreement should be reached during the audit as to the validity of the findings.

The findings should be described in depth with substantiating information. It is helpful to obtain photocopies of pertinent documents if this is acceptable to the auditee and practicable.

5.11.1 Consolidation of Findings

Each auditor should review and consolidate their findings prior to the audit team critique or caucus. It is a good practice to read over all findings and cross-check information where there is more than one auditor to ensure that the meaning is still clear, and the terminology correct, before the post-audit conference.

5.11.2 Audit Team Critique

The audit team leader should ensure that sufficient time is scheduled for an audit team critique before the post-audit conference. At the critique, the team leader should accomplish the following:

a. Direct a discussion of observations and findings
b. Evaluate findings to determine if there are generic problems identified that may be consolidated into one finding
c. Act as sounding board to ensure findings are definitive and substantiated

5.12 Evaluation and Analysis of Audit Observations

Each auditor should evaluate and analyze their own observations throughout the conduct of the audit. Resulting conclusions may alter the course of the audit activities.

5.12.1 Information Exchanges

There should, however, be frequent exchange of information between members of the audit team during the audit. This will allow the team leader to make any required changes in the direction and assignments of the audit to better evaluate a situation and achieve the audit objective. It will also allow each member to relay information that may be pertinent to another part of the audit.

5.12.2 Team Leader Review

The audit team leader should review all observations to determine if there may be some weaknesses which by themselves are not significant but which when grouped show a generic problem. Some of these observations may then become audit findings.

5.12.3 Presentation of Observations

Observations made during the audit may lead to recommendations that are presented at the post-audit conference. The specific method for identifying and presenting observations and/or recommendations should be described in the auditor's procedures and may include one or more of the following:

    a. Presented at the post-audit conference
    b. Included in the audit report
    c. Discussed with the auditor's management for possible future audit activity
    d. Discussed informally with the auditees

5.13 Post-Audit Conference

The primary objective of the post-audit conference is to ensure that the audited organization understands all findings and observations. The post-audit conference should be conducted immediately following the conclusion of the audit. Attendees will normally be the audit team, a representative of management from the audited organization, and other personnel from the audited organization deemed appropriate by its management.

A preliminary discussion of the findings is normally held by the audit team leader and interface person of the audited organization. This discussion will allow the auditee to become aware of the findings, resolve any questions, and determine who should attend. As part of the wrap-up, the audit team leader should give a summary evaluation of the audited program.

The audit team leader will normally moderate the conference. The team leader should ensure that all findings and observations are presented in an impersonal sense with no conjecture by an auditor as to personnel competence or performance. Findings may be presented in one of the two following methods:

    a. Each auditor presents their own findings.
    b. The team leader presents all findings and relies on assistance from the appropriate auditor to clarify and answer questions.

The audit team leader has the additional responsibility of using tact to keep any discussions pertinent and brief. The only discussion items pertinent are those needed to clarify the findings and not to justify the audit method.

During the post-audit conference, the auditors should express their thanks to the organization being evaluated for its assistance during the audit. The auditor should identify good as well as bad conditions discovered during the audit. This will give the organization being audited the general results, removing the impression that the auditor's purpose was to find deficiencies only.

REPORTING AUDIT RESULTS

5.14 Communications

5.14.1 Preliminary Report

Audit findings and recommendations should be reviewed with those being audited as early as possible, preferably prior to the post-audit conference. This will allow the organization being audited sufficient time to review the facts before the post-audit conference to ensure there are no surprises. Differences should be resolved prior to the post-audit conference.

The auditor should prepare a typed or handwritten draft of their findings and recommendations as early as possible. They may distribute copies to those present at the post-audit conference.

5.14.2 Final Report

The findings in the final report should not significantly differ from what was described in the draft copies of the findings, unless specifically explained in the formal audit report.

5.15 Objective/Subjective Reporting

It may be worth the effort to explore the degree to which audit report drafts get reviewed and revised internally before being issued, and at what level. Such information must be treated with great caution because revisions may result from the use of auditors whose writing talent fails to match their other sterling qualities. Nonetheless, evidence of the consistent suppression or softening of adverse findings against sister organizations, or of rationalization in the checklist observations, clearly indicates lack of independence.

5.16 Reporting Format and Content

The final audit report should be prepared as soon as possible after the audit and should be signed by the audit team leader. Procedures may dictate the final report schedule and distribution. See Figure 4.2 for a sample format.

The body of the report must be easily readable, factual, understandable, and only concern the audit. The report must be edited for content and errors. It should be sincere and courteous, contain appropriate language, and not name individuals or highlight their mistakes.

Positions, titles, or systems may be referenced to identify deficiencies. The writing should be simple, using statements indicated in the conclusions to the summary portion of the formal audit report. If considered appropriate, an executive summary may be directed to top management addressing the areas of major concern.

Distribution of the report should include responsible management of both the audited and auditing organizations. The audit report should describe the audit and include:

a. Name of the organization, group, or area being audited, and names of persons contacted during the pre-audit, audit, and post-audit activities.

b. Provision for indicating the purpose of the audit. The audit should be identified by name, number, location, and date.

c. A summary of audit activities and results, including an evaluating statement regarding the effectiveness of the QA program elements that were audited. Deficiencies that have been corrected during the audit should be noted in the report summary with a statement that corrective action has been taken.

d. The audit findings in the appropriate format.

e. A response date specified for replies, if required.

5.16.1 Transmittal Letter

A letter of transmittal should accompany the audit report. The letter of transmittal should be addressed to the management of the audited organization and include:

    a. Reference to the audit by name or number, location and date

    b. A short summary to indicate general audit results

    c. A response date for findings if applicable

    d. Copy distribution that includes the auditor's management and interested departments

5.16.2 Findings

There are many different formats or styles used in reporting audit findings. The reporting can be done by letter or on a form (see Figures 4.3 and 5.1). The formal report format should include the following:

    a. The audit finding number.

    b. The specific requirement.

    c. Provision for specifying the details of a nonconformance or program deficiency. Identify and describe the nonconformance or program deficiency in sufficient detail to ensure that corrective action can be effectively carried out by the audited organization.

    d. Provision for the auditor, as appropriate, to offer recommendations for correcting the nonconformance or improving the QA program to prevent recurrence and to indicate the significance of the finding, if known.

    e. The name of the auditee representatives contacted, date, and signature of the auditor.

    f. Provisions for response by the auditee including completed corrective action, future corrective action to prevent recurrence, if appropriate, and the date that the corrective action was or will be completed.

    g. Provisions for recording verification of corrective action and follow-up.

5.16.3 Recommendations

The auditor should, where appropriate, make recommendations for correcting the reported nonconformances or deficiencies in the QA program.

CORRECTIVE ACTION AND FOLLOW-UP

5.17 Corrective Action

Management of the audited organization should be requested to review and investigate the audit findings to determine the appropriate corrective action needed and should be asked to respond to the report in writing. The response should clearly state the corrective action taken to prevent recurrence, if the finding is significant, and the scheduled completion date for the corrective action. If corrective action is not appropriate, the

EXTERNAL	☐ Program	☐ Specific Element		AUDIT No. __2016__

EXTERNAL ☐ Program ☐ Specific Element
              ☐ Survey   ☐ Inquiry
                                    ☐ Contract
INTERNAL ☒ Program ☒ Specific Element

Jack W. Lang
Signature of Auditor
9/18/2016
Date

AUDIT WORKSHEET

Organization: **SHOP OPERATIONS**

Section: **PRESSURE VESSEL SHOP AND MACHINE SHOP**

I.   **REQUIREMENT OR FINDING:**

Technical Procedure 12-2-ST-11, Rev. 2 requires grinding wheels, files, wire brushes, etc. be properly color-coded prior to use on carbon steel or stainless steel material. This requirement is not being complied with by the tool cribs and fabricating shops.

RECOMMENDATION:

(1) All tool cribs should be given a copy of 12-2-CT-11, Rev. 2.
(2) Responsible personnel should be instructed as to the pertinent and applicable requirements.
(3) All equipment (as referenced in 12-2-GR-11) should be properly color-coded prior to issuance to fabricating shop personnel.
(4) QA should perform a follow-up audit to insure compliance.

Representative Notified: **John Doe (foreman)**   219 Shop Manager
                             Bill Smith (foreman)   204 Shop Manager
                     Date: **9/18/2016**   Signed: *Jack W. Lang*

II. **REPLY:**

The above recommendations shall be complied with.

Shop Managers
Dave Smouse Shop 219

Corrective action completion date: **9/25/2016**   Signed: *Jim Walker, Shop 204*

III. REPLY REVIEW: Proposed corrective action is (SATISFACTORY) UNSATISFACTORY

IV. FOLLOW-UP TO VERIFY IMPLEMENTATION   **REQUIRED**

REMARKS: The auditor performed a follow-up of the above finding   **1**   and found the tool cribs and manufacturing shops to be in compliance with the recommendations.
                                                     Lead Auditor
                   Date: **10/2/2016**   Signed: *Jack W. Lang*

Figure 5.1 Example of Audit Work Sheet

response should specify the reason for no action. Action should be taken by the auditee to ensure that corrective action is accomplished as scheduled.

Corrective action by the audited organization may or may not be the same as the auditor's recommendation, depending upon its interpretation of the requirement or the practicality of the recommendation.

5.18 Follow-Up

The audit team leader or management of the auditing organization should follow up by:

    a. Obtaining the written response to the audit report
    b. Evaluating the adequacy of the response
    c. Verifying that corrective action has been accomplished as scheduled
    d. Determining that the action was effective in preventing recurrence

Follow-up action may be accomplished through written communication, review of revised documents, re-audit after the reported implementation date, or other appropriate means. The audit team leader should develop a formal follow-up log system to ensure they are informed of those responses still open and needing disposition.

Section 6
Audit Techniques

This section outlines the various techniques used in performing functions to accomplish the audit objective. The many variables that contribute to the ways these techniques are implemented include the type and size of the organization being audited, the function of the organization being audited, and the relationship between the auditee and the auditor. The audit organization may have a procedure designating acceptable technique for some situations discussed here.

It is the responsibility of the lead auditor to recognize the environment in which the audit is being performed and adjust the mode of auditing accordingly.

ASSEMBLING AND REVIEW OF AUDIT MATERIALS

Subsections 6.1–6.4 outline the various ways that different types of documents may be obtained and reviewed for the preparation of an audit.

6.1   Program Documents

One of the most important documents is the auditee's QA manual and its associated operating procedures and standards. This manual and associated operating procedures and standards or instructions may be:

a. Requested from the auditee as a condition of the bid or "Request for Quote"
b. Specified in the purchase order, contract, or specification as a requirement
c. Requested via the auditor's "Notification of Audit" letter to the auditees
d. Requested separately by mail
e. Picked up at the auditee's location by the auditor prior to start of the actual audit

Situations with no approved QA program may include purchase of commercial grade items/services. Further evaluation of a vendor with no approved ASME NQA-1/10 CFR 830 QA program requires source verification or survey to determine vendor qualification for fabrication or testing of safety structure, system, or component for conformance of critical characteristics ensuring item end-use performance.

6.2   Ancillary Documents

It is important to note whether the auditor is to retain the auditee's QA manual and procedures, and, if so, if they must be kept on controlled distribution for updating. The manual revision level should be identified in the "Request for Quote" or purchase order/contract for the audit subject. Documents such as auditee guidelines, NRC license commitments, technical specifications, NRC regulatory guides (as applicable), previous audit reports, drawings, and applicable industry and federal codes and standards should be obtained prior to the audit for auditor familiarization, planning, and scheduling of the audit.

Other documents pertinent to the audit may include those referenced in the "Request for Quote" or purchase order/contract, records of previous audits, correspondence (letters, memos) pertaining to the audit subject matter, any audit attribute checklists or sheets that may be used as a guide during the audit, special instructions, applicable diagrams, sketches, drawings, or procedures.

There are several acceptable methods of obtaining these other documents: by mail, memo, or letter, or through the auditor's or the auditee's files. They may also be requested at the time of audit. The auditor should verify that all such documents, QA manuals, procedures, correspondence, and drawings are current for the activity under audit.

6.3 Trace Back of Requirements

The auditor should review the requirements listed on the audit checklist (see Figures 6.1 and 6.2) for verification to the purchase order/contract for supplier audits or to the QA manual for internal audits. Note that Figure 6.2 may be used as an attachment to Figure 6.1.

The audit checklist should be reviewed to verify that the following documents used in preparation of the checklist are properly identified as being applicable to the procurement document(s)/QA manual:

a. Observations and recommendations from previous audits

b. Notes, letters, and other data relating to the audit checklist

c. Records of previous audits for trends or problem areas, noting where the audited item may require additional emphasis

d. Requirements of procurement documents for specific criteria that will be identifiable with current audit activities

e. All other necessary internal and external (to the auditor's organization) documents, correspondence, manuals, and other sources of information pertinent to the audit subject—particularly key points or major requirements of the codes, standards, owner preferences, procedures, or instructions

f. Design specifications, purchase orders, work orders, instructions, procedures, or drawings, that are identified with the purchase order/contract number to the documented instructions and procedures

6.4 Review of Quality Assurance Manual

The QA manual should be reviewed by the auditor(s) who will conduct the audit so they will be familiar with the scope and contents as they apply to either the utility/ owner or to purchase order/contract requirements. If there is more than one auditor, each should be assigned separate sections of the QA manual to review and prepare the applicable audit checklists for those sections. The manual should be reviewed for:

a. Compliance to purchase order/contract requirements

b. Compatibility to SAR, ASME, and other regulatory requirements

c. Conformance to a prepared QA manual review checklist

   d. Verification that the supplier's QA procedures also address all the applicable
       requirements of the purchase order/contract

AUDIT CHECKLISTS

Several different kinds of checklists have been or are being used for system audits. They
are not all equally effective, and some are clearly inadequate. Subsections 6.5–6.9 present typical examples of completed checklists that indicate the range of checklists and
define the main criteria to be used in selecting or designing them.

TITLE:	NUMBER **80 - 07**	
	TYPE: **Division**	
AUDIT/CHECKLIST – DOCUMENT CONTROL	DATE: **10/17/2015**	PAGE 1 of ___**4**___
	PREPARED BY: **E.F. Merrill**	
	APPROVED BY: **J.T. BARNES**	

1.0 GENERAL AUDIT INFORMATION

Organization
Audited ____**Engineering (Power Div)**_____   Audit Date ____**10/18-21/2015**

Auditor(s) ____**E.F. Merrill**____   Representative(s) of
Organization Audited ____**T. Connors/J. Powers**

Audit Supervisor Approval _____*J.T. Barnes*_____

2.0 AUDIT INSTRUCTIONS

2.1 The purpose of Document Control, as specified in Criterion VI of Appendix B to 10 CFR 50, is to ensure
    that properly approved and up-to-date documents are distributed to and used by activities affected
    by the documents.

2.2 Since the approval of documents is covered by other audit plans, this audit covers only the control
    of distribution of documents and the upkeep or maintenance of document files.

2.3 This audit is to be conducted on an organization basis; i.e., a specific organization such as a project,
    division, or section is to be audited for its distribution of documents as well as its upkeep of documents
    which it holds.

2.4 This audit is intended to cover only those types of documents which have an effect on the adequacy of
    the engineering, design, construction, and quality assurance aspects of Facility X, Y, Z work.

2.5 For those audit checks which verify implementation of a requirement, the auditor is to indicate how
    he assessed the implementation. For example, if he is auditing the distribution of drawings, he
    is to indicate the time period he looked at, the approximate quantity of drawings distributed in that
    period, the quantity of drawings he checked, and the identity of drawings found unsatisfactory.

Figure 6.1   Example of Audit Plan/Checklist Form

3.0 **AUDIT PROCEDURE**

3.1   The two attachments to this plan contain the audit checks; Attachment 1 covers Document Distribution and Attachment 2 covers Document Maintenance.

3.2   Enter below the types of documents audited and apply the audit checks in the appropriate checklist using a separate checklist for each type.

DOCUMENT DISTRIBUTION	DOCUMENT MAINTENANCE
EAP - 3.1 Rev. C
EAP - 4.6 Rev. A	**not audited**
EAP - 15.2 Rev. A	**during**
EAP - 16.7 Rev. B	**this audit**
EAP - 18.0 Rev. D
EAP - 18.1 Rev. D

Figure 6.1   Example of Audit Plan/Checklist Form (Cont'd)

There should be a means of identifying the name of the organization that was audited, the audit dates, audit numbers, and auditor's name associated with each completed checklist. There are various ways of doing this, such as showing that information on the checklist, or having unique identification on the checklist to tie it to an audit report that would have the above information.

A *system audit* may be described as the examination of objective evidence to determine the adequacy of a system to ensure compliance with requirements, or to verify

DOCUMENT DISTRIBUTION

Audit #   2015

Organization Audited   **Engineering Dept. (Power Div.)**   Audit Date   **10/18-21/2015**

Type of Document   **Engineering Assurance Procedures**

AUDIT CHECK	RESULTS
1. Is there a procedure for distribution of the documents and their revisions?	**YES EAP 2.1**
2. Does the procedure specify distribution to all who need the documents and their revisions?	**YES**
3. Are distribution lists for the documents maintained up-to-date?	**YES**
4. Are the documents distributed according to the procedure?	**YES – use acknowledgment system**
5. If there is no distribution procedure, is the distribution of the documents adequate?	**N/A see remarks**
6. If the procedure requires a receipt acknowledgment system, is it being implemented?	**YES – however lead engineer has not acknowledged receipt of several procedures**
7. If a receipt acknowledgment system is used, does the distributing organization follow-up on delinquent acknowledgment?	**NO – see attribute #6**
8. Is the list or index updated and reissued frequently enough to be useable for determining which documents are current?	**YES**
9. Is the list or index distributed to all who have need for it?	**YES**
10. Is the latest list or index correct?	**YES – 10/1/80**

Figure 6.2   Example of Document Distribution Checklist Form

performance of controlled activities in accordance with the established system. The checklist for a particular audit should then identify each requirement element the audit is intended to address.

6.5   Requirement Checklist

Requirement elements may be identified by direct quote or paraphrase, or they may be identified implicitly by appropriate questions. When questions are used, they should be

DOCUMENT DISTRIBUTION

AUDIT CHECK	RESULTS
11. In the case of documents such as SARs and procedure manuals, which may be issued to a holder after revisions have been made to them, are they distributed in an up-to-date condition?	**YES**
12. If some documents are issued on a noncontrolled basis (i.e., revisions and changes, will not automatically be sent to the receipts), are they marked as such before being distributed?	**unable to verify**

EXAMPLE OF AUDIT CHECK (BACK)

REMARKS:

#5   Procedure EAP 2.1, paragraph 5.6 requires revision to delete "no distributor system" as a distribution acknowledgment system is in effect.

#6   See audit report – finding number 1.

#7   See audit report – finding number 2.

Figure 6.2   Example of Document Distribution Checklist Form (Cont'd)

phrased in such a manner that a YES answer corresponds to compliance and a NO to noncompliance.

It is not necessary that the checklist consist of questions or key phrases. It may consist, instead, of quoted requirements or requirement elements. The checklist illustrated in Figure 6.3 uses the latter technique for identifying audit items.

The chief disadvantage of quoting basic requirements is the possibility of losing specifics. To avoid this, modified requirement checklists, such as the example shown in Figure 6.4, overcome that problem by quoting the pertinent requirement element and amplifying it by posing highly specific questions. Otherwise, the format is the same as that shown in Figure 6.3.

REQUIREMENT	SAMPLE DOCUMENT				
	1	**2**	**3**	**4**	**5**
A program for inspection of activities affecting quality shall be established and executed.	QAD 7.1 Source Inspection	QAD 7.7 Receipt Inspection	QAD 10.2 In-process Inspection	QAD 9.6 Magnetic Particle Inspection	QAD 11.1 Hydro-Static Testing
The inspection program shall verify conformance with the documented instructions, procedures, and drawings for accomplishing the activity.	QAD 7.1 Para. 6.1	QAD 7.7 Para. 5.2.1	QAD 10.2 Para. 6.2	QAD 9.6 Para. 6.2	QAD 11.1 Para. 5.4
Such inspection shall be performed by individuals other than those who performed the activity being instituted.	"	"	"	"	"
Examinations, measurements, or tests shall be performed for each work operation where necessary.	QAD 7.1 Para. 6.4	N/A	QAD 10.2 Para. 6.3	QAD 9.6 Para. 6.2	QAD 11.1 Para. 5.5
Process control may be substituted where direct inspection is impossible or disadvantageous.	N/A	N/A	QAD 10.2 Para. 6.6	N/A	N/A
If mandatory inspection hold points are required, the specific hold points shall be indicated in appropriate documents.	QAD 7.1 Para. 6.9	N/A	QAD 10.2 Para. 6.12	QAD 9.6 Para. 6.1	QAD 11.1 Para. 5.1

Figure 6.3 Example of Requirements Audit Checklist

The checklist shown in Figure 6.5, while using the same basic format as that shown in Figures 6.3 and 6.4, provides the auditor with a special space (for each audit item) in which to record either remarks and conclusions relevant to more than one of the items in the audit sample or information volunteered by individuals in the audited activity.

REQUIREMENT	AUDIT POINT	SAMPLE DOCUMENT				
		1	2	3	4	5
Audit personnel shall be selected for . . . auditing assignments based on experience or training (establishing) qualifications commensurate with the complexity or special nature of the activities to be audited.	Is there documented evidence of the use of predefined auditor selection criteria?	QAD 18.1 Para. 2.4.1				
	Is there documented evidence of evaluation of the experience and/or training of potential auditors against established criteria?	C. WOLFE	W. DURE	C. NOBLE	C. MARKS	D. BOTTOMS
		Sat.	Sat.	Unsat.	Sat.	Unsat.
	Were evaluations conducted in the selection of currently assigned auditors?	"	"	No Evidence	"	No Evidence
	If so, do the documented details regarding experience and/or training substantiate the selections?	YES	YES	NO	YES	NO
	Are the established criteria and the evaluations compatible with the complexity or special nature of the activities to be audited?	YES	YES	Unable to Verify	YES	Unable to Verify

Figure 6.4 Example of Requirements Audit Checklist with Special Questions

REQUIREMENT	AUDIT POINT	SAMPLE DOCUMENT				
		1	2	3	4	5
Audit personnel shall be selected for . . . auditing assignments based on experience or training (establishing) qualifications commensurate with the complexity or special nature of the activities to be audited.	For the audits examined, do documented details of the assigned auditor's experience and/or training support the assertion that he (or she) had qualifications commensurate with the complexity or special nature of the activity audited?	C. Wolfe Sat. Document Control Audit #3 - 2016	W. Dore Sat. Procurement Control Audit #4 - 2016	C. Noble Unsat. Welding Audit #7 - 2016	C. Marks Sat. Records Audit #10 - 2016	D. Bottoms Unsat. Test Audit #1 - 2016
	There are no auditor qualification records available to substantiate the assignment of Noble and Bottoms as lead auditors.					
	Is there any evidence of special abilities that led to assignment of the particular auditor to the audit examined?	YES	YES	YES	YES	NO
	Noble is a qualified welding engineer, however he has no auditor training. No evidence to justify selection of Bottoms. **Refer to audit finding.**					
	Did the assigned auditor have any special technical training, prior pertinent experience, or other unique qualifications?	YES	YES	YES	YES	NO

Figure 6.5 Example of Requirements Audit Checklist with Special Questions, and Remarks Section

AUDIT CHECKLIST

Audit No.: _____   Date: _____
Subject: _____   Page _____ of _____
_____   Auditor: _____

Personnel Contacted	Organization	Date

Item No.	Doc. No.	Para. No.	Items Audited/Deficiencies/Comments	Conform Yes/No

Figure 6.6   Example of Blank Audit Checklist

6.6   Auditor's Option Checklist

The examples shown in Figures 6.6 and 6.7 deserve serious attention. Figure 6.6 consists of a blank form with preprinted spaces for the vital information identifying the audit and auditor but without any checklist items. The auditor, having determined the scope and depth of the upcoming audit and analyzed the pertinent requirements, constructs their own questions, as in Figure 6.7. Obviously, they are free to borrow techniques from any of the previous examples or can create variations best suited to the specific audit. By the same token, they can use as much or as little space as seems appropriate. As we shall note in the following analysis, this degree of flexibility has certain disadvantages, not the least of which is the danger of wide disparity among auditors and a resulting lack of consistency in the audit program.

This type of checklist, with some modification, can be utilized to audit the process flow of materials, either hardware or software.

AUDIT CHECKLIST

Audit No.: _____15-7_____   Date: _____9-17-15_____
Subject: __Control of Special Process__   Page __1__ of __5__
      __(Procedure QAD 9.16 Rev.B)__   Auditor: __Knowhow__

Personnel Contacted	Organization	Date
K. Willis	QA Engineering	9/17
R. Beatrice	" "	9/17
J. Lannon	QA Records	9/17
C. Nagomi	Weld Shop	9/17
R. Peterson	Mfg. Engineering	9/17

Item No.	Doc. No.	Para. No.	Items Audited/Deficiencies/Comments	Conform Yes/No
1	9-16	2.0	Not audited. These requirements addressed in detail in subsequent check list items.	N/A
2	9-16	3.1	Does the mfg. weld engineer develop the weld specs? Evidence: WS-28E, WS-112, WS-116, WS-194, W5-561	YES
3	"	"	Does the mfg. weld engineer recognize his responsibilities for weld specs, welding operators? Welding machines? EVIDENCE: Interview 9/17; above WS's Report of Qualifications due (dtd) 9/3/15	YES
4	9-16	3.2	Are the operations necessary to qualify a procedure, welder, or weld machine documented in manufacturing planning? WS 116 Trvlr #66201, WS19 + Trvlr #66267, WS 28E Trlv #66113	YES
5	"	"	Does the qualifying mfg. planning identity the materials their P.O. Numbers and the heat numbers? WS 116 traveler, WS 194 Traveler, WS 28E	YES
6	9-16	3.3	Are the weld test samples identified by steel stamping? Evidence: WS 116 Trvlr #66201-1 WS 19 + Trvlr #66267-1	YES

Figure 6.7 Example of Completed Audit Checklist

6.7 One-Item Trace Back vs. List of Questions Checklist

The example shown in Figure 6.8 appears not to meet many of the above criteria. It does not identify the requirements audited against; it provides no identified space for noting compliance or noncompliance; it also lacks the desired provision for identifying information concerning the audit itself (e.g., organization audited, audit number, audit date, and the name of the auditor). However, it does provide for documentation of substantiating data, the recording of observations, and clear identification of the audit sample. Further, the actual checklist, of which Figure 6.8 shows only the first page, does contain a designated space at the end for auditor observations, findings, and conclusions, as well

1. Drawing Revision Verification:

		Shop Folder	Eng. File	Remarks
a.	Panel assembly drawing no. __MCC - 21975 Rev.1__	✓	✓	——
b.	Test specification no. _____TP - MODY Rev.6_____	✓	✓	——

		This Date	Calib. Due	Remarks
2.	Test Instruments:			
a.	_____Weston Serial #1575_____	12/4/15	1/4/16	
b.	_____Test Fixture #3_____	12/4/15	12/15/16	
c.	_____ —— _____			

3. Spot-Check of Component Parts:

   a. Part name   **Relay**
   b. Part number   **75877-2**
   c. Indication of QC acceptance **YES**
   d. Inspection file on part number **10/16/15 – 15 units**
      (date and quantity accepted)
   e. Workmanship   **Sat.**
   f. Remarks   ——

4. Witness (or repeat) test per spec no.: _____**TP - MOD4 Rev.6**

   a. Observed variations from test procedure: _____**None**

   b. Observed product nonconformance to requirements: ____**None**

   c. Workmanship of panel assembly: _____**Sat.**

   d. Identification of acceptance: _____**Test tag dated 12/4/15**

Figure 6.8 Example of Panel Assembly and Test Checklist

as a block for the auditor's signature and the date. Although the form is designed for the examination of a single item, two or more copies could be used if more than one item were to be audited. Such a checklist becomes quite useful in the performance of a product audit, or for any audit of activities involving a specific item of hardware/software.

6.8 Procedures as Checklists

Like every other facet of the QA program, the establishment of a QA audit system requires that one or more written procedures or instructions be generated to describe responsibilities and present general ground rules and guidelines to the auditors. Of necessity, such procedures must be sufficiently general to apply to all audits performed within the system.

Procedures may be more useful to the auditor than checklists under certain conditions. Specifically, the use of individual audit procedures should be seriously considered for the following cases:

a. Where the audit personnel are relatively inexperienced and/or variations between individual audit techniques might cause problems

b. Where one or more members of the audit team are technical specialists with little or no prior QA audit experience

c. Where circumstances demand more than the ordinary evidence required to demonstrate the validity of the audit activity

d. Where the auditor, in preparing their audit plan, determines that a step-by-step procedure would be advantageous in performance of the particular audit

6.8.1 Inexperienced Personnel

Inexperienced personnel may result from a QA organization having recently converted an experienced QA engineer into an auditor, or from hiring or transferring someone. In the latter case, the individual may have considerable QA audit experience but will be encountering an audit program philosophy that reflects the preferences of the management in their new company, as well as a new set of conditions and operating relationships. While the procedure illustrated in Figure 6.9 may be too detailed and basic for use in many programs, the level of detail can easily be adjusted, either during initial preparation of a standard set of these procedures or as use reveals areas in which improvement can or should be made.

6.8.2 Technical Experts

It is unlikely that any function would find it worthwhile to maintain a file of prepared procedures for the occasional technical expert borrowed for a specific audit. However, the time needed to generate such a procedure when it is recognized that a technical participant is going to be required will more than pay for itself. By providing the consultant with a carefully structured procedure, the audit function gets the most for their time. A normally competent engineer can be surprisingly uninformed about the most basic principles and techniques of a system audit. Figure 6.10 indicates how simple the basic form can be, and Figure 6.11 shows one way in which the desired procedure could be constructed.

6.8.3 Procedural Plan

In planning the individual audit, the more experienced auditor is likely to use a procedural approach. This technique is especially useful where the audit will involve two or more areas that are widely enough separated to make physical travel a consideration. The auditor may prepare such a procedure as a separate attachment to the plan itself, as the format of the example in Figure 6.12 would suggest, or they might make it an integral part of the plan.

TITLE:	Audit of Design Controls				
DOC. NO.: SA - 30	**Issue:** C		**Date:** 9/10/14	**Page**	17 of 38

3.1	Audit of Design Adequacy Verification for Design Changes.
3.1.1	Identification of changes to be audited.
3.1.1.1	Obtain and review the list(s) of design changes released since last audit of Design Controls.
3.1.1.2	Identify those changes involving safety-related items.
3.1.1.3	Determine and itemize the design specifications and drawings affected by each safety-related change.
3.1.2	Audit sample selection.
3.1.2.1	Establish a numbered list of the documents itemized in step 3.1.1.3.
3.1.2.2	Using a standard table of random numbers, perform a random selection of five documents from the enumerated listing of step 3.1.2.1.
3.1.2.3	Identify the random numbers table used: **Table A** ANSI X 9.82-1-2006 (R 2013)
3.1.2.4	Identify the starting point and order of progress for the random numbers obtained. **Column 2 line 10 + line 10 Column 3 to 12**
3.1.2.5	List the specification or drawing number, revision letter, and little of each document selected for the audit sample:

1.   **NMP COLIN**   **Rev 2**
2.   **DV 72B**   **Rev 3**
3.   **2472.12310.548**   **Rev 0**
4.   **257.12186.327**   **Rev 0**
5.   **CR 207**   **Rev 5**

3.1.3	Examination/Evaluation of sample.
3.1.3.1	Verify that the design bases were readily available to the engineer(s) who accomplished the change to the design.

YES ✓   NO _____

(Remarks: _____**Had original calculations**_____

_____)

3.1.3.2	Determine whether verification of adequacy was accomplished and documented.

Figure 6.9   Example of Audit Procedure

6.9   Standard Audit Checklists and Procedures

Experience shows that the preparatory phase of an audit may require a day or more dependent upon the scope of the audit. Preparation of a checklist will take up half of that time. A review of some 200 actual audit checklists prepared that way also showed considerable inconsistency from checklist to checklist, not only between auditors, but from audit to audit for a single auditor. The quality of the checklists, and consequently of the audits, varied similarly.

The obvious solution is development of a set of standard audit checklists and/or procedures covering all of the audits identified as normal criteria of the audit schedule.

Audit: _____   Team Leader: _____

Technical Auditor: _____

Topic of Technical Audit: _____

Figure 6.10   Example of Blank Audit Procedure

Initial preparation of these standard checklists and/or procedures will be costly if they are to satisfy the quality requirements of this industry. It may not be feasible to do the whole job at one time. If not, it could be undertaken on the basis of one checklist per auditor per week or per month, with appropriate reviews and consultation by the responsible individual in the program. It could also be undertaken over a longer period of time by an individual auditor.

If no provision can be made in your program for a formal effort in that direction, you would be well advised to establish it as a personal objective. Devote the necessary care to the checklist for each audit you conduct, with the thought that you will place a

Audit: __Independent Review of Calculations__ Team Leader: __W.W. Alexander__

Technical Auditor: ____E.B. Goodenough (Staff Engineering Adviser, Structures)__

Topic of Technical Audit: ____Verify technical adequacy of independent review calculations__

---

1. Select one crititcal system involving safety-related structural elements.

   System: ____Safety Injection Pump Foundation__

2. List and enumerate structural design calculations performed for the system selected. Attach list.

3. By random number selection, choose one member of the list of calculations. Verify that the selected calculation was not referred to you at any time for technical comment or guidance. (If you did comment or provide guidance, reject the choice and randomly select a replacement.)

   Calculation Identification: ____SI — 2015____ – 1

4. Obtain the independent review package (or report) for the calculation. Verify that its format and sign-off comply with IP3.4.3 of QP-3.

   YES __✓__   NO _____

5. Verify that the reviewer was properly qualified.

   YES _____   NO __✓__

   Remarks: __Reviewer was engineer's supervisor - was not independent however qualifications were adequate.__

6. Verify that the reviewer performed an adequate evaluation of the assumptions used by the engineer responsible for the design. (Interview reviewer if necessary to clarify or verify rationale and/or possible alternatives he considered.)

   YES __✓__   NO _____

   Remarks: __Performed evaluation using actual data rather than extrapolation__

7. If the reviewer used an alternate method of calculation, verify that it was appropriate to the calculation involved.

   YES __✓__   NO _____

   Remarks: __Extrapolation did not obtain finite results.__
   __Actual data was more accurate.__

Figure 6.11 Example of Complated Audit Procedure

copy of that checklist in your "Standard Checklists" file, to be used the next time you are responsible for auditing the same part of the program.

If you are responsible for the QA audit activity in your organization, use whatever means are available to you to create such a file and insist on your auditors using the standard checklists whenever they perform an audit for which a standard exists.

6.9.1 Tailored Checklists

It sometimes is advantageous to an auditor to make up individual checklists for specific audits. Forming questions from the QA manual or program documents helps the auditor to read and understand what will be examined or investigated. Questions will be in

---

PROCEDURE FOR CONDUCT OF AUDIT #314, DESIGN DOCUMENT CONTROL

1. Obtain copies of the document distribution lists (for controlled distribution) from the Plant Document Center. From among the individual (as opposed to controlled files) recipients, select two at random. Note the documents each are listed as receiving.

2. Select three documents at random from each of the document indices maintained in the Document Center.

3. For each document selected during step 2, determine the current status (revision letter, changes outstanding but not yet incorporated) and record on checklist.

4. Examine the selected individual recipients' copies of the documents of the sample to verify that they are current. Record results on checklist.

5. Examine the copies of the document of the sample at each controlled document file outside the Document Center to verify that they are current. (NOTE: At each controlled file, make a brief survey to verify that no oudated or superseded copies of the documents in the sample are in the area.) Record results on the checklist.

6. Walk through plant areas in which work is actively in progress. Examine any drawings in use by craftsmen or inspectors. Note drawing number, revision letter, and title of each drawing observed.

7. Check data of step 6 against status data in the Document Center. Document results on checklist. (NOTE: If any such in-use drawings are found during this status check to be out-of-date or superseded, notify the QA Manager immediately.)

8. Conduct exit interview; obtain corrective action commitments.

9. Prepare audit report.

Figure 6.12   Example of Audit Procedure

the context of the QA manual or program. Such checklist preparation often allows the auditor to detect changes or differences that would, under normal circumstances, not be obvious.

PRE-AUDIT CONFERENCE

Handling of the pre-audit conference is extremely critical and can have a significant effect on the success of the audit. The pre-audit conference is the time when the tone of the audit is established. The groundwork laid at this time and the impressions formed by the auditee will aid in the performance of the audit.

6.10 Rapport Establishment

A rapport should be established with the management of the organization being audited. In addition, it should be clearly understood that the audit team is there for a very definite purpose: to evaluate adequacy and implementation of the auditee's QA program or procedures. The pre-audit conference is also an excellent platform to briefly bring out each auditor's background and areas of expertise. Source verification for commercial grade item acceptance may employ a more informal approach with a single auditor/inspector coordinating with the vendor's QA manager for verification of safety critical characteristics or test performance within acceptable limits at pre-specified hold points.

6.10.1 Questions

To further establish a rapport with the auditee, the auditor should encourage the auditee to ask questions that result from reading the written notice or that arise during the conference. All questions should be answered honestly, using discretion in sensitive areas.

6.10.2 Audit Team Leadership

Audit team leadership should be evident at the conference. That is, the audit team leader must speak for the team and make it clear that the team leader is in charge of the team. This may be done through actions in conducting the pre-audit conference, rather than a definite statement to that effect.

6.10.3 Handling Diversion

An exchange of formalities is conducive to establishing rapport. This exchange should be limited and should not touch on controversial subjects. Any attempts by the auditee to divert the audit team's attention and time, such as the telling of stories, experiences, etc., should be handled by the audit team leader in a diplomatic manner (e.g., the team leader should politely emphasize that there are many areas to cover in a limited amount of time and that he would like to adhere to his schedule). In many cases the auditor may request, or the auditee may offer to give, a verbal description of the auditee's QA program. The auditor must guard against this presentation taking up too much valuable time, either due to the auditee presenting too much detail or using the presentation as a diversion from the audit. This will allow the audit team maximum time for the performance of the audit.

AUDIT CONDUCT

Audit conduct includes the operational phase of the audit during which document reviews, interviews, and evaluation of objective evidence are completed. Audit conduct may be either in person or virtual.

6.11 Fact Finding and Verification

The auditor's real challenge lies in dealing with people, rather than in examining records. In every audit, the auditor has the dual objective of evaluating evidence for compliance with the contractual requirements and exploring the methods that are used to accomplish the activity. The auditor will find certain requirements capable of audit only through interviews, and they should do a certain amount of questioning during every audit.

6.11.1 Basis for Questioning

The auditor should, at all times, maintain an appropriate mood and manner in interviews. The use of preliminary discussion in asking questions concerning the individual's job function, how they go about dispatching responsibilities, information about the product or service, some personal ideas, etc., can help establish rapport. This is necessary in establishing a basis for the evaluative questions. In order to establish full candor and disclosure, the auditor must first establish a permissiveness to talk freely. The auditor should clear any discussions with auditee personnel through an escort or contact if they are part of the function being audited.

Note-taking during the discussion should be a matter of judgment. If the auditee is reserved in conversation, taking notes will probably increase their fear and concern. On the other hand, if the auditee is a willing subject and wishes to express opinions and provide facts and information, then note-taking is appropriate in order to preserve the conversation exactly. In this latter situation, copies of exhibits may be requested as back-up information to the discussions without increasing anxiety.

6.11.2 Questioning Methods

A judgment must be made at the opening interview as to the type of reaction that may be expected from the individual. In all circumstances, the questioning methods should create minimum hostility to the auditee. Approaching the subjects in a manner in consonance with the individual's attitudes may suggest the use of simple, minimally probing questions in the initial portion of the interview. A series of simple questions with a sincere expression of concern to understand the answers will minimize anxiety. If the person being interviewed is outgoing, and the auditor wishes to minimize time, a more direct questioning technique may be employed. This situation requires sensitivity and judgment by the auditor. However, a conservative approach should be used in the framing of questions until the personality of the individual being interviewed can be determined.

6.11.3 Avoid Value Judgments

One of the quickest ways to terminate a dialogue with candor is for the auditor to interject value judgments about the operations that do not have full substance and assured validity. This form of discussion turns the auditee off and identifies the auditor as being an "instant armchair expert." The purpose of a meaningful dialogue is for the auditor to listen, understand, and evaluate the facts of the situation so that appropriate judgment concerning the conformance or appropriateness of the situation may be made. Long stories about "how we do it at our organization" or "how we used to do things" are inappropriate in an auditor's dialogue.

6.11.4 Get the Facts

Since the auditor's basic purpose is to objectively evaluate the supplier's QA program activities to the contractual requirements, the auditor should be concerned with the why, when, where, who, which, and how the activities satisfy the audit plan. Examples of the type of questions that will help "get the facts" are:

    a. Why does only the Purchasing Department review invitations for proposal?
    b. When does the QA Department get to review customer's requirements?
    c. Where are QA records stored?
    d. Who will conduct and witness tests?
    e. Which processes are considered special?
    f. How are inspection personnel trained?

6.11.5 Opinion vs. Facts

One of the most difficult facets of maturing, especially in the field of system audit, involves learning the differences between opinion and fact. The individual who hopes to become a good auditor would do well to spend whatever time is necessary learning that. There are practical exercises that can be performed, which are as effective as the judicious use of weights to improve muscle definition.

No matter how experienced, the system auditor should regularly practice expressing an observation in two contrasting forms—once as pure fact, without interpretation, and once as fact colored by judgment. Despite the arguments of most schools of philosophy (that every "factual" observation is shaped by the perceptive bias formed by interaction between the observer and that which they observe), everyone is capable of producing at least two significantly different forms of description.

For example, you discover that two of the five design documents you select for your audit sample fail to indicate whether the designs they depict are safety-related or not. You might use that observation for your day's practice.

Your factual observation might be expressed thus:

Of five design documents examined, two (Design Specification 42-10011, "Locking Mechanism, Control Rod Drive," and Drawing 31-44205-300, "Valve, High Pressure Relief") lacked any notation as to whether they concerned safety-related items.

Your contrasting judgmental exaggeration might take the following form:

Forty percent of the audit sample violated a primary control requirement. Engineering judgment as to safety classification is not being exercised.

You could make the contrast even sharper:

A significant out-of-control situation exists with regard to the identification of safety-related items in the design stage.

The truly immature auditor might be tempted to write:

Controls are clearly ineffective. Lack of identification of safety-related designs suggests that engineering safeguards (such as design verification, provision of alternate capabilities, etc.) are probably not being planned or accomplished.

All of the above judgmental statements may be true in any one instance; none constitutes a statement of substantiated fact, and every one constitutes a legitimate cause for management concern. By making it a habit to prepare such contrasting statements at intervals, even the most mature auditor does a better job of keeping their perspective.

6.12 Sampling

During the quality system audit, it is generally impractical to examine all the detailed items that could be observed or to evaluate all the available evidence of compliance. Auditing, therefore, may involve the use of sampling techniques. Sampling by the QA auditor is primarily applied to checking drawings, procedures, and records.

If a sampling plan is used, it will probably be worked out separately from the rest of the audit checklist. It should be documented, at least briefly, and any special assumptions or rationale should be specified clearly. If the sampling plan was not part of the audit plan, it should be attached to that document.

While it is not mandatory, it is desirable to document the actual sampling process. The auditor will often exclude items from their sample; each exclusion should be indicated, with the reason for the action. The important element in documenting the reason is that each exclusion rules out some portion of the possible data field, and in any reconstruction of the audit it will be of considerable interest to know whether areas were excluded that could have had a significant impact on the audit results. Exclusion of an item because it was not readily available, for example, could mean that the most likely sources of quality degradation escaped the auditor's examination.

Example: The sample to be audited shall consist of documents that have been issued since the last audit was performed on the activity. However, this shall not prevent the auditor from reviewing earlier work or documents if audit findings indicate this should be done.

The documents to be audited shall be reviewed against the audit plan and other requirements such as regulatory guides, facility guidelines, codes, standards, and the auditee's QA program manual. The auditor should also refer to any auditing records of authorized deviations. The documents should be audited to the requirements in effect when the documents were issued, unless superseding requirements specify back fitting.

6.12.1 Sample Plan Uses

The lot size from which the sample is taken should be recorded, such as number of calculations, total number of fuel rods inserted, total number of cement pours, or number of drawings reviewed, etc. At times the lot size will be unknown and an estimated lot size may be used based on an evaluation of the audit item to be sampled.

When a discrepancy from the audit plan is found during the audit, the auditor should fill out a discrepancy report, identifying the discrepancy to the audit plan; any drawing or purchase document reference, including the issue date of the major controlling document; and auditor identification.

Whenever a finding appears to be repetitious, the auditor should:

a. Complete the total audit plan for the normal audit sample

b. Determine if the audit sample is large enough

c. Examine additional documents for only those findings that were repetitious to confirm that a trend exists. These additional examinations should be recorded on the audit plan.

Whether the audit sample is obtained by statistical sampling or not, documents or any other evidence that the auditor examines should be identified to retrieve them at a future date.

The auditor will discover numerous cases in which controls are still in an evolutionary stage, have been recognized as marginal by responsible management and are well along in the process of remedial action, or have suffered some temporary inadequacy of application because of organization or program changes. Some of those cases, while they cannot be reported as having been in full compliance with requirements, also cannot be reported as being out of compliance at the time of the audit. The circumstances observed, and the auditor's analysis, should be documented. The audit checklist can be used for this purpose, or they may be documented separately and attached to the checklist.

6.12.2 Document Lists

Two kinds of documents concern the auditor: the kind that *prescribe* and the kind that *describe*. Figure 6.13 lists examples of each type. Basically, those that prescribe tell what, when, or how. A memorandum transmitting results of a thermal calculation contains

	PRESCRIPTIVE DOCUMENTS	DESCRIPTIVE DOCUMENTS
Design Calculations	—	X
Design Calculation Checks	—	X
Design Specifications	X	—
Design Drawings	X	—
As-Constructed Drawings	—	X
Design Procedures/Manuals	X	—
Design Review Reports	—	X
Design Reports	—	X
Procurement Specifications	X	—
Safety Analysis Report	X (Prelim.)	X (Final)
Stress Report	—	X
System Audit Reports	—	X
Purchase Orders	X	—
Receiving Records	—	X
Certificates of Personnel Qualification	—	X
Certificates of Compliance or MTRs	—	X
Special Process Procedures	X	—
Travelers, Work Orders, etc.	X (Prior to Work)	X (After Work)
Nonconformance Reports	X (For Disposition of Corrective Action)	X (After Disposition)
Pile Drive Log	—	X
Pile Loading Reports	—	X
Preoperation Test Procedures	X	—
Preoperation Test Reports	—	X
Radiation Exposure Records	—	X

Figure 6.13 Example of Prescriptive and Descriptive Type of Documents

data that will be used in the design, so the memo belongs in the prescriptive category. A work order (or traveler, or shop order), which contains the sequential planning for a job, prescribes the way the job is to be done. A material certification or inspection test report describes the chemical content of material or what was found during inspection testing; each document describes something about the product. A more general way of saying the same thing is that the latter two documents are evidence of how something was actually done.

It is a fundamental principle of control that descriptive (i.e., design) documents and prescriptive documents (i.e., constituting evidence that work has been performed in accordance with established requirements) be identified in appropriate indices or lists. Both types of documents are particularly essential to qualification of items/services for CGD as the vendor's QA program was determined insufficient to produce items with critical characteristics adequate to ensure suitability for intended end-use application.

The auditor's initial approach to any field of documentary evidence should be made through listings of the documents in question. As the auditor considers the index of a particular kind of document, it can be expected that many of the listed documents are of no concern to the audit. One may be able to establish the relevant items by information on the list. In some cases, the list will not contain sufficient information for such a determination. In any event, the auditor will normally find it most efficient to begin sampling as if every item on the list were usable.

6.12.3 Working Documents

A considerable fraction of the system audits in manufacturing activities or at the construction site for the plant will be concerned with documents that are (or are supposed to be) in use at the time of the audit. Work orders often fall into this category. The auditor will want to establish the data field by reviewing the master job schedule. This will show how many work orders are currently being worked on and where each job is being performed.

6.12.4 Procurement Documents

A system audit of procurement activities warrants careful prior familiarization by the auditor. The document logging system will be as dynamic as any logging system in the entire program, and again the auditor should direct preparatory effort toward it. Closed items on the log will be carefully stored and protected; the auditor will seldom encounter a situation where procurement documents are lost or even misplaced. Open items may require the greatest persistence on their part; the responsible buyer will most likely have such items (packages) in the immediate area.

The auditor is also likely to find the procurement area the most demanding in terms of the amount of educating they will have to do. When a buyer clearly understands what is required and has the criteria in mind for each of the alternative courses of action that involve QA, they can generally be relied upon; in practice, the education process usually is a one-on-one situation.

Procurement documents for commercial grade items/services may specify hold points for source verification and critical attributes with allowable tolerances. Vendor identification of dates during the fabrication process or machine capability may be required responses for auditor evaluation of adequacy of item/service performance.

6.12.5 External Audit Sample Selection

The time allocated to an audit of a contractor or supplier seldom allows much extra time for learning the working details of the multitude of document systems. The team leader for such an audit should request copies of pertinent logs, tabulations, and/or other listings of the types of documents they will want to examine. They may have a problem in scoping their request in such a way as to avoid questions of proprietary rights or program applicability; personal liaison via telephone, followed up by written confirmation, is almost always advisable.

The audit sample may be selected by random selection techniques applied to such listings. Before that decision is made, the team leader should check with their engineering and/or project people; they will more often than not have some concern about some part of that contractor's work, and a systems audit will frequently uncover ragged controls at the heart of areas of concern. Procuring commercial grade items/services will only authorize acceptance of activities and items being evaluated unless a more extensive commercial grade survey of the vendor is performed, evaluating processes, programs, documentation, and personnel qualification to provide assurance of reproducibility.

6.13 Environment for Interview

If full rapport and candor is expected in an interview, the environment should be conducive to these results. As an example, attempting to interview a line foreman in the noise and interruption of floor duties often will lead to so many interruptions and other inabilities to communicate that a full exchange of views, identification of problems, obtaining of supporting evidence, etc., may not be possible. Also, probing questions asked in the presence of subordinates or peers is a sure-fire way of putting the individual on the defensive. A remote location that is private will be more conducive for such interviews. Obviously, if the desired information can only be obtained by a tour of the shop and its associated activities, then this must be tolerated. However, it is often appropriate to establish a second interview in a more favorable environment to review and to ensure complete understanding of what was observed and discussed during the shop tour. It is essential that a complete and full understanding and/or disclosure of the facts be recorded.

6.13.1 Fairness

The auditor may observe minor conditions that do not warrant inclusion as a recommendation or discussion in the final report. Often the auditor can discuss these items with the responsible person, indicating concern for the practice. The auditor may suggest possible alternative or corrective actions that would be appropriate to the subject and state that this item is being discussed in a personal manner and will not be made a part of the formal report or discussions. This approach demonstrates fairness on the part of the auditor in not exploring unlikely sources or continuing to investigate until something, however insignificant, to report is found. Successfully motivating the organization for corrective action lies in the formal reporting of the few really important items and in avoiding discussion of the many insignificant items that are observed during the audit.

6.13.2 Empathy

The auditor must carefully maintain a role of empathy rather than sympathy. *Empathy* is described as "the common identification and understanding of the experience, feelings, and thoughts or attitudes of the other person." In expressing empathy, the auditor suggests that "I understand your situation, your feelings, your thoughts and attitudes, but I do not necessarily agree that these are appropriate or right." If sympathy is expressed for these conditions, then there is reinforcement to the person being interviewed that these factors are valid and should be retained. In the matter of attitude change and acceptance of behavioral change, it is imperative that empathy be expressed in the interview and sympathy avoided. This allows the auditor to exit with a neutral position that, on further evaluation of the facts identified, may lead to a recommendation for change. The auditee, in recalling the discussion, may recognize that the auditor fully understood but did not necessarily support the position, and therefore is more prepared to accept change.

6.14 Auditor's Obligation

The auditor has a clear and overriding obligation to identify all items adversely affecting quality/safety. Unless such information bears directly on something within the scope of the immediate audit, the most fruitful course of action seems to be to make it the subject of a special audit or investigation. Upon initially receiving the information, the auditor should make written note of it, identify the individual from whom they heard it, and determine from that individual where and how more information (or confirmation) can be obtained. Depending on the urgency of the subject matter, the auditor may immediately bring the matter to the attention of their own supervisor or to that of the appropriate level of management in the company they are auditing, or they may defer such action until the immediate audit has been completed. In either event, they should exert their own influence toward a complete, conscientious examination of the facts.

6.14.1 Reporting Noncompliances

Since the auditor will only be able to observe a very limited sample size in terms of compliance to requirements, care should be exercised in reporting any item of a significant magnitude and symptomatic to the quality system. The auditor is not responsible for, nor should they undertake, extended investigations to lay the groundwork for definitive corrective action. The earlier the auditee apprises management of that kind of finding, the sooner it can get the required investigation(s) underway.

6.14.2 "Drilling Down"

The more dramatic a disclosure or finding, the more careful the auditor must be. Make it a habit to see for yourself, or to talk with whomever the information is supposed to have originated with, if the information could indicate a serious problem.

6.14.3 Volunteered Information and Tip-Offs

During questioning of working individuals in an audited activity, the auditor should be conscious of the fact that they represent authority. The individual being audited may feel that an auditor's adverse opinion could affect their standing with their own supervisor. What is less often recognized before the fact is that an employee may well see in the auditor a useful tool. The employee may believe that they can, by presenting the auditor with the right bit of information, get the auditor to accomplish some end they, the employee, cannot or has not been able to accomplish alone.

It should be pointed out that the individual who volunteers information deserves attention. In nuclear power plant projects, that individual either may know something or they may be building a case. The auditor should listen and try to discern the truth by further questioning and investigation to obtain objective evidence.

6.15 Tactics

The subsection covers some of the many tactics used to avoid the potential unpleasantness of audits.

6.15.1 Diversions

Diversion of the auditor is occasionally resorted to as a means to limit available evaluation time. Tactics such as showing new products being developed, touring a sister plant, or long lunch hours are typical examples. The auditor must ensure that available time is utilized to the utmost in the direct conduct of the audit, and that any obvious diversionary methods are tactfully resisted so as to accomplish the mission in a timely and thorough manner.

6.15.2 Deception

Sometimes personnel anticipating the audit may develop data, statistics, or other information that is offered to the auditor as evidence of corrective action or purports to demonstrate that no problem exists. Some people are adroit at using statistical data in a manner that is deceptive, and such data should be accepted and used only if there is a thorough investigation as to its validity and the appropriateness of its use. Usually checking other sources such as inspection and material control records, nonconforming material, hour tabulations, work standard performance, and corroborative data to validate the information provided is necessary before such information may be accepted and utilized in the audit.

6.15.3 Handling Internal Conflicts

The auditor, while investigating or interviewing, may become involved with internal conflicts between persons in a functional organization, or most usually between persons in peer functions. Some of these may take the form of accusations of who did what, when, why, etc. Discussion with the other side may prove equally confusing in terms of what the facts are.

The auditor should avoid involvement in any internal conflicts unless there is enough evidence that these conflicts are in fact a source of quality problems, such as where a required function is not being satisfactorily performed because of a dispute over the responsibilities of the persons involved in the conflict. Under no circumstance should the individuals involved be identified by name in the report; however, functions or organizations should be named when appropriate.

6.15.4 Premature Disclosure

The auditor, during the evaluation of a problem, may have obtained partial information from one or more sources prior to a thorough analysis as to the validity of the problem.

Care must be exercised in discussing such information and its sources prematurely. Such discussion may create concern and possible counteractions prior to the final determination of the facts and the appropriate presentation of the problem.

FINDINGS

A *finding* is any defect, characteristic, noncompliance, or activity that is a condition adverse to quality of products and/or services and could have a credible impact to the intended function of the product and/or service. A finding also includes an undesirable or abnormal pattern of events, conditions, and programmatic issues, such as failure to implement any aspect of an approved QA Program. See Subpart 3.1-16.1, para. 302 for classification of conditions adverse to quality as to significance. The auditing organization should promptly notify affected management of the finding so they can take appropriate prompt action to correct the issue. Additionally, the auditing organization should consider the need to stop work to address any immediate safety concerns.[*]

6.16 Objectivity

The auditor should always maintain a conscious objectivity toward the subject they are evaluating. This requires concentrating on the objectives and eliminating factors that are external to the audit. Previous practices or personal beliefs are factors that may adversely affect full understanding of conditions and their relationships to the QA program and the quality systems being evaluated.

6.17 Keeping Notes

The value of keeping good, understandable notes during an audit cannot be overemphasized. Most audits cover many areas and involve a great many details that, unless noted as they occur, could become lost during the review prior to the post-audit conference and subsequent written report. Such documentation need not be in detail, nor written in a polished manner. However, the keeping of brief notes of enough detail to be deciphered later is highly recommended. The keeping of notes may also serve to highlight adverse conditions that are symptomatic, and if they are noted for consideration, other data may be combined with them to indicate a pattern that would otherwise not be noted.

The use of a tape recorder in the performance of an audit may be helpful to the auditor; however, extreme caution is recommended in its use. Tape recorders should only be used with the knowledge and approval of the auditee. The auditor should recognize that many people are reluctant to speak freely knowing the conversation is being recorded, and this may have an adverse effect on feedback received during an audit. The use of a tape recorder in place of written notes can be an effective time-saving tool during an audit.

6.18 Backup Data

In line with keeping adequate notes, backup data should be collected/accumulated and made available to substantiate the audit findings. Backup data include names, places, documents, etc.; whatever detail that would be necessary to reconstruct the events of the audit should the need arise.

---

[*] NQA 2019 definition of finding in SUBPART 3.1-18.2 Implementing Guidance on Classification and Handling Audit Issues

There are different categories of backup data or objective evidence, and some kinds of evidence achieve the status of objectivity only by the way they are treated at the time of the observation.

6.18.1 Documentation

Documents that are part of a permanent (or semi-permanent) record and that are signed by responsible authority form the least controversial objective evidence.

6.18.2 Nonpermanent Documentation

Reports that are not identified as part of the permanent record, correspondence that will also not become part of the record, worksheets, and notebooks that may be lost or destroyed, and unofficial notes from which formal records will be generated, are acceptable as objective evidence.

6.18.3 Observations of Activities

Activities that the auditor observes and immediately enters on the audit checklist may constitute a controversial kind of objective evidence. The careful avoidance of judgment-type language and the presence of a concurring signature by a member of the audited activity, or by another member of the audit team, is reasonably effective in establishing the validity of such evidence.

6.18.4 Oral Statements

Responses to prepared questions, if documented on the questionnaire or at the appropriate point on the audit checklist, constitute firm evidence only if accompanied by objective evidence or acknowledged by the signature of the individual providing such responses. They are most effective if recorded as direct quotes rather than as paraphrased statements.

6.18.5 Opinions and Judgments

Occasionally, an auditor confuses a statement of opinion or judgment for audit evidence. The auditor may assert that a situation of poor control exists while observing apparently confused operation of controls being audited. While the observation may be entirely valid, it may not be evidence. If, on the other hand, the auditor makes notes of the specific actions that led to such a conclusion, the written descriptions do become a form of evidence.

6.19 Reproduction of Copies

In the accumulation of data, it is sometimes easier to reproduce copies of the material in question rather than take the time to write down the necessary information. While this can save the auditor time and is often worthwhile, if it is the policy of the auditee not to permit reproduction of information the auditor must respect this policy.

The auditor should be selective when requesting copies of documents. While initial requests may be granted, repeated requests may encounter resistance. An auditor's rapport with the auditee may aid or hinder the request. Should requests for copies be granted with conditions, such as their return at the conclusion of the audit, these conditions should be honored in all cases.

6.20 Discussion of Findings During Audit

The results of a systems audit are of considerable interest to several groups of people. The chartering authority has an obvious concern. The managers directly responsible for the audited activities have an equally valid, and perhaps even more immediate, interest. The working-level individuals who perform the audited task also have considerable concern about what is being discovered.

The best auditors tend to keep people informed. During the actual course of examining specific material to determine the degree of compliance, the auditor will normally be working with someone who has been assigned either as an escort or to produce necessary records when the need arises. It is a useful practice to be frank with that individual, pointing out what you are looking for, what criteria you are using to determine compliance or noncompliance, and what you are finding.

It is surprising but true that the working-level people will often not be aware of the requirement to which you are auditing, particularly if you are using the top QA program document as your audit base. Because the detailed procedures and instructions for getting the job done and satisfying all of the mandatory control requirements (of which QA program requirements are usually only part) are second- or third-tier documents, it is not really necessary for every individual at the working level to know the policy provisions of the QA program. To that extent, your communication with your escort may include a considerable amount of mutually beneficial information.

If an instance of noncompliance is discovered, it should be revealed to the individual who is escorting or helping you to ensure understanding of the deficiency. Some auditors suggest that the individual be asked to initial the finding when it is recorded on the checklist, and such a practice does have merit. If the supervisor responsible for the activity in which discrepancies are observed is readily available, it is sometimes worthwhile to ask them to verify your finding on the spot. It is also worthwhile to give verbal comments that are below the threshold of establishing an actual finding. Noncompliances identified for CGD of items/services must be corrected prior to procurement with verification of no adverse impact to item fitness for intended end-use (services require no alteration of critical characteristics).

Finally, significant findings or safety infractions should be brought to the immediate attention of the auditee's management. The obvious purpose is to give them time to digest the information for the appropriate corrective action.

Periodic caucuses or critique sessions should be held among the auditors at the end of each phase, element, or day of the audit to assemble notes and critique the activities completed. This will aid in the thoroughness of the audit and serve as a method of arrangement of notes for the post-audit conference.

POST-AUDIT CONFERENCE

The post audit conference offers a discussion of audit observations and findings to the auditee organization, permitting any disagreements to be considered prior to the audit reporting phase. Disagreements are discussed with auditee prior to the post audit conference; however, greater attendance during the conference is typical.

6.21 Overall Presentation

Both at the beginning and end of the post-audit conference, the team leader should express appreciation for the help and courtesies extended by the audited organization. There may have been little of either, but such an expression tends to frame the conference in goodwill. The team leader should follow with a summary assessment of the program based on the results of the audit. This assessment should have a positive flavor, if possible, introducing the subject of adverse findings as exceptions to an acceptable program. Regularly scheduled debriefing sessions with the auditee should ensure mutual understanding of deficiencies identified. Source verification of vendor performance for CGD of items/services may require a single auditor/engineer/inspector, with post-audit conference attendance including only vendor manufacturing/testing/QA personnel involved during the assessment.

6.21.1 Use Impersonal Language

All reported findings and recommendations, including the discussion and backup, should be impersonal in nature. The use of names should be avoided and replaced by a definition of the functions that were evaluated and/or the level of the persons in that function that were interviewed. Individual names can be retrieved from the audit checklist. In no way should any conjecture with respect to personal competence or capability of people contacted be made a part of the findings and recommendations, if any, or the discussion of those findings and recommendations. If names are requested by the auditee, they should be given discreetly at the end of the post-audit conference.

6.21.2 Team Leader Presentation vs. Auditor Presentation

If the audit was performed by one auditor, the auditor must review and organize findings carefully before the post-audit conference. When an audit team is involved, the team leader must accomplish the same task with the help of the team members. The team leader may choose to present all the findings, relying on each member of the team to field questions and/or expand on the deficiencies they identified. The more common technique is for the team leader to have members present their own findings.

6.22 Presentation of Findings

Organization of the findings can greatly affect the effectiveness of the post-audit conference. The vendor will be aware that noncompliances identified for commercial grade items/services will result in deferral or cancelation of procurement activity because SSC could be altered with performance unknown. Preferably, all findings concerning a single requirement or, in the case of an audit of broader scope, findings concerning a single control, should be presented first, moving from group to group, before anything is said about the observations that will not require corrective action. In presenting findings, certain elements of information are indispensable:

   a. What was the requirement (document, paragraph, and sentence)?
   b. What was the deficiency?
   c. Where was the deficiency observed (organizational unit, physical location)?

It is not unheard of for the people in the post-audit conference to demand to see the discrepancy themselves. Such an attitude does not necessarily imply a question as to the auditor's veracity. Those present may not be totally familiar with the form or other document under discussion, and the actual nature of the discrepancy may not be clear to them. On the other hand, they may suspect that the auditor has misunderstood the control system, believing the document in question to occupy a greater role in the system than it actually does. In any event, such a request must be treated without excitement. The conference can proceed to the next finding while the necessary document is being obtained.

It will happen occasionally that a finding is either not valid or is worded in such a way as to imply something different from what the auditor intended, or what the audited activity is willing to concede. The post-audit conference may be the best place to get questions of fact resolved and to correct wording that creates the wrong intent. However, when this is done, discussion should be held to a minimum.

As chairman of the conference, the team leader faces the normal challenges of such a position. The team leader must keep discussion on track, soothe ruffled feelings if they develop, and end those discussions that threaten to drag on too long. The team leader may often suggest that a subject be deferred until after the post-audit conference, at which time it can be resolved by those directly concerned.

6.23 Presentation of Recommendations

The post-audit conference should also address the question of corrective action. For many findings, agreement will be reached that a noncompliance does exist, and the audited organization will be able to define corrective action and establish an approximate schedule for its accomplishment on the spot. In some cases, however, it is appropriate to make recommendations regarding corrective action to a finding. It is important that the team leader recognize that recommendations are just that—recommendations—and not mandates that the audited organization must follow. It is normally improper to recommend specific elements of reorganization since the organization and the staffing thereof is a line function of the division being evaluated, and from the facts presented and the recommendations it is the responsibility of the auditee management to consider staffing competence or organizational relationships. Agreement with the recommendations of the auditor by management of the function is desirable on an informal basis. Such an agreement should not be quoted unless a definite commitment is made at an appropriate level of management.

6.24 Presentation of Observations

Observations noted during the course of an audit may, by themselves, be insignificant. However, when grouped together, observations may indicate a generic problem that should be noted as an audit finding and reported.

Although many observations do not warrant classification as an audit finding, some may indicate possible trends that deserve mention in the post-audit conference and/or audit report. Any reference to observations by the auditors should be carefully worded in order that all concerned are aware that:

a. An audit finding does not exist

b. The auditors feel the matter is serious enough to warrant evaluation by the auditee

c. The auditor may investigate the matter further at some future time

HUMAN FACTORS

The auditor's qualifications should include human factors, such as skills in communication and interaction.

6.25 Fact vs. Opinion

To be an effective auditor, one must be able to communicate freely with everyone with whom one comes in contact. This is especially true when questioning auditees, who may or may not be willing to respond to the auditor's questions. The first impression that an auditee forms of the auditor usually determines the outcome of the audit. The best way to communicate with the auditee is to begin in a friendly way using a disarming mood and manner and to demonstrate an attitude that suggests the auditor is on an equal basis with the auditee. This approach usually establishes the rapport necessary to effect good communications.

Clues as to how the auditees are to be approached during the interview stages of the audit can usually be obtained during the pre-audit conference. If the manager appears to be aggressive, this trait may be reflected in their subordinates. In this instance, the auditor can expect to encounter many arguments and reasons as to why the auditee's way of doing things is the correct and only way. This atmosphere will normally produce the greatest resistance to change that an auditor will encounter. At the other extreme is the nonaggressive manager, who, together with his subordinates, will accept almost any suggestion to change that the auditor may recommend. In this case, the auditor must be careful not to be overbearing or act superior as the auditees would already be on the defensive because of fear of the unknown and will only answer the question directly with very little explanation. This situation can lead to a very good QA program being inadequately explained, which will require further exploration by asking more questions.

The auditor should communicate, through actions and self-confidence, a thorough knowledge of the subject being audited. They should not, however, indicate through communications or actions that they are "the expert" on the subject.

No matter how boring an auditee may be in replying to a question, the auditor must always display an interest in the reply by such means as smiling, nodding their head in agreement, or interjecting an occasional comment. The auditor must not display impatience with the auditee who has to illustrate the response with examples, experiences, or the best way to do it. The knack here is for the auditor to realize when the question has been answered and redirect the interview back to the objective of the audit.

The auditor always has to demonstrate objectivity during the interview to maintain the rapport established. Asking loaded questions or making value judgment statements will indicate that the auditor is not objective or interested in the reply but has already formed an opinion. This action can and often does place the auditee on the defensive and make them unwilling to cooperate.

The auditor must always be alert and listen carefully to what auditees are saying to understand their views and values. The auditor must constantly maintain awareness that there are many ways to accomplish a function, and that the auditees have usually chosen the way most efficient for their operation, which should be documented in the procedures. During external audits, it is not the auditor's place to determine the efficiency of the system, but to determine the system's compliance with the procedural/

contractual requirements. If the auditor is requested to make a suggestion for system improvement, they may do so but should emphasize that it represents personal opinion only, which may or may not be acceptable to other organizations.

During the interview, the auditor must maintain empathy, not sympathy. Despite all the rapport, empathy, humility, and objectivity on the part of the auditor, the auditor must always expect a test of understanding by the auditee. These tests must always be responded to with complete honesty and candor, as the auditor has no devious methods to hide or reason to misrepresent the true mission and objectives of the audit. To ensure that these tests are passed, the auditor must never criticize, condemn, or complain about the system, people, or organization under audit, nor make value judgments during the interviews. The purpose of the interview is to listen, understand, and evaluate the facts of the situation so that the conformance or appropriateness of the situation may be judged. Any wording or action that curtails meaningful dialogue should be avoided. To affect a meaningful conversation, the auditor should understand and practice "The Ten Commandments of Effective Communications" (see Figure 6.14). If effective rapport is established and empathy maintained during the interview, the auditor can be assured that appropriate facts and not opinions will be obtained.

The Ten Commandments of Effective Communication	
1. Judgment/evaluation	Thou shalt not judge nor evaluate until thou hast understood
2. Non-critical inference	Thou shalt not infer thoughts, facts or ideas in addition to those stated; avoid embellishment
3. Plural inference	Thou shalt not attribute thine own thoughts and ideas to the speaker
4. Lack of attention	Thou shalt not permit thy thoughts to stray nor thy attention to wander
5. Attitude	Thou shalt not close thy mind to others
6. Wishful hearing	Thou shalt not permit thy heart to rule thy mind
7. Semantics	Thou shalt not interpret words and phrases except as they are interpreted by the speaker
8. Excessive talking	Thou shalt not become infatuated with the sound of thine own voice
9. Lack of humility	Thou shalt not consider thyself too good to learn from any man
10. Fear	Thou shalt not fear improvement, correction, or change

Figure 6.14 Guidelines for Effective Communications During an Audit

6.26 Report Writing

Despite any rapport that a team establishes during the audit and post-audit conference, the audited organization's real feelings of the evaluation may never surface until receipt of the report. The reaction is dependent upon how the report is written, and this reaction will affect how corrective or preventive action is undertaken. A poorly presented report can negate all the constructive aspects of the audit itself.

The report must reflect the objectivity, impersonality, and empathy displayed during the audit. In order to do this, the report must reflect the results and impressions left with the audited organization during the post-audit conference. The report should not contain any observations or findings not discussed with the auditees unless the report explains that the finding was omitted through oversight. Internal audit reports can contain such findings, as it was explained at the conference that additional research was necessary back at the auditor's home base of operations. The report should be written to express what the audit uncovered and should only state facts, not opinions, and should not place the blame for any deficiencies. The auditor must constantly guard against personal feelings being revealed in the report.

The report should be written in the simplest terms possible in order that the findings can be clearly understood by all recipients. The audit report is no place to try to impress anyone with one's knowledge of the English language; however, the report must reflect proper grammatical construction. The audit report should be written in the third person. It must reflect an honest and objective appraisal of the audited organization's QA/control program in agreement with the contractual requirements.

Again, it should be remembered, as in the case of personal conduct at the audited organization's facility, that the audit report is a means by which the auditor's organization is measured. A clearly written report reflects clear thinking and is indicative of an effective audit.

6.27 Understanding People

Interfacing with various organizations and levels of management requires that a lead auditor be a good communicator. The auditor must be alert to ensure that the communication channels are always kept open during the audit.

Sometimes, these channels are suddenly closed for no apparent reason. This is usually due to the auditor saying something that appears to be minor in nature but is in fact very important to the auditee. To understand why these channels are closed, the auditor should have a fundamental understanding of human behavior, organizational motivation, fear of the unknown, and resistance to change, and should be capable of coping with personnel conflicts. To understand the auditee's behavior and motivation, the auditor should be sensitive to the auditee's feelings and needs rather than words or logic, because most people respond to basic needs.

6.27.1 Maslow's Hierarchy of Needs

Valuable insight can be gained into an individual's reaction to an audit question from the well-known formulation of human needs developed by A. H. Maslow. According to Maslow, "Man is an animal of ever-expanding needs. Once one need is satisfied, another takes its place." The following lists Maslow's hierarchy of these needs and attempts to reflect how individuals satisfying these needs would react during the interview stage of an audit.

Physiological needs—These are human needs of survival—food, clothing, and shelter. These needs are usually satisfied by wages. Once these needs are satisfied, they cease to be a motivator of behavior and are replaced by higher needs. Individuals attempting to satisfy these needs will offer little resistance to an auditor during an interview for fear of losing their jobs.

Safety needs—People have an instinctive need to protect themselves, family, and job from danger and threat, and to make their position as safe as possible. These needs are satisfied through insurance, religion, pension plans, management backing, etc. Individuals attempting to satisfy these needs, like those attempting to satisfy their physiological needs, will offer an auditor very little resistance during an audit interview.

Social needs—People are basically beings who do not want to be alone, and as a result have a great need for belonging, for acceptance, for association, and for receiving and giving love and friendship. People with an urge to satisfy these needs are usually members of some social organization but not necessarily the country club or jet set. Individuals with an urge to satisfy these needs will have a tendency to give the auditor the answer they think the auditor would like to hear, not necessarily the correct one. This condition would require the auditor to ask additional questions to accomplish the audit objective.

Ego or esteem needs—Ego or esteem needs are divided into two classes: those that relate to one's reputation such as status, recognition, appreciation, and respect and those that relate to one's self esteem such as self-confidence, achievement, competence, independence, and knowledge. People seeking fulfillment of these needs usually will live in an elaborate house in an exclusive neighborhood and belong to an exclusive social club. Individuals seeking to satisfy these needs will probably demonstrate the most resentment and antagonism to an auditor during the audit. To most of these people, self-image is based on job performance, which they perceive as the only real opportunity to build self-esteem. Any situation, such as an audit, that is likely to undermine that self-esteem will be considered as a serious threat by these individuals.

Self-fulfillment needs—Many people, but not all, feel that they must fulfill a role in life. Self-fulfillment needs include the realization of one's own potentialities, continued creativity, continued self-development, and self-expression. In today's society, this is known as "doing your own thing." Individuals attempting to satisfy these needs may perceive the auditor as being beneath them and will probably react negatively and sometimes violently to any audit finding presented at the post-audit conference if the finding jeopardizes any of their needs.

A preliminary discussion using exploratory questions of the auditee's job responsibilities, hobbies, interests, and ideas prior to questions directly related to the audit checklist can give an auditor an idea of where the auditee stands in this social scale. There is no definite way for an auditor to know which individual occupies a precarious ego position; however, the discussion period can assist in this regard. The auditor should be able to recognize the symptoms of individuals who perceive the audit as a threat to their safety, social, ego, and esteem needs and react accordingly. Indications such as antagonism at the pre-audit conference or beginning of the interview, unreasonable resentment, overreaction to observations, excessive nervousness, unwarranted perspiration, shakiness, unusual breathing, or a rise in the pitch of the voice during the audit require appraisal on the part of the auditor.

An auditor should ask himself such questions as "Have I inadvertently overstressed the seriousness of an observation?"; "Have I overdone the cold formal image?"; "Has my suspicion of the presence of a serious deficiency prompted a more aggressive approach than normal?"; and "Have I somehow given the impression that I have questioned the individual's integrity or motivations?"

In the case of imagined threat by the auditee, the auditor needs to extract the immediate sting from the situation. The most effective technique is the adoption of an attitude of quiet good humor. A shift from the audit checklist questions to general exploratory questions of the auditee's other interests also helps alleviate the situation. Another technique in combating the auditee's fears is for the auditor to demonstrate some permissiveness through the use of "gimmies or freebies" in minor nonsystematic problem situations that can be corrected on the spot. This tactic, in addition to demonstrating fairness, should help dissolve the auditee's fear of the auditor being a "nitpicker." This technique should be used carefully to prevent distraction from the audit objective.

In every case, except that in which the individual reacts strongly at the very outset of the audit, the auditor must recognize that when something happens during the interview that constitutes a threat to the auditee, the auditor's most appropriate action is to deemphasize the negative impact of the situation and concentrate on the positive, such as a cooperative search for effective methods for corrective action. Such a technique tends to replace the threat to the auditee's ego or esteem needs because the auditee is given an opportunity to help resolve the problem and satisfy job performance and reputation at the same time.

The auditor should also recognize, in such situations, that there may be something personal that the auditee dislikes and for which there is no solution. If the situation does not detract from the audit objective, the auditor should complete the audit. If it does detract from the objective, and the auditor is a member of a team, the auditor should relate the conditions to the team leader, who should make a reassignment. If the auditor is the sole member of the team and the conditions detract from the audit objective, the auditor should complete the audit as best as possible and relate the conditions to the audit supervisor for appropriate future action.

In summary, an auditor must do everything possible to establish a good rapport with the auditees and must not do anything through words or action that can adversely affect the delicate balance of the auditee's feelings and fear of the unknown with which the word *audit* is associated.

The following are suggested as additional reading on the subject of "understanding people":

a. A. H. Maslow, *Motivation and Personality* (New York: Harper Bros., 1954).
b. A. H. Maslow, "A Theory of Human Motivation," *Psychological Review* 50, no. 4 (1943), 370–396.
c. D. McGregor, *The Human Side of Enterprise* (New York: McGraw Hill, 1960).
d. E. F. Thomas, "People: Causes and Effects," *ASQC Technical Conference Transactions* (1976), 185–195.

6.28 Analytical Ability

An auditor should be capable of separating the trivial from the important facts during the interview stage of the audit. A knowledge of quality principles and practices can be applied to analyze the findings for trends. During the audit, several minor discrepancies may be indicative of a major breakdown in a QA program. It is the auditor's responsibility to analyze all findings to determine if this in fact the case.

The technique for determining if there is a common trend between findings is to determine the key reason underlying each finding, for example by asking oneself "What happened to the applicable system or process that led to the finding?" Once the cause is revealed for each finding, the auditor will realize that there may be a common cause for all the findings. If so, this usually will indicate at least a partial breakdown in the QA program. With this information, the auditor will be in a position to present the trend to the auditee for corrective action. If the real cause of the problem is found, the corrective action taken by the auditee should prevent repetition.

It may be that one audit will not reveal the true cause of all the findings. A team leader should not be discouraged if the true cause is not found, for some problems may not come to light for years. When this occurs, the team leader should review all past audits performed on the auditee and by combining past and present information, the trend should appear.

6.29 Audit Team Motivation

The team leader is responsible for supervising the audit team during the audit and as such should provide guidance and leadership to the team in all facets of auditing. Satisfactory work during the audit by an auditor should be recognized by assigning increased responsibilities in subsequent audits, praise, and recommendations to the appropriate supervisor. Conversely, the team leader must recognize any auditor or technical specialist who is not performing up to standard and be ready to take the necessary corrective action to improve the performance of such an individual during the audit. Unsatisfactory performance during an audit should be discussed with the auditor and if necessary reported to the individual's supervisor by the team leader in order that proper corrective action (retraining or replacement of the individual) may be taken.

Team leaders should be employee-oriented individuals who recognize the individual needs and goals of each member of the audit team and the factors for motivating each auditor as an individual. If team leaders are employee-oriented, they will create an environment that is conducive to the productivity of the audit team because groups or teams working for employee-oriented supervisors are likely to have a higher level of morale and quality of output than those working for a production-oriented supervisor.

When selection of a one-member external audit team is required, a qualified team leader desiring recognition should be selected. Usually, the chance to conduct audits external to one's own company will be enough motivation for an individual who desires recognition. Knowing that management recognizes their ability to act as the company representative is the motivation that many individuals seek. As the company representative, an auditor must demonstrate high moral character, responsibility, ethics, and the ability to communicate with all levels of management because the auditor is the standard by which the company is measured by the audited organization.

The assignment of higher-level management personnel or technical specialists to the audit team may cause the team leader motivational challenges. Technical specialists usually want to get involved in solving problems related to their field of expertise rather than determining a system breakdown. In attempting to solve the problem, the specialist may not accomplish the audit objective. The team leader must be alert to this type of involvement on the part of the specialist. As specialists are usually assigned to the team because of their expertise, the team leader should oversee and review the audit checklist development to ensure that the checklist will accomplish the audit objective.

During the conduct of the audit, it is usually a good policy to have the specialist accompany a trained auditor to listen to the interview and evaluate the technical aspects of the auditee's responses. The specialist can then advise the auditor on the technical adequacy of the responses. If this is not possible, another technique available to the team leader is to hold frequent meetings with the specialist to ensure that the specialist is completing the checklist in enough detail to permit the preparation of detailed findings. These meetings should also ensure that the specialist is making enough progress to cover the audit subject in its entirety.

The ground rules by which higher-level management personnel are assigned to an audit team as team members should be discussed in detail and clearly understood by the team leader, the team leader's supervisor, and the individual involved. These ground rules should outline that the team leader is responsible for the audit activities and that the individual is working with the auditor during the audit. If during the audit the individual fails to comply with the ground rules and is interfering with the audit objective, the team leader should politely remind the individual of the ground rules in a private meeting. Should the meeting fail to resolve the problem, the team leader should refer the matter to the supervisor.

Another technique to maintain high auditor morale is to permit the audit team member who identified an audit finding to present that finding at the post-audit conference. This will usually make the audit team member certain of the facts to be presented and avoid controversial discussions at the conference. The team member should also be permitted to review the audited organization's corrective/preventive action reply during the follow-up phase of the audit. As the initiator of the finding, an auditor should be keenly interested in assuring that the problem is resolved. The team member should be the judge, under guidance of the team leader, in determining the acceptability of the audit response and be given the responsibility of preparing a rebuttal letter to the reply if it is determined that the response is unsatisfactory. The team member should explain why the response is unsatisfactory and request the audited organization to reconsider its response. In this way, the auditor is kept involved with some of the decision-making aspects of the organization.

6.30 Audit Ethics

This section deals with ethics in a professional sense only. The ASQ Code of Ethics describes the fundamental ethics that should be considered as a guide for auditors (see Figure 6.15). Although all those who perform quality audits may not be members of ASQ, these are still underlying principles that apply to the ethics of audits. One fundamental principle outlined by ASQ that is appropriate to auditors is impartiality. In performing an audit, the auditor should always strive to be objective in judgment and pronouncements. Only the facts should enter into the assessments of whether conformance exists between criteria and established programs. The auditor should express an opinion on a subject only when it is based on adequate knowledge and honest conviction. In all cases, the facts should speak for themselves. No embellishments or subjective expressions are necessary.

The team leader of an audit team serves as a supervisor and should always be willing to recognize good work and offer constructive criticism for improvement in performance. As the leader of the team, the lead auditor must demonstrate through actions how the audit team should act. A leader must demonstrate leadership and set a good example. The team leader should require the team to comply fully with the

ASQ Code of Ethics   February 2019

Introduction

The purpose of the American Society for Quality (ASQ) Code of Ethics is to establish global standards of conduct and behavior for its members, certification holders, and anyone else who may represent or be perceived to represent ASQ. In addition to the code, all applicable ASQ policies and procedures should be followed. Violations to the Code of Ethics should be reported. Differences in work style or personalities should be first addressed directly with others before escalating to an ethics issue.

The ASQ Professional Ethics and Qualifications Committee, appointed annually by the ASQ Board of Directors, is responsible for interpreting this code and applying it to specific situations, which may or may not be specifically called out in the text. Disciplinary actions will be commensurate with the seriousness of the offense and may include permanent revocation of certifications and/or expulsion from the society.

Fundamental Principles

ASQ requires its representatives to be honest and transparent. Avoid conflicts of interest and plagiarism. Do not harm others. Treat them with respect, dignity, and fairness. Be professional and socially responsible. Advance the role and perception of the Quality professional.

Expectations of a Quality Professional

1. **Act with Integrity and Honesty**
   1. Strive to uphold and advance the integrity, honor, and dignity of the quality profession.
   2. Be truthful and transparent in all professional interactions and the activities.
   3. Execute professional responsibilities and make decisions in an objective, factual, and fully informed manner.
   4. Accurately represent and do not mislead others regarding professional qualifications, including education, titles, affiliations, and certifications.
   5. Offer services, provide advice, and undertake assignments only in your areas of competence, expertise, and training.

2. **Demonstrate Responsibility, Respect, and Fairness**
   1. Hold paramount the safety, health, and welfare of individuals, the public, and the environment.
   2. Avoid conduct that unjustly harms or threatens the reputation of the Society, its members, or the Quality profession.
   3. Do not intentionally cause harm to others through words or deeds. Treat others fairly, courteously, with dignity, and without prejudice or discrimination.
   4. Act and conduct business in a professional and socially responsible manner.
   5. Allow diversity in the opinions and personal lives of others.

3. **Safeguard Proprietary Information and Avoid Conflicts of Interest**
   1. Ensure the protection and integrity of confidential information.
   2. Do not use confidential information for personal gain.
   3. Fully disclose and avoid any real or perceived conflicts of interest that could reasonably impair objectivity or independence in the service of clients, customers, employers, or the Society.
   4. Give credit where it is due.
   5. Do not plagiarize. Do not use the intellectual property of others without permission. Document the permission as it is obtained.

Figure 6.15 ASQ Code of Ethics (February 2019)

rules, regulations, and customs of the organization under audit. This entails compliance with working hours, dress, lunch hours, and other requirements. Team members should attempt to blend into the environment in which they are auditing. Any action that makes the team stand out will reduce its effectiveness in dealing with the audited organization.

In dealing with any problem between the team and audited organization, the team leader must demonstrate fairness between both parties. The leader must deal with objectivity in obtaining the facts and eliminate any personality conflicts. If there is significant doubt remaining as to verification of the facts or the correctness of the finding, and additional evaluation fails to eliminate the doubt, the item should be dropped or offered in terms that acknowledge the degree of uncertainty at the post-audit conference. This type of action expresses the objectivity and fairness of the audit.

Should personality conflicts occur between members of the audit team, the team leader has the responsibility to step in immediately and resolve the conflict. The resolution should take place in an area not exposed to the audited organization and should be resolved to the benefit of the entire audit team and organization being audited.

It should be the clearly defined policy of any audit team leader that there are no surprises involved with the audit at any time. An audit is no place for cloak-and-dagger tactics or the identification of situations that are sprung at a critical time. Ethical audits require full disclosure of any finding with responsible members of the audited organization to test its validity prior to formal exposure at the post-audit conference or formal audit report.

The team leader must ensure that they and the team members maintain their integrity. They should not accept gifts or entertainment of a nature or degree that might possibly prejudice the audit or affect the relationship between the two organizations. If members of the audited organization offer to take the audit team to lunch, it is the team leader's responsibility to clarify the rules by which the lunch is accepted, such as limiting the time away from the facility.

During the conduct of the audit, auditors often have access to proprietary information of the audited organization. Auditors have a moral obligation not to divulge this information to anyone. Divulging proprietary information is a violation of this moral obligation and is not in the best business or professional interest of either organization. The discloser betrays a trust and in so doing gains a reputation that is not conducive to building better business relations for the auditor's company or themself.

Auditors must avoid the temptation during external audits to discuss another audited organization's performance with the people they are presently auditing. To do so is almost as bad as disclosing proprietary information and is in bad taste. Exceptions to this may be taken during internal audits, if part of the audit objective is to assess the efficiency of a quality system that is applicable to more than one facility.

Auditors must avoid making false, unsupported, or misleading statements that tend to injure or discredit the audited organization's reputation. This requirement is self-evident and must be adhered to in every respect.

In summary, all auditors must act in an ethical manner that will bring credit to themselves, their company, and the audit.

6.31 Psychology of Auditing

Auditing is viewed differently by each organization involved. Higher management of some organizations look on it as responding to mandatory licensing commitments or contractual requirements, while others view it as a good management tool.

No matter which view is taken, the first reaction to any audit group or function is usually one of suspicion due to the association of audits with uncovering fraud, deceit, or gross lack of compliance. The individual managing the overall QA program may be threatened by the establishment of an independent audit function that audits the internal quality system.

In most cases, QA system audit reports should be reviewed with the QA management before they are presented to management. However, reports of findings should not be diluted or censored if they are to have any value.

Organizations being audited may also react negatively based on the connotation that an audit is directed solely toward uncovering deficiencies rather than showing the degree of compliance to recognized standards and practices. When auditors encounter a negative reaction, they should point out the positive aspects that the audit will achieve for both organizations, such as better management methods evolved from evaluation of current practice. Where a QA system audit program is a way of life, it has a definite favorable effect on the quality of work.

Audit psychology means two things to the auditor. The first involves the climate that the responsibilities create for personal growth; the second the personal characteristics that contribute to making the individual an effective auditor.

The implied authority the auditor exercises can have destructive effects. It is no secret that some individuals choose roles of authority as a result of a background that has produced an authoritarian personality. In staffing an audit team, the lead auditor should avoid individuals who exhibit marked self-righteousness, overly active tendencies toward assessing blame, or excessive assuredness in stating matters of opinion.

The team leader should constantly be on guard against the growth of a sense of being on a disciplinary mission. The team leader faces another hazard, too: frequently suspicion and antagonism arise related to intrusion into areas defended by individuals whose concepts of responsibility and authority conflict with the idea of independent evaluation. If the auditors lack self-confidence, or have inner defenses, they may have difficulty in preventing such negative reactions in others from arousing their own defense mechanisms.

A lead auditor must maintain a constant awareness that the overall objective of a quality system audit is not to police but to participate in the development and maintenance of a quality system that permeates the entire audited organization's operation with a dedication to quality workmanship.

Section 7
Industry Initiatives and Developments (Updated 2021)

7.1 Commercial Grade Dedication

7.1.1 Reference Documents Added to Appendix A

1. ASME NQA-1 2008/2009, Part II, Subpart 2.14, "QA Requirements for Commercial Grade Items and Services"
2. ASME NQA-1a-2009, Part I, Requirement 7, Section 700, "Control of Purchased Items and Services"
3. ASME NQA-1a-2009, Part II, Subpart 2.14, "Quality Assurance Requirements for Commercial Grade Items and Services"
4. DOE Office of Environmental Safety and Quality, "Guidance for Commercial Grade Dedication," June 2011
5. NRC 10 CFR 21.3, "Definitions"
6. NRC DG-1292, "Dedication of Commercial Grade Items for Use in Nuclear Power Plants," June 2016
7. EPRI 1016157, "Information for Use in Conducting Audits of Supplier Commercial Grade Item Dedication Programs," Final Report, June 2008
8. EPRI 3002002982, "Plant Engineering: Guideline for the Acceptance of Commercial-Grade Items in Nuclear Safety-Related Applications," 2014, Revision 1 to EPRI NP-5652 and TR-102260
9. EPRI 3002006066, "Typical Format for Documenting Commercial-Grade Item Dedication Technical Evaluations," Final Report, August 2015
10. EPRI NP-6406, "Guidelines for the Technical Evaluation of Replacement Items in Nuclear Power Plants (NCIG-11)," December 1989
11. NRC GL 91-05, "Licensee Commercial Grade Procurement and Dedication Programs"
12. NRC IN 2011-01, "Commercial-Grade Dedication Issues Identified during NRC Inspections"
13. NRC IP 35007, "Quality Assurance Program Implementation during Construction and Preconstruction Activities," December 2016
14. NRC IP 36100, "Inspection of 10 CFR Part 21 and 10 CFR 50.55(e) Programs for Reporting Defects and Noncompliance," April 2011
15. NRC IP 43004, "Inspection of Commercial Grade Dedication Programs," January 2017
16. NRC IP 88114, "Quality Affecting Item Procurement (10 CFR Part 21) and Commercial Grade Item Dedication Process (Reactive)," October 2006

7.1.2 Glossary

10 CFR 21.3

Basic component.

1. (i) When applied to nuclear power plants licensed under 10 CFR Part 50 or Part 52 of this chapter, basic component means a structure, system, or component, or part thereof that affects its safety function necessary to assure:

   (A) The integrity of the reactor coolant pressure boundary;

   (B) The capability to shut down the reactor and maintain it in a safe shutdown condition; or

   (C) The capability to prevent or mitigate the consequences of accidents that could result in potential offsite exposures comparable to those referred to in § 50.34(a)(1), § 50.67(b)(2), or § 100.11 of this chapter, as applicable.

   (ii) Basic components are items designed and manufactured under a QA program complying with appendix B to Part 50 of this chapter, or commercial grade items that have successfully completed the dedication process.

2. When applied to standard design certifications under subpart C of Part 52 of this chapter and standard design approvals under Part 52 of this chapter, basic component means the design or procurement information approved or to be approved within the scope of the design certification or approval for a structure, system, or component, or part thereof, that affects its safety function necessary to assure:

   (i) The integrity of the reactor coolant pressure boundary;

   (ii) The capability to shut down the reactor and maintain it in a safe shutdown condition; or

   (iii) The capability to prevent or mitigate the consequences of accidents that could result in potential offsite exposures comparable to those referred to in §§ 50.34(a)(1), 50.67(b)(2), or 100.11 of this chapter, as applicable.

3. When applied to other facilities and other activities licensed under 10 CFR Parts 30, 40, 50 (other than nuclear power plants), 60, 61, 63, 70, 71, or 72 of this chapter, basic component means a structure, system, or component, or part thereof, that affects their safety function, that is directly procured by the licensee of a facility or activity subject to the regulations in this part and in which a defect or failure to comply with any applicable regulation in this chapter, order, or license issued by the Commission could create a substantial safety hazard.

4. In all cases, basic component includes safety-related design, analysis, inspection, testing, fabrication, replacement of parts, or consulting services that are associated with the component hardware, design certification, design approval, or information in support of an early site permit application under Part 52 of this chapter, whether these services are performed by the component supplier or others.

Commercial grade item.

1. When applied to nuclear power plants licensed pursuant to 10 CFR Part 50, commercial grade item means a structure, system, or component, or part

thereof that affects its safety function that was not designed and manufactured as a basic component. Commercial grade items do not include items where the design and manufacturing process require in-process inspections and verifications to ensure that defects or failures to comply are identified and corrected (i.e., one or more critical characteristics of the item cannot be verified).

2. When applied to facilities and activities licensed pursuant to 10 CFR Parts 30, 40, 50 (other than nuclear power plants), 60, 61, 63, 70, 71, or 72, commercial grade item means an item that is:
    (i) Not subject to design or specification requirements that are unique to those facilities or activities;
    (ii) Used in applications other than those facilities or activities; and
    (iii) To be ordered from the manufacturer/supplier on the basis of specifications set forth in the manufacturer's published product description (for example, a catalog).

Critical characteristics. When applied to nuclear power plants licensed pursuant to 10 CFR Part 50, critical characteristics are those important design, material, and performance characteristics of a commercial grade item that, once verified, will provide reasonable assurance that the item will perform its intended safety function.

Dedicating entity. When applied to nuclear power plants licensed pursuant to 10 CFR Part 50, dedicating entity means the organization that performs the dedication process. Dedication may be performed by the manufacturer of the item, a third-party dedicating entity, or the licensee itself. The dedicating entity, pursuant to §21.21(c) of this part, is responsible for identifying and evaluating deviations, reporting defects and failures to comply for the dedicated item, and maintaining auditable records of the dedication process.

Dedication. (1) When applied to nuclear power plants licensed pursuant to 10 CFR Part 50, dedication is an acceptance process undertaken to provide reasonable assurance that a commercial grade item to be used as a basic component will perform its intended safety function and, in this respect, is deemed equivalent to an item designed and manufactured under a 10 CFR Part 50, Appendix B, Quality Assurance Program. This assurance is achieved by identifying the critical characteristics of the item and verifying their acceptability by inspections, tests, or analyses performed by the purchaser or third-party dedicating entity after delivery, supplemented as necessary by one or more of the following: commercial grade surveys; product inspections or witness at hold points at the manufacturer's facility, and analysis of historical records for acceptable performance. In all cases, the dedication process must be conducted in accordance with the applicable provisions of 10 CFR Part 50, Appendix B. The process is considered complete when the item is designated for use as a basic component.

Defect means:

1. A deviation in a basic component delivered to a purchaser for use in a facility or an activity subject to the regulations in this part if, on the basis of an evaluation, the deviation could create a substantial safety hazard;
2. The installation, use, or operation of a basic component containing a defect as defined in this section;
3. A deviation in a portion of a facility subject to the early site permit, standard design certification, standard design approval, construction permit, combined

license or manufacturing licensing requirements of Part 50 or Part 52 of this chapter, provided the deviation could, on the basis of an evaluation, create a substantial safety hazard and the portion of the facility containing the deviation has been offered to the purchaser for acceptance;

4. A condition or circumstance involving a basic component that could contribute to the exceeding of a safety limit, as defined in the technical specifications of a license for operation issued under Part 50 or Part 52 of this chapter; or

5. An error, omission or other circumstance in a design certification, or standard design approval that on the basis of an evaluation, could create a substantial safety hazard.

Deviation means a departure from the technical requirements included in a procurement document, or specified in early site permit information, a standard design certification, or standard design approval.

Evaluation means the process of determining whether a particular deviation could create a substantial hazard or determining whether a failure to comply is associated with a substantial safety hazard.

EPRI 5652

Dedication plan. A CGD plan shall be established early in the CGD process to document the critical characteristics for acceptance, the methods for acceptance of the critical characteristics, and the acceptance criteria. Dedication plans may be developed for a specific item, service, or generic group of items or services. The CGD plan is based on the technical evaluation.

Technical evaluation. An evaluation performed to assure that the correct technical requirements for an item are specified in a procurement document. [EPRI NP-5652] [US Nuclear Regulatory Commission Inspection Procedure (NRC IP 43004)]

Failure modes and effects analysis. An evaluation of an item's credible failure mechanisms and their effect on system/component function.

Certificate of conformance. A document signed or otherwise authenticated by an authorized individual certifying the degree to which the items or services meet specific requirements.

Certified material test report. A document attesting that the material is in accordance with specified requirements, including the actual results of all required chemical analyses, treatments, tests, and examinations.

Characteristic. Any property or attribute of an item, process, or service that is distinct, describable and measurable as conforming or nonconforming to specified quality requirements. Quality characteristics are generally identified in specifications and drawings that describe the item, process, or service.

Equivalency evaluation. A technical evaluation performed to confirm that an alternative item not identical to the original item will satisfactorily perform the design function(s) of the original item, thereby providing evidence that this item is not a Design Change.

Receipt inspection. Activities conducted upon receipt of items, including commercial-grade items, in accordance with ANQA-1 or other applicable QA standard, to check such elements as the quantity received, part number, general condition of items, and damage.

Verification. An act of confirming, substantiating, and ensuring that the critical characteristics of the item meet the specified requirements.

7.1.3 Basics of Commercial Grade Dedication

Nuclear operations require rigorous controls for items and processes to ensure continuing safety and reliability of systems for decades of operation. The original equipment manufacturers (OEM) and service providers may not be available throughout the entire system lifetime, and replacement items or providers with the same pedigree will be required. CGD of items and services can ensure that replacements meet the original design intent and safe performance continues when the original sources are no longer available. An overview of CGD for items or processes is depicted in Figure 7.1.

When does CGD apply? Why are we doing this?

CGD applies to only safety items (safety structures, systems, and components) or processes that perform a 10 CFR 50/10 CFR 830 safety function. Safety-related structures, systems, and components (10 CFR 50.2) are:

i. those structures, systems and components that are relied upon to remain functional during and following design basis events to assure:
(1) The integrity of the reactor coolant pressure boundary
(2) The capability to shut down the reactor and maintain it in a safe shutdown condition; or
(3) The capability to prevent or mitigate the consequences of accidents that could result in potential offsite exposures comparable to the applicable guideline exposures set forth in §50.34(a) (1) or §100.11 of this chapter, as applicable.

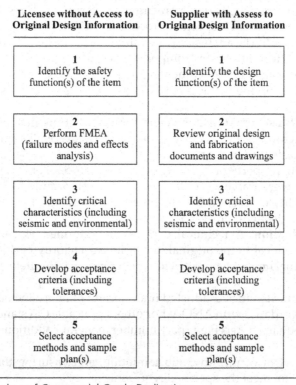

Figure 7.1 Overview of Commercial Grade Dedication

Which industries employ CGD? How common is it?

Nuclear QA applications of CGD will encompass both of the following:

- The commercial nuclear industry, which is regulated by NRC 10 CFR 50 provisions including nuclear fuel design and fabrication, NRC licensee power reactor operations, services and component suppliers supporting reactor operations, resultant 10 CFR 72 spent nuclear fuel storage and nuclear waste including cask licensing, 10 CFR 71 nuclear material transportation criteria, and subsequent reactor decontamination and decommissioning
- Nuclear facilities regulated by DOE 10 CFR 830 provisions including both management and operating contractors and national laboratories with programs incorporating 10 CFR 830 nuclear QA and nuclear safety provisions

How rigorous is CGD? How much is enough?

CGD results from reverse engineering to determine significant design and performance attributes for replacement components that were not certified to code (e.g., BPVC) by the original manufacturer or vendor. These attributes provide reasonable assurance that the replacement item will perform its intended function (same function as the design that was originally qualified).

The original design was qualified by performance of qualification tests to verify that a component's design is suitable (function, complexity, performance, and application). Suitability determinations also include material composition and processing to ensure component operability, maintainability, fit, form, process, and interfaces for effective performance in the specified environment.

What steps are employed to transition from the qualified/certified design (original SSC) to the suitable replacement SSC accepted by CGD methods?

1. A technical evaluation of the original design is performed by an engineer to specify the critical characteristics, ensuring that both the approach is appropriate and results are based on the failure modes and effects analysis (FMEA) to identify the most severe application. Evaluation of the 10 CFR 50 NRC/10 CFR 830 DOE Hazard/Accident Analysis section of the Documented Safety Analysis with review of the technical safety requirement controls specified will provide the most severe performance criteria to identify the critical characteristics that need to be specified. Specifying these critical characteristics essential for safe performance ensures adequacy or suitability of the CGD replacement component (see Figure 7.2).
2. The dedication plan documents critical characteristics to be verified (physical, performance, or dependability including justification for their selection) derived from the technical evaluation, including methods for acceptance and tolerances for acceptance. Critical characteristics must be verifiable—if not, then the item or service is not a candidate for CGD (see Figure 7.3). This provides reasonable assurance that the item's critical characteristics are conforming based on objective evidence to ensure subsequent performance (EPRI 5652 and TR-102260).
3. NRC IP43004 discusses additional controls for performing technical evaluations and acceptance of commercial grade items or processes using the criteria established in Criterion VII of 10 CFR 50, Appendix B/ASME NQA-1. Additional requirements that are outlined in NRC IP43004 include ASME Section XI, which provides rules for the examination, in-service testing and inspection, and repair and replacement of components and systems in light water-cooled and liquid-metal-cooled nuclear power plants.

Date: 12/21/16

Component: Nilar International—Shielded Shipping Cask for Irradiated PWR Fuel Assemblies Transportation Cask Inner Steel Lid/Inventory Control #Nilar-27 Type 304 Stainless Steel product for further processing

Safety Application: Spent Nuclear Fuel Storage—Structural Integrity; Containment Boundary

Safety Specification: NRC CoC #9235 Rev. 11 Package ID USA/9235/B(U)F-96

Supplier Identification: Hanover Forge, 1406 Longview Road, Pittsburgh, PA

Critical Characteristics for Acceptance:

Dimensions:

1. Diameter   (86.700' +/– 0.500" required / 85' 11.125" actual)

2. Thickness   (9.000" +/– 0.125" required / 8.946" actual)

Fabrication Process: Form and Finish (grind, polish to #7 finish, buff) Disc from Nilar Stock provided to final specification per Procedure #HF-M13 Rev B 10/14/12 as specified on Nilar Drawing #9235-423G Rev C 3/17/09

Raw Material: Type 304SS

Operator: JNW

Procedure: #HF-M13 Rev B

Training Records of Operator: Recertified 10/12/16

Calibration:

Records Critical Characteristics Attributes Inspection: 12/4/16 Calibration of Instruments used for Mechanical Inspection

Sub-Tier Suppliers for CGI: Votive Instruments—Qualified for instrument calibration by NAC Corporate QA 11/7/16

Qualification Method: Nilar Corporate QA Assessment of Votive Instruments (ASME NQA-1 2008 with 2009 Addenda)

Tandem Source Inspector <u>James T. Randall</u> Date <u>2/23/17</u>

Figure 7.2   Source Verification of Supplier for Dedication of Commercial Grade Item

Section A) Item Description

Tandem International—Tandem 100 Spent Nuclear Fuel Cask #72-1014

- Storage Overpack—Concrete Lid with Shield Block and Exit Vents
- Inventory Control #HSO-1

Section B) End-Use/Parent/Host Equipment Information

1. Safety-Related Yes X No Safety-Significant
2. Passive X Active
3. Basic Safety Function
   a. Structural Integrity—Maintain Confinement (Redundant Seals retain Spent Nuclear Fuel within Cask). Ensure Retrievability of SNF Contents. Each cask has passive heat removal maintaining thermal environment independent of intervening actions.
   b. Radiation Shielding—Radiation Protection (gamma and neutron shielding to the Public and On-site Worker i/a/w 10 CFR 72.104, 10 CFR 72.106, 10 CFR 21

Section C) Eligibility for Dedication

1. Commodity or Standard Item Yes <u>No</u>
2. Codes Applicable—Plain Concrete/American Concrete Institute Code #349-85; ASME Code 1995 Edition with Addenda through 1997

Section D) Failure Modes and Effects Analysis (SAR Credible Accidents Involving Cask Lid)

1. Credible Failure Modes:
   a. Thermal—
      i. Off-Normal conditions resulting from Temperature variations from cask contents of 10% failed fuel rods could cause failure of Confinement Boundary.
      ii. Temperature increase caused by Burial in soil with partial blockage of air inlets in concrete overpack lid and without potential for cooling.
   b. Cask Drop/Tip-over Accidents credible
   c. Immersed in Flame—Modeled by ANSYS Computer Code; Risk accepted by NUREG 1536
2. Basis for Selection: 6/1/2000 NRC Safety Analysis Report, Section 9.1 Accident Analysis

Figure 7.3 Commercial Grade Item Dedication—Technical Evaluation

Section E) Critical Characteristics

1. Dimensions/SAR License Overpack Dimensions—Cask Lid:
   a. Dimension: 63.000" +/− 0.003"
   b. Thickness: 48.000" +/− 0.002"
2. Concrete Testing—ASTM C39 Test Specimens
   a. Compressive Strength Criteria—Compressive Strength 4000 psi and Strength Loss considerations at Temperatures >300°C—no strength loss after 4 months per ACI 316/ASTM C1107: Pass
   b. Volume Change—ASTM C1107 criteria
      i. Weight Loss < 0.666%—Pass
      ii. Density (146 lbs/cubic ft) changes to maintain Hydrogen content: Original Density 2.22 g/cc with <0.015 g/cc variation permissible—pass

Review and Approval

Prepared by Thomas Jenson   Date   March 16, 2016
Reviewed by Johnathon Abbott Date   March 29, 2016

Figure 7.3   Commercial Grade Item Dedication—Technical Evaluation (Cont'd)

What are the CGD methods for acceptance?

1. **Inspection and test/receipt inspection** (ASME NQA-1 Part II, Subpart 2.14, 601) requires supplier data regarding the material pedigree (e.g., drawings/specifications, material composition, and processing history) permitting the verification of critical characteristics.
2. **Commercial grade survey** (ASME NQA-1 Part I, 602; Part II, Subpart 2.14, 601) ensures the supplier quality system is adequate through performing a more extensive evaluation with a certificate of conformance submitted for the initial and each subsequent delivery to verify that the system approved earlier has remained unchanged and adheres to procurement contract. The Nuclear Energy Institute (commercial nuclear energy applications) currently endorses the International Laboratory Accreditation Cooperation for international applications to perform accreditation as a substitute for commercial grade surveys and has applied for NRC approval.
3. **Source verification** (ASME NQA-1, Part I, 704.2) establishes that critical characteristics for acceptance (CCFA) are verified using appropriate methods and that the test/inspection instrumentation is adequate with current instrument calibration records ensuring measurements are valid. Objective evidence of information examined during the dedication process and activities observed must be retained including recording the verification method for CCFA (see Figure 7.2 and Case Study 6).
4. **Supplier/item performance record** (ASME NQA-1 Part I, 704.3; Part II, 2.14 604.3) may supplement the previous three acceptance methods but does not suffice for CGD approval. Performance records sufficient to comply with this verification method are stipulated in ASME NQA-1-2009 (see Figure 7.4).

Date Received: 11/6/2016

Commercial Grade Item: MoveX 125 Ton Totem Transfer Cask (for use in Tandem 100 Cask System)

Safety Application: The function of the transfer cask is to provide radiation and structural protection of the Spent Nuclear Fuel during loading, unloading, and transfer operations.

(The MoveX 125 transfer cask is used for various plant operations, such as normal onsite transport of spent nuclear fuel. In the event of a postulated accident, the transfer cask must not suffer permanent deformation to the extent that the ready retrievability or confinement integrity of the Spent Nuclear Fuel is compromised. Structural characteristics as specified in 10 CFR 72.24.)

Supplier: Atlas Fabrication Corporation

Date Qualified: 2/17/16

Specification Stress Limits per ASME Code, Section III, Subsection NF, Class 3; MoveX transfer cask is a carbon steel, lead, steel layered cylinder (steel structural material, SA-516 Grade 70) that possesses sufficient fracture toughness to preclude brittle fracture.

Critical Characteristics for Acceptance: Fracture Toughness to ensure intact following drop accident

Acceptance Method: Charpy V-Notch Test at minimum Service Temperature

Critical Characteristic	Test Method	Specification	Acceptance Criteria	Accept Y/N
Fracture Toughness for Side-Drop Test	Charpy V-Notch Testing at 0 F	ASME Code, Section III, Subsection NF, Articles NF-2300 and NF-2430	Totem 125: Horizontal (side) drop; meet level D Totem stress limits for NF Class 3 components: Shell—3.4.9.1 away from the impacted zone; show lids stay in-place. Transfer Lid- 3.4.4.3.3.3 Show primary and secondary impact Slapdown—3.4.9.2 decelerations are within design basis. (This case is only applicable to Totem.)	Y

Figure 7.4 Commercial Grade Item Acceptance Record

The transfer cask and overpack materials are Charpy V-notch tested in accordance with the ASME Code, Section III, Subsection NF, Articles NF-2300 and NF-2430. Table 3.1.18 in Section 3.1 of the SAR provides the fracture toughness test criteria and temperature for the Charpy V-notch test.

Observations: Acceptable

Technician: James F. Whitmore Date: 12/3/16

Comments: Tandem cask may be made of SA516 Gr. 70, SA515 Gr. 70, or SA36 (with some components having an option for SA203E or SA350-LF3 depending on material availability).
ASQ Energy and Environmental Division
Nuclear Quality Assurance Auditor Training Handbook 2017
ASQC Quality Systems Auditor Training Handbook 1986

Figure 7.4 Commercial Grade Item Acceptance Record (Cont'd)

Section 7.2 Software Used in Design Analyses

7.2.1 Reference Documents Added to Appendix A

As well as the reference documents added by Section 7.1, the following two documents have been added:

1. EPRI 3002002289, "Plant Engineering: Guideline for the Acceptance of Commercial-Grade Design and Analysis Computer Programs Used in Nuclear Safety-Related Applications," Revision 1 of 1025243, Final Report, December 2013
2. NRC RG 1.231, "Acceptance of Commercial-Grade Design and Analysis Computer Programs Used in Safety-Related Applications for Nuclear Power Plants," January 2017

7.2.2 Glossary

EPRI 3002002289

Computer program. A combination of computer instructions and data definitions that enables computer hardware to perform computational or control functions.

Development. The process by which computer programs (including source code) are written or modified.

Legacy software. A term used to describe computer software that has been accepted by means other than those described in the most current regulatory/licensing/QA requirements.

Non-process computer program. Computer program applications that do not run on permanent plant equipment; that is, they are not installed in plant systems, structures, or components.

Process computer program. Any computer program that controls, monitors, interfaces, or communicates with permanent plant equipment governed by the design change process.

Qualification: computer program. The process for ensuring that a computer program design is suitable for its intended application (see *software verification and validation*).

Reasonable assurance. A justifiable level of confidence based on objective and measurable facts, actions, or observations from which adequacy can be inferred.

Software. Computer programs and associated documentation and data pertaining to the operation of a computer system.

Software configuration management. Procedures that include, but are not limited to, configuration identification, change control, and status control.

Software life cycle. The period of time that begins when a software product is conceived and ends when the software is no longer available for use.

Software quality assurance (SQA). The program that establishes quality controls for the development, procurement, operation, use, maintenance, and retirement of software commensurate with its importance to nuclear safety.

Software verification and validation. Process that determines whether the development products of a given activity conform to the requirements of that activity and whether the software satisfies its intended use and the user needs.

Validation. Confirmation by examination and provisions of objective evidence that the particular requirements for a specific intended use are fulfilled.

Verification. Confirmation by examination and provisions of objective evidence that specified requirements have been fulfilled.

7.2.3 Use of Computer Programs in Design Analyses

As the features and capabilities of computer programs becomes greater, emphasis on the use and control of software in the nuclear industry has increased significantly. This section looks at the key elements of computer programs used in design and analysis that are most relevant to an auditor.

The first requirement once the decision has been made to use a computer program in a design analysis is to determine if the application is, in fact, safety-related (important to safety). Computer programs are not, in themselves, safety-related but may be used in safety-related applications.

Computer program applications are classified as safety-related if any function(s) performed by the computer program could prevent associated SSC from performing their safety-related functions. If a postulated failure of a computer program could impact the ability of an associated SSC to perform its safety-related function(s), the computer program application is safety-related.

If the computer program is not being used in a safety-related application, NQA-1-2008/2009 does not apply. However, organizations may apply a graded approach to the NQA-1 process to programs not being used in a safety-related application in case the program might be used in a safety-related application at a later time or just because NQA-1 presents a well-defined software quality method for developing software.

Regardless of the quality method selected, software must be maintained under configuration control. Software configuration management (SCM) includes, but is not limited to configuration identification, change control, and status control. Configuration items shall be maintained under SCM until the software is retired. If an auditor were to apply the principles of configuration management (CM) to the configuration management of software, they would find the process and often the tools for SCM are very similar to CM of facility equipment and engineering documents.

Organizations must also establish a process for documenting, evaluating, and correcting software problems. Software problems include errors and other types of problems (e.g., user mistake) identified by either the software supplier or internal developer. If the problem is determined to be an error, the methods must include not only an evaluation of how the error affects current use of the software but must also address previous uses of the software. The process used to address software problems must address the appropriate requirements of ASME NQA-1-2008/2009, Part 1, Requirement 16. The process to address software problems could be in lieu of or in support of the organization's corrective action program.

7.2.4 Choice of Software

To determine the acceptability of a computer program, the first decision the organization needs to make is whether they will use a pre-verified computer program or verify the computer program within the design analysis.

If the computer program is pre-verified, the computer program shall be verified to show that it produces correct solutions for the encoded mathematical model within defined limits for each parameter employed. One of the aspects related to this requirement that is frequently overlooked by organizations using software for safety-related/ important to safety applications is ensuring that the tests conducted to validate the software include the full range of parameters that will be used during the design or analysis process. If the analysis will include temperatures from 100°C to 300°C, test cases that only go to 250°C are not acceptable. The computer program results may also be verified within the design analysis itself by including the verification and the basis for using the particular computer program for the application.

Documentation of computer programs used in design analyses needs to include identification of any computer calculation, including identification of the computer type; computer program name; and revision, inputs, outputs, evidence of or reference to computer program verification, and the bases (or reference thereto) supporting application of the computer program to the specific physical problem. The detail of the documentation must be sufficiently detailed that a person technically qualified in the use of the computer program can review and understand the documentation and the adequacy of that documentation, with recourse to the originator.

7.2.5 Developed Software

Software developed to be used in safety-related/important to safety applications must be developed in accordance with the process defined in ASME NQA-1-2008/2009, Part 1, Requirements 3 and 11, and ASME NQA-1-2008/2009, Part II, Subpart 2.7.

With the release of the 2008 edition of ASME NQA-1, software development requirements were significantly changed to recognize the various models used to develop software. With the more prescriptive requirements of previous editions removed, the onus is now on the design organization to define the specific model and associated processes to ensure software is developed in a manner compliant with NQA-1-2008/2009.

During an audit of developed software, it is critical that the auditor first ensure that the organization's procedures fully implement the requirements of NQA-1-2008/2009 and then ensure that the organization complies with their own procedures in the development process. Organizations often define stricter requirements than necessary, and it is important for the auditor to remember that if the organization violates its own procedures, even if they are compliant with NQA-1, there still is a potential audit finding.

NQA-1-2008/2009 includes a nonmandatory appendix, NQA-1-2008/2009, Part IV, Subpart 4.1, "Application Appendix: Guide on Quality Assurance Requirements for Computer Software." Section 101.1 presents the concept of "simple and easily understood computer programs," which may be used outside of the controls of NQA-1-2008/2009, Part II, Subpart 2.7. These programs must be fully documented within the design analysis itself.

7.2.6 Acquired Software

Rather than develop the software necessary for a safety-related design analysis, an organization may choose to acquire the software from outside the organization. This includes any source of software, not just commercial suppliers (e.g., professional organizations, university groups, internet open source software). Software may be acquired from a supplier compliant with 10 CFR 50 Appendix B or a non-quality supplier.

7.2.7 10 CFR 50 Appendix B Supplier

A software supplier may submit to the requirements of 10 CFR 50 Appendix B and develop the software in accordance with NQA-1-2008/2009, Part I, Requirements 3 and 11, and Part II, Subpart 2.7. Such a supplier would be subject to audit just as any other approved supplier. Once all the supplier approval processes are completed, the organization can add the software development organization to their approved supplier list. Software acquired from an approved software supplier may be used without further testing, but the procuring organization is responsible for justifying the use of that particular software for that particular application and ensuring that testing encompassed the entire range of parameters that will be used during the design analysis. The organization is also responsible for assuring that the computer program works in the organization's operating environment. Some organizations view this as a form of receiving inspection for software.

There are two pitfalls that auditors need to be aware of when auditing software procured from a 10 CFR 50 Appendix B supplier:

1. Many major software companies do not sell their software directly but rather deal only through "channel partners" or other distribution activities. The auditor needs to ensure that the organization has audited the distributor and added them to their approved supplier list or there is a documented process that allows organizations to procure safety-related software from a supplier not on the approved supplier list.
2. Many major software companies sell "QA Packages" that include such things as problem sets and a commitment to an error notification process. They contend that if the organization does not buy the QA Package, their software is not 10 CFR 50 Appendix B and 10 CFR Part 21 compliant. The auditor needs to ensure that if the supplier requires the buyer to purchase a QA Package to be 10 CFR 50 Appendix B and 10 CFR Part 21 compliant, that the organization being audited did procure the QA Package and kept it up to date.

7.2.8 Commercial (Non-10 CFR 50 Appendix B) Supplier

This includes software downloaded for free or otherwise acquired from a supplier who does not offer 10 CFR 50 Appendix B software (also see Section 7.3.6 for other examples). Such software must be dedicated (see Section 7.3).

7.2.9 Documentation

Development, acquisition, and use of software generates a large number of documents. These documents are typically referred to as **configuration items**. Auditors need to review these documents against the criteria of NQA-1-2008/2009, Part I, Requirement 6, Section 100, which requires that the preparation, issue, and change of documents that specify quality requirements or prescribe activities affecting quality that include instructions such as development standards and user manuals, procedures such as plans and best practices, and drawings such as logic diagrams and architecture descriptions must be controlled to ensure that correct documents are being employed. Such documents, including changes thereto, shall be reviewed for adequacy and approved for release by authorized personnel. One example within the software realm would be a test plan that must be controlled, reviewed, and approved before using the plan to conduct software testing activities.

Software configuration items such as computer programs and data need to be controlled as well and may be a part of organization's document control program; however, they are often controlled by the organization's information technology department. This is an acceptable approach, and the auditor could use NQA-1-2008/2009, Part I, Requirement 3, Section 802, "Software Configuration Management," and Part II, Subpart 2.7, Section 203, to verify acceptable SCM practices for control of configuration items.

Section 7.3 CGD of Software Used in Design and Analysis

7.3.1 Reference Documents Added to Appendix A

1. ASME NQA-1-2008/2009, Part I, Requirement 3, "Design Control," August 31, 2009
2. ASME NQA-1-2008/2009, Part I, Requirement 6, "Document Control," August 31, 2009
3. ASME NQA-1-2008/2009, Part II, Subpart 2.7, "Quality Assurance Requirements for Computer Software for Nuclear Facility Applications," August 31, 2009

7.3.2 Glossary

EPRI 3002002289

Validation. Confirmation by examination and provisions of objective evidence that the particular requirements for a specific intended use are fulfilled.

Verification. Confirmation by examination and provisions of objective evidence that specified requirements have been fulfilled.

7.3.3 Purpose

CGD is used to accept commercially procured computer programs that are used in safety-related design and analysis applications in which the results provided by the software are not independently verified for each calculation. A commercially procured computer program is one that is developed in a commercial environment and not developed under a QA program that meets the requirements of 10 CFR 50 Appendix B. Figure 7.5 illustrates the CGD of process.

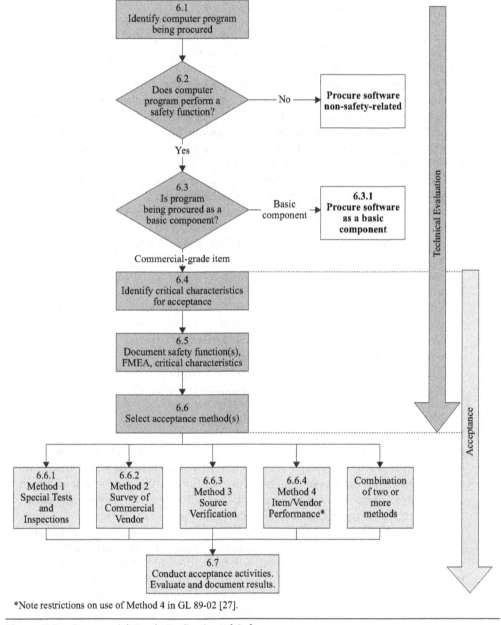

*Note restrictions on use of Method 4 in GL 89-02 [27].

Figure 7.5   Commercial Grade Dedication of Software

Computer programs are classified as safety-related if any function(s) performed by the computer program could prevent associated SSC from performing their safety-related functions. If a postulated failure of a computer program could impact the ability of an associated SSC to perform its safety-related function(s), the computer program is safety-related.

ASME NQA-1-2008/2009, Part I, Requirement 3, Section 401, permits commercial grade programs to be used in safety-related applications without being dedicated if the results are verified as part of the design or analysis.

7.3.4 Technical Evaluation

The dedication process begins with a technical evaluation completed by the responsible engineering organization. The technical evaluation consists of:

- Identifying the computer program scope of use and function;
  - This is based upon the dedicating entity's proposed application for which the computer program is being procured. The organization preparing the technical evaluation should include other possible uses of the program and perhaps expand the dedication to address multiple uses of the program.
- Determining the safety classification of the computer program being procured, and identifying applicable safety functions;
  - The safety classification of computer programs is performed to determine if any of the function(s) performed by the computer program could prevent associated SSCs from performing their safety-related functions. If a postulated failure of a computer program could impact the ability of an associated SSC to perform its safety-related function(s), the computer program is safety-related. Therefore, functions of a computer program associated with SSCs should be identified as part of the safety classification process for computer programs.
  - Note that computer programs are not, of themselves, safety-related or non-safety-related. It is the intended use of the program that determines the classification. Program X might be used in a non-safety-related application today and in a safety-related application tomorrow.
  - Programs being used in non-safety-related applications cannot be dedicated. For simplicity's sake, organizations might use the same process to qualify non-safety-related computer programs as for dedicating safety-related codes, but it is not actually dedication.
- Performing FMEA to help identify if failure of the computer program could result in failure of the plant SSCs and to identify characteristics of the computer program necessary to ensure that it will perform its safety function;
  - The dedicating entity postulates failures of the computer program and then evaluates whether or not those postulated failures could prevent associated SSCs from performing their designated safety-related function.
  - While the EPRI guide discusses various failure mechanisms (i.e., conceptual error, arithmetic error, and interface error), it is probably more useful to determine if the postulated errors will be evident to the analyst/designer.
  - FMEA is not usually very useful for software because it is almost impossible to identify postulated failures without detailed analysis of the code that is not possible for commercial grade computer programs. However, there are instances where FMEA is possible and is worthwhile.

- Identifying the critical characteristics and acceptance methods that will be used to verify critical characteristics;
  - It is important to remember that acceptance is not validation.
  - Identifying critical characteristics is an essential step in the dedication process. Critical characteristics identified during the technical evaluation are verified during the acceptance process to provide reasonable assurance that the computer program being accepted is capable of performing its intended safety-related function.
  - The number and nature of the critical characteristics are to be based on the intended safety function, application requirements, complexity, credible failure modes and effects, and performance requirements.
  - It is absolutely essential that, just like validation, the range of parameters specified in defining the critical characteristics must include the range of parameters being used during the design/analysis. If the technical evaluation author states that the results must be accurate from 100°C to 400°C, the design/analysis cannot include temperatures above 400°C.
  - Critical characteristics should almost always include tolerances. Complex computer programs often do not produce a single number as a result so the acceptance criteria may have to define a distribution or even a plane as a result.
  - In addition to critical characteristics, the technical evaluation shall include the capabilities and limitations for intended use.
- Specifying the appropriate technical, quality, and documentation requirements;
  - Technical requirements should be a translation of the design of the software into procurement requirements. The licensee should develop procurement documents that specify the software requirements to ensure that the vendor meets the design intent.
  - The quality requirements for computer software should be developed and specified in the procurement document to invoke the necessary supplier controls over manufacturing, design, purchasing, and error reporting activities that ensure that the specified technical requirements of the software are met. Supplier documentation requirements should correlate with the specified technical and quality requirements and be specific as to the content.
- When necessary, performing an equivalency evaluation to determine the suitability of the proposed replacement computer program that is not identical to the original;
- Documenting the technical evaluation and ensuring that provisions are in place to document the acceptance process and results of acceptance activities;
  - Results of the technical evaluation may be documented in various formats. For example, critical characteristics might be identified by the dedicating entity in various types of documentation, such as:
    - Software requirement specification
    - Procurement specification
    - Verification plans
    - Test or inspection results
    - Procedures or work instructions
    - User guides including installation instructions
  - The basis or reasons for critical characteristic selection should also be evident in the documentation.

7.3.5 Select Acceptance Methods

The same four acceptance methods are available for dedication of software as with other dedications:

1. Special tests and inspections
2. Commercial grade survey
3. Source verification (that is, inspections or witness hold points)
4. Acceptable item and supplier performance record (that is, historical records of acceptable performance)

Because of a supplier's interest in protecting intellectual property, it is unlikely that methods 2 or 3 will be possible. But, if the supplier allows it, they are acceptable for dedication. As with other dedication activities, method 4 can only be used in conjunction with one of the other methods.

7.3.6 Documenting Results

The results of acceptance activities should be documented and clearly identified as acceptable or not acceptable. Documentation should be clear and understandable enough to ensure that another person with similar training and qualification can easily arrive at the same conclusions included in the evaluation and acceptance package.

Documentation shall be reviewed and approved (ASME NQA-1-2008/2009, Part I, Requirement 6). The documentation and associated computer program(s) shall establish the current baseline.

7.3.7 Configuration Management

The acquired software shall be identified and controlled during the dedication process. Subsequent revisions of accepted software received from organizations not required to follow ASME NQA-1-2008/2009, Part II, Subpart 2.7, shall be dedicated.

Section 7.4 Control of Electronic Records

7.4.1 Reference Documents Added to Appendix A

Authority	Citation	Comments
Regulations	NQA-1-2008/2009, Part I, Requirement 17, "Quality Assurance Records" NRC 10 CFR 50 Appendix B "Quality Assurance Criteria for Nuclear Power Plants and Fuel Reprocessing Plants" Though not dealing with electronic records specifically, NRC documents refer back to this appendix as the primary requirements for records. "Safety Evaluation of Duke Energy Carolinas, LLC, Amendment 40 to the Quality Assurance Topical Report (TAC Nos. MF5055, MF5056, MF5057, MF5058, MF5059, MF5060 and MF5061)" https:// www.nrc.gov/docs/ML1509/ML15099A561.pdf	

Authority	Citation	Comments
Standards	IEEE Std. 730-2014, "Standard for Software Engineering Quality Assurance Plans" IEEE Std. 828-2012, "Standard for Software Configuration Management Plans" IEEE Std. 1012-2016 (R1992), "Standard for Software Verification and Validation Plans" IEEE Std. 1028-2008 (R1993), "Standard for Software Reviews and Audits" IEEE Std. 1062-2015, "Recommended Practice for Software Acquisitions" IEEE Std. 14764-2006, "Standard for Software Maintenance" IEEE Std. 1228-1994, "Standard for Software Safety Plans" http://www.ieee.org/index.html "Electronic Records Management Software Applications Design Criteria Standard" [a DOD standard that has been reissued by DOE] https://www.energy.gov/sites/prod/files/cioprod/documents/DOD5015.2Standard.pdf	
Guidance	NQA-1-2008/2009, Part III, Subpart 3.1, Nonmandatory Appendix 17A-1, "Guidance on Quality Assurance Records" NQA-1-2008/2009, Part III, Subpart 3.1, Nonmandatory Appendix 17A-2, "Guidance for Electronic Records" NRC GL 88-18, "Plant Record Storage on Optical Disks" https://www.nrc.gov/reading-rm/doc-collections/gen-comm/gen-letters/1988/gl88018.html NRC RIS 00-018, "Guidance on Managing Quality Assurance Records in Electronic Media" https://www.nrc.gov/reading-rm/doc-collections/gen-comm/reg-issues/2000/ri00018.html NUREG-0800 17.5, "Quality Assurance Program Description—Design Certification, Early Site Permit and New License Applicants" https://www.nrc.gov/docs/ML1503/ML15037A441.pdf "Change to Quality Assurance Topical Report, Amendment 40" [letter from Duke Energy Carolinas, LLC, related to the above regulation] https://www.nrc.gov/docs/ML1430/ML14300A011.pdf	

Authority	Citation	Comments
	"Regulatory Information Summary 00-18, 'Guidance on the Management of Quality Assurance Records on Electronic Media'" [letter from NIRMA related to the above RIS]. https://www.nrc.gov/docs/ML1120/ML11200A122.pdf This NIRMA letter contains an important table at the end showing the difference between the 1998 versions and 2011 versions of the four NIRMA TGs listed below. NIRMA TG-11, "Authentication of Records and Media" NIRMA TG-15, "Management of Electronic Records" NIRMA TG-16, "Software Configuration Management and Quality Assurance" NIRMA TG-21, "Electronic Records Protection and Restoration" DOE Records Management homepage https://energy.gov/cio/office-chief-information-officer/services/guidance/records-management [US Food and Drug Administration] 21 CFR 11 "Electronic Records; Electronic Signatures" https://www.accessdata.fda.gov/scripts/cdrh/cfdocs/cfcfr/CFRSearch.cfm?CFRPart=11 http://www-pub.iaea.org/MTCD/publications/PDF/trs467_web.pdf NRC presentation on "Electronic Signatures" (n.d.) https://www.nrc.gov/docs/ML1125/ML11256A069.pdf NRC presentation on "Guidance for Electronic Submissions to the NRC" (2017) https://www.nrc.gov/docs/ML1303/ML13031A056.pdf International Atomic Energy Agency (IAEA), "Long Term Preservation of Information for Decommissioning Projects," Technical Report No. 467 (Vienna: IAEA, 2008) The Nuclear Information Technology Strategic Leadership (NITSL) group is a nuclear industry group of all nuclear generation utilities that exchange information related to information technology management and quality issues. https://www.nitsl.org/about	
Directives (Requirements)	NRC IP 88113 "Control of the Electronic Management of Data" https://www.nrc.gov/docs/ML0605/ML060530433.pdf	

7.4.2 Glossary

NARA glossary https://www.archives.gov/files/records-mgmt/rm-glossary-of-terms
.pdf

21 CFR 11.3

1. *Digital signature* means an electronic signature based upon cryptographic methods of originator authentication, computed by using a set of rules and a set of parameters such that the identity of the signer and the integrity of the data can be verified.
2. *Electronic record* means any combination of text, graphics, data, audio, pictorial, or other information representation in digital form that is created, modified, maintained, archived, retrieved, or distributed by a computer system.
3. *Electronic signature* means a computer data compilation of any symbol or series of symbols executed, adopted, or authorized by an individual to be the legally binding equivalent of the individual's handwritten signature.

Requirements to keep records pertaining to quality issues have been around for years. Only in the past few decades have we gained the ability to move from paper records in mass warehouses (perhaps similar to the scene at the end of *Indiana Jones and the Raiders of the Lost Ark*) to having quickly retrievable, compact electronic storage. Even with all of the advantages of electronic records, we are faced with the challenge of how to maintain them for the long durations required. Mission tapes from the 1960s/1970s Apollo missions are nearly unreadable 40 years later. Will PDF files on hard drives be readable 40 years from now, even if the hardware is?

Primary issues to consider with electronic records are:

- Verification
- Validation
- Authentication (especially control of digital signatures)
- Storage management
- Standards applied to the digital and physical environment
- Security
- Access control
- Records management programs (application and infrastructure)
- Disaster recovery methods

7.4.3 10 CFR 50 Appendix B Regulatory Requirements for Records

Section XVII, "Quality Assurance Records," of 10 CFR 50 Appendix B serves as the foundation for the requirements for maintenance of records, whether hard copy, microfiche, or electronic:

Sufficient records shall be maintained to furnish evidence of activities affecting quality. The records shall include at least the following: Operating logs and the results of reviews, inspections, tests, audits, monitoring of work performance, and materials analyses. The records shall also include closely related data such as qualifications of personnel, procedures, and equipment. Inspection and test records shall, as a minimum, identify the inspector or data recorder, the type of observation, the results, the acceptability, and the action taken in connection with any deficiencies noted. Records shall be identifiable and retrievable. Consistent with applicable regulatory requirements, the applicant shall establish requirements concerning record retention, such as duration, location, and assigned responsibility.

7.4.4 NRC Requirements

A primary current document for records requirements is NUREG-0800 17.5 "Quality Assurance Program Description—Design Certification, Early Site Permit and New License Applicants," Section Q, "Quality Assurance Records (Criterion XVII)." Salient points include "measures are required to be established that ensure that sufficient records of completed items and activities affecting quality are appropriately stored (ANSI/ANS 3.2)." The standard further specifies the types of information that should be treated as records: "Records shall be identifiable and retrievable" is listed as a requirement. The applicant is also expected to establish requirements for retention duration, location, and protecting records from destruction "from destruction by fire, flooding, tornadoes, insects, and rodents and from deterioration by extremes in temperature and humidity."

GL No. 88-18 "Plant Record Storage on Optical Disks" was published by the NRC in 1988 in order to "approve the use of optical disk document imaging systems for the storage and retrieval of record copies of quality assurance records." RIS 00-018 "Guidance on Managing Quality Assurance Records in Electronic Media" was published soon after in order to provide "additional guidance on the acceptability of new information management technologies." This document referenced four 1998 Nuclear Information and Records Management Association (NIRMA) TG for use. Nine IEEE documents that nuclear facilities "may use" to supplement the NIRMA guidelines were also listed.

In May 2015, the NRC Office of New Reactors published the "Evaluation of Duke Energy Carolinas, LLC, Amendment 40 to the Quality Assurance Topical Report." This letter approved a requested change to the subject document to reference the 2011 NIRMA TGs rather than the1998 version of the guides referenced in RIS 00-018. The letter states:

> The newer 2011 NIRMA . . . changes are based on the development and imple-
> mentation of enterprise content management systems, web-based technolo-
> gies, and higher capacity LAN/WAN networks. The key difference between
> the 1998 and 2011 NIRMA technical guides is that the newer technical guides
> provide better understanding and controls for an integrated approach to the
> creation, capture, and maintenance of records using electronic tools.

The letter authorized the following newer versions of the NIRMA TGs listed in RIS 00-018 for use at the subject plant locations:

TG-11-2011, "Authentication of Records and Media,"
TG-15-2011, "Management of Electronic Records"
TG-16-2011, "Software Quality Assurance Documentation and Records"
TG-21-2011, "Required Records Protection, Disaster Recovery and Business Continuation"

Information from these documents will be included in the requirement/subject list below. One could assume that this letter is a precedent for future NRC direction, and perhaps permission for others to use will be forthcoming. However, the older versions from RIS 00-018 are still official NRC policy at the time of this writing.

The following subsection cover the specific requirements for electronic records that the QA program must address.

7.4.5 Usage

NUREG-0800 17.5 contains provisions for the generation, distribution, use, maintenance, storage, and disposition of electronic records, as well as administration, receipt, retrieval capabilities for all records. NIRMA TG-15-98 states that "due to the unique vulnerabilities of electronic records, special measures should be taken to ensure their usability." The document states electronic records must be retrievable, intelligible, understandable and reliable, and requirements are listed for each of these four terms. Original records/media should not be used for work purposes or maintained online.

Refer to "Guidance for Electronic Submissions to the NRC" (included in the References) when sending electronic reports/records to the NRC.

7.4.6 Procedures

NIRMA TG-16-98 contains requirements for a Software Quality Assurance Plan (SQAP), a Software Configuration Management Plan (SCMP), a Software Quality Assurance (SQA) Policy, and a SQA Program. The SQA Policy should "consider interfaces with":

- Information services/information technology
- Regulatory compliance
- Engineering management
- Configuration management
- Information and records management
- Site corrective

NRC IP 88113 states the following:

If the licensee intends to rely on the electronic record as its official record, it is of the utmost importance that a statement of intent to rely on the electronic record exists. . . . The official record, once designated by the licensee, must be subject to rigorous procedures for creation, modification, and destruction under a records-management program. A statement designating the electronic record as the official record must exist as part of the licensee's overall records-management program.

7.4.7 Media

NUREG-0800 17.5 includes guidance on acceptable media on which electronic records are created and stored. Provisions to verify that the media is appropriate, suitable for the capture or storage of records, and error-/defect-free are also listed.

NIRMA TG-11-1998 provides a detailed listing of types of media and storage requirements. Microform and magnetic media requirements are provided. A general guidance in the document is that the media should outlive the required retention period or be able to be regenerated or migrated to other media before the end of life of the media.

7.4.8 Software

NIRMA TG-15-1998 provides a listing of "several existing and de facto standards [that] may be used." These include (but are not limited to) JPEG, MPEG, AVI, HTML, RTF, and PDF formats.

NRC Inspection Procedure 88113 points out that most file formats are patented by proprietary companies, and those companies may go out of business and/or stop supporting the format. As a result, the licensee may be unable to access and view their electronic records. IP 88113 notes that "there is no guaranteed way to avoid this, but if the format adopted is widely used, it is more likely to be supported for years to come." It adds: "The licensee should adopt media that are mainstream, widely-used devices that comply with industry standards—avoid both cutting-edge and obsolete technologies."

The software itself used to manage electronic records should meet software QA requirements. NIRMA TG-16 calls for several software QA documents, a graded approach, and classification of software and life cycle development practices. The TG does make reference to NITSL-SQA-2005-02. Further discussion of software QA is contained in Section 7.3 of this Handbook.

7.4.9 Hardware

NUREG-0800 17.5 lists requirements to safeguard against equipment malfunction or human error related to electronic records storage.

7.4.10 Access/Security

NUREG-0800 17.5 requires that access controls, user privileges, and other appropriate security controls must be established. NIRMA TG-15-1998 states that "physical security is required for designated electronic data (i.e., limiting physical access to the hardware, assuring fire protection, maintaining an inventory, maintaining data security)." Also, sensitive data should not be stored on unsecured systems, and "special measures" should be taken for removable media.

NIRMA TG-15-1998 contains the following specific security requirements:

- When a master list of access identifiers is maintained in a text file, it should be encrypted
- Access rights should be revoked on transfer, retirement, resignation, or termination of the employees to whom they were assigned
- Access identifiers should be associated with specific privileges, such as the ability to retrieve records or to add records to a file
- Whenever a predefined number of consecutive invalid attempts to access the system by a single user are made, the system should invalidate that access identifier
- Continuing need for specific access privileges should be verified at regular intervals
- Additional security measures may be applied to certain specific records or quality data (i.e., proprietary, safeguards or confidential) as deemed appropriate
- Four types of document access controls or levels of permission are used by systems: read (browse), write (update), delete, and approve permissions

7.4.11 Audits/Inspections

NUREG-0800 17.5 states that "magnetic and optical media should be tested periodically to identify any loss of data, to ensure that they are free of permanent errors, and that the record system hardware/software still supports the retrieval of the records."

NIRMA TG-11-1998 also lists specific testing for magnetic media, including cleaning requirements, inspections every three years, and limitations on the number of errors found on the media.

NIRMA TG-15-1998 calls for performing and documenting audits and inspections of systems, applications, media, and processes used in the generation of electronic records to ensure electronic record integrity. "A statistical sample of media records should be read each year to identify any loss of data and to discover and correct the causes of data loss. If errors are discovered, other media which might have been affected by the same cause (i.e., poor quality media, high usage, poor environment, improper handling) should be read and corrected as appropriate." "Magnetic computer tapes should be tested no more than 6 months prior to using them to store electronic records that are scheduled for permanent or long-term retention."

Review NRC Inspection Procedure 88113 when developing inspection criteria.

7.4.12 Training

NUREG-0800 17.5. Training should be provided for individuals or organizations in charge of electronic records. NIRMA TG-15-1998 provides specific training requirements and roles and responsibilities of managers of electronic records.

7.4.13 Labels/Retention/Retrievability

NUREG-0800 17.5. In addition to indexing information requirements, the software name, version, and equipment (hardware) used to produce and maintain the electronic media must be recorded.

NIRMA TG-11-1998. Labels for electronic media should include the originating office, title, data begin and end dates, software version used, record density, type of internal labels and system on which it was produced.

NIRMA TG-15-1998 contains extensive requirements for record retention schedules and retention system requirements.

7.4.14 Authentication

NUREG-0800 17.5 contains a number of authentication requirements. "Authentication is accomplished by manually affixing seal, signature, an electronic representation (user ID/password combination, digital signature) or other acceptable process control that ensures genuineness, validity, or reliability." Users should have a unique user ID/password for access. Controls to ensure data integrity and prevent unauthorized alteration or erasure are required.

NIRMA TG-11-1998. Electronic media are allowed to be treated as "record copies" after proper certification as an exact duplicate of the original record.

NIRMA TG-15-1998. "Electronic records and media should be turned over to the authorized storage organization/facility as soon as the document has been authenticated."

7.4.15 Correction

NUREG-0800 17.5. Records are corrected in accordance with procedures that provide for appropriate review or approval by the originating organization. The correction includes the date and the identification of the person authorized to issue such correction. For records stored in electronic media, a new record is to be generated when substantial corrections or changes to previous electronic records are required.

NIRMA TG-11-1998 provides guidance for how to correct electronic media, and "Corrections, changes or supplements to records should have the same review and authentication requirements as the original record."

7.4.16 Copying/Migration

NUREG-0800 17.5. An electronic record migration/regeneration program is implemented for electronic records stored in media with a standard life expectancy that fails to meet the specific retention period. This program is implemented in accordance with documented procedures that provide for appropriate record authentication, quality verification of the completion, and accuracy of the data transferred. NIRMA TG-11-1998 also provides similar controls.

7.4.17 Storage/Disaster Planning

NUREG-0800 17.5 states that "electronic media should be stored in a dust-free environment, away from electronic devices and demagnetizing equipment. Media should be maintained at the constant temperature of 40 to 80 degrees Fahrenheit, with a constant relative humidity of 30 to 50 percent." The applicant's program must implement GL 88-18, "Plant Record Storage on Optical Disks" (Appendix B/RIS 00-18).

NIRMA TG-11-1998 provides temperature and humidity specifications for optical media (such as CD-ROM).

NIRMA TG-15-1998 requires maintaining a duplicate copy of designated data as a backup in case recovery is needed: "Backup copies should be stored in a different area from the on-line copy to prevent possible destruction by the same source that destroyed the on-line copy." The original hard copy record is allowed to be destroyed if the electronic record has been approved and indexed, if this meets other regulatory, business, or insurance requirements. It is "strongly recommend[ed]" that draft documents of records should not be retained unless necessary for a business need.

NIRMA TG-15-1998 states the following requirements for storage facilities. "All electronic records storage should be conducted inside the storage facility. Electronic devices or demagnetizing equipment are not allowed in the facility. All media and containers should be examined on entry or exit from the facility. Electronic media should be shielded from electronic signals."

NIRMA TG-21 contains full information on emergency planning and response for electronic records. The document includes the following sections:

- Section 4, "Disaster Response Team Responsibilities"
- Section 5, "Disaster Response Plan Development"
- Section 6, "Prevention Planning"
- Section 7, "Response and Recovery Planning"
- Section 8, "Post-Disaster Planning"
- Section 9, "Testing and Maintenance"

Appendix A of TG-21 is a table of "Recovery Options for Water-Damaged Collections and Records." For example, the options for CD-ROMs are air-dry and "dehumidification-dry."

7.4.18 Destruction

NIRMA TG-15-1998 contains the following requirements for destruction of electronic records:

- Electronic records scheduled for destruction are reviewed electronically on-screen to facilitate disposition action decisions
- Electronic records scheduled for destruction are disposed of in a manner that ensures protection of sensitive, proprietary, or confidential information
- Computer media previously used for electronic records containing sensitive, proprietary, confidential, or security information are not reused
- The records destruction process is suspended in the case of foreseeable, pending, or actual litigation or government investigation
- The responsible party assigned to destroy the records should decide the appropriate method of destruction for the media contained on the Destroyed Records Inventory Form. Burning, shredding, disposal in an on-site landfill, or electronic erasure are approved methods for the destruction of records. For security, proprietary, or confidential electronic records, electronic erasure SHOULD NOT be used as the means of destruction.
- Only by degaussing, or by using a program that writes an alternating pattern of zeros and ones over the data to be erased can destruction be assured

Section 7.5 Counterfeit, Fraudulent, and Suspect Items

7.5.1 Reference Documents Added to Appendix A

Authority	Citation	Comments
Regulations	NRC RIS 2015-08, "Oversight of Counterfeit, Fraudulent, and Suspect Items in the Nuclear Industry" https://www.nrc.gov/docs/ML1500/ML15008A191.pdf	
(Excerpt from Section 7.5)	From 10 CFR 50 Appendix B Criterion VII, "Control of Purchased Material, Equipment, and Services" Criterion VIII, "Identification and Control of Material, Parts, and Components" Criterion X, "Inspection" Criterion XV, "Nonconforming Materials, Parts, or Components" Criterion XVI, "Corrective Action"	

(Excerpt from Section 7.5)	From 10 CFR 830.122(c) Criterion 3, "Management/ Quality Improvement" (1) Establish and implement processes to detect and prevent quality problems. (2) Identify, control, and correct items, services, and processes that do not meet established requirements. (3) Identify the causes of problems and work to prevent recurrence as a part of correcting the problem. (4) Review item characteristics, process implementation, and other quality-related information to identify items, services, and processes needing improvement.	
Directives (requirements)	DOE O 414.1D Chg 1 (Admin Chg), Quality Assurance https://www.directives.doe.gov/directives-documents/400-series/0414.1-BOrder-d-admchg1	
Standards (invoked)	ASME NQA-1, "Quality Assurance Requirements for Nuclear Facility Applications"	
(Excerpt from Section 7.5)	**REQUIREMENT 8, Identification and Control of Items** **100 BASIC** Controls shall be established to assure that only correct and accepted items are used or installed. Identification shall be maintained on the items or in documents traceable to the items, or in a manner that assures that identification is established and maintained. **REQUIREMENT 15, Control of Nonconforming Items** **100 BASIC** Items that do not conform to specified requirements shall be controlled to prevent inadvertent installation or use. Controls shall provide for identification, documentation, evaluation, segregation when practical, and disposition of nonconforming items, and for notification to affected organizations. [Sections 200, 300, and 400 refer to Identification, Segregation, and Disposition, respectively] **REQUIREMENT 16, Corrective Action** **100 BASIC** Conditions adverse to quality shall be identified promptly and corrected as soon as practicable. In the case of a significant condition adverse to quality, the cause of the condition shall be determined, and corrective action taken to preclude recurrence. The identification, cause, and corrective action for significant conditions adverse to quality shall be documented and reported to appropriate levels of management. Completion of corrective actions shall be verified.	

Practice	http://www.gidep.org/GIDEP (Government-Industry Data Exchange Program) is a cooperative activity between government and industry. Does include a reporting database as well as product information, metrology, engineering, and reliability reports and documentation.	
Guidance	NRC Main Page and Library of CSFI documents https://www.nrc.gov/about-nrc/cfsi.html; https://www.nrc.gov/about-nrc/cfsi/guidance.html#policy-issues NRC SECY-11-0154, "An Agency-Wide Approach to Counterfeit, Fraudulent and Suspect Items" https://www.nrc.gov/docs/ML1122/ML112200150.pdf NRC GL 89-02, "Actions to Improve the Detection of Counterfeit and Fraudulently Marked Products" https://www.nrc.gov/reading-rm/doc-collections/gen-comm/gen-letters/1989/gl89002.html NRC IN 2008-04, "Counterfeit Parts Supplied to Nuclear Power Plants" https://www.nrc.gov/docs/ML0936/ML093620098.pdf NRC IN No. 89-70, "Possible Indications of Misrepresented Vendor Products" https://www.nrc.gov/reading-rm/doc-collections/gen-comm/info-notices/1989/in89070.html NRC IN 2013-15, "Willful Misconduct/Record Falsification And Nuclear Safety Culture" https://www.nrc.gov/docs/ML1314/ML13142A437.pdf Includes descriptions of willful record falsification, and counterfeit parts. https://www.nrc.gov/docs/ML1507/ML15075A434.pdf NEI 14-05A "Guidelines for the Use of Accreditation in Lieu of Commercial Grade Surveys for Procurement of Laboratory Calibration and Test Services," Revision 0 https://www.nrc.gov/docs/ML1507/ML15075A434.pdf Primarily CGD but does contain information on CSFI on pp. 18 and A-1. **EPRI Documents** "Plant Support Engineering: Counterfeit and Fraudulent Items Mitigating the Increasing Risk, Revision 1 of 1019163" https://www.epri.com/#/pages/product/000000003002002276/ See also https://www.nrc.gov/docs/ML1424/ML14245A078.pdf	

| | "Keeping Counterfeit and Fraudulent Items Out of the Nuclear Supply Chain," an article by an EPRI author overviewing EPRI SFCI efforts. http://www.nuclear-exchange.com/pdf/tp_counterfeit_tannenbaum.pdf DOE Suspect/Counterfeit Items Resource Handbook https://www.standards.doe.gov/standards-documents/1200/1221-bhdbk-2016/@@images/file DOE Office of Health, Safety and Security, "Suspect/Counterfeit Items Awareness Training Manual" https://energy.gov/ehss/downloads/suspectcounterfeit-items-awareness-training-manual DOD Counterfeit Part information, published by the Defense Acquisition University (DAU). https://dap.dau.mil/acquipedia/Pages/ArticleDetails.aspx?aid=5ea0eba7-13f0-40be-9ec7-0e1fa52934ad Several references to other documents and websites. Government Accountability Office, "Counterfeit Parts: DOD Needs to Improve Reporting and Oversight to Reduce Supply Chain Risk," February 2016 http://www.gao.gov/assets/680/675227.pdf Lockheed Martin, "Counterfeit Materials Prevention," February 2019 https://www.lockheedmartin.com/content/dam/lockheed-martin/eo/documents/suppliers/rms/rms-quality-counterfeit.pdf A document listing expectations for suppliers to Lockheed Martin. Focused on DOD, it does, however, contain several valid principles and is a good example of documenting procurement expectations. | |

7.5.2 Glossary

10 CFR 21.3

Basic component. (1)(i) When applied to nuclear power plants licensed under 10 CFR Part 50 or Part 52 of this chapter, basic component means a structure, system, or component, or part thereof that affects its safety function necessary to assure:

A) The integrity of the reactor coolant pressure boundary;

B) The capability to shut down the reactor and maintain it in a safe shutdown condition; or

C) The capability to prevent or mitigate the consequences of accidents that could result in potential offsite exposures comparable to those referred to in § 50.34(a)(1), § 50.67(b)(2), or § 100.11 of this chapter, as applicable.

(ii) Basic components are items designed and manufactured under a QA program complying with appendix B to Part 50 of this chapter, or commercial grade items which have successfully completed the dedication process.

(2) When applied to standard design certifications under subpart C of Part 52 of this chapter and standard design approvals under Part 52 of this chapter, basic component means the design or procurement information approved or to be approved within the scope of the design certification or approval for a structure, system, or component, or part thereof, that affects its safety function necessary to assure:

    (i) The integrity of the reactor coolant pressure boundary;

    (ii) The capability to shut down the reactor and maintain it in a safe shutdown condition; or

    (iii) The capability to prevent or mitigate the consequences of accidents that could result in potential offsite exposures comparable to those referred to in §§ 50.34(a)(1), 50.67(b)(2), or 100.11 of this chapter, as applicable.

(3) When applied to other facilities and other activities licensed under 10 CFR Parts 30, 40, 50 (other than nuclear power plants), 60, 61, 63, 70, 71, or 72 of this chapter, basic component means a structure, system, or component, or part thereof, that affects their safety function, that is directly procured by the licensee of a facility or activity subject to the regulations in this part and in which a defect or failure to comply with any applicable regulation in this chapter, order, or license issued by the Commission could create a substantial safety hazard.

(4) In all cases, basic component includes safety-related design, analysis, inspection, testing, fabrication, replacement of parts, or consulting services that are associated with the component hardware, design certification, design approval, or information in support of an early site permit application under Part 52 of this chapter, whether these services are performed by the component supplier or others.

Defect means:

(1) A deviation in a basic component delivered to a purchaser for use in a facility or an activity subject to the regulations in this part if, on the basis of an evaluation, the deviation could create a substantial safety hazard;

(2) The installation, use, or operation of a basic component containing a defect as defined in this section;

(3) A deviation in a portion of a facility subject to the early site permit, standard design certification, standard design approval, construction permit, combined license or manufacturing licensing requirements of Part 50 or Part 52 of this chapter, provided the deviation could, on the basis of an evaluation, create a substantial safety hazard and the portion of the facility containing the deviation has been offered to the purchaser for acceptance;

(4) A condition or circumstance involving a basic component that could contribute to the exceeding of a safety limit, as defined in the technical specifications of a license for operation issued under Part 50 or Part 52 of this chapter; or

(5) An error, omission or other circumstance in a design certification, or standard design approval that, on the basis of an evaluation, could create a substantial safety hazard.

Defective item. A defective item or material is any item or material that does not meet the commercial standard or procurement requirements as defined by catalogues, proposals, procurement specifications, design specifications, testing requirements, contacts or the like. It does not include parts or services that fail or are otherwise found to be inadequate because of random failures or errors within the accepted reliability level. Manufacturers generally notify their customers when defective items are identified through such mechanisms as recall notices. Such notices may be directly sent to customers or may appear in Federal agency or industry.

DOE Suspect/Counterfeit Items Awareness Training Manual

Counterfeit item. A counterfeit item is a suspect item that is a copy or substitute without legal right or authority to do so or one whose materials, performance, or characteristics are knowingly misrepresented by the vendor, supplier, distributor, or manufacturer.

Deviation. Deviation means a departure from the technical requirements included in a procurement document, or specified in early site permit information, a standard design certification or standard design approval.

Nonconformance. A deficiency in characteristic, documentation, or procedure that renders the quality of an item or activity unacceptable or indeterminate.

Suspect item. A suspect item is one in which there is an indication by visual inspection, testing or other information that it may not conform to established Government—or industry—accepted specifications or national consensus standards.

EPRI 1019163

Counterfeit. Counterfeit items are items that are intentionally manufactured or altered to imitate a legitimate product without the legal right to do so. Examples of a counterfeit item include one that has been fabricated in imitation of something else with purpose to defraud by passing the false copy for genuine or original or an item copied without the legal right or authority to do so.

Enhanced inspection/testing. Inspection/testing performed in addition to the standard receiving inspection/testing process in order to reasonably ensure that the items received are authentic.

Fraudulent item. Fraudulent items are items that are intentionally misrepresented as something other than they actually are, with intent to deceive. Fraudulent items include items with falsified or inaccurate trademarks, manufacturer names, markings, test results and/or certifications. Fraudulent items also include used items sold as new as well as manufacturing overages sold by entities that have acquired the legal right to manufacture a specified quantity of an item (such as an integrated circuit) but produce a larger quantity than authorized and sell the overage as legitimate inventory.

7.5.3 Counterfeit, Suspect, Fraudulent Items

Counterfeit, suspect, fraudulent items (CSFI or CFI in NRC parlance) or suspect/counterfeit items (S/CI in DOE parlance) are a significant quality threat. Although not specifically called out in 10 CFR Energy laws, quality requirements of 10 CFR 50 Appendix B and 10 CFR 830.122(c) apply as follows:

From 10 CFR 50 Appendix B:
Criterion VII, "Control of Purchased Material, Equipment, and Services"
Criterion VIII, "Identification and Control of Material, Parts, and Components"
Criterion X, "Inspection"
Criterion XV, "Nonconforming Materials, Parts, or Components"
Criterion XVI, "Corrective Action"

From 10 CFR 830.122(c) Criterion 3, "Management/Quality Improvement":
(1) Establish and implement processes to detect and prevent quality problems.
(2) Identify, control, and correct items, services, and processes that do not meet established requirements.

(3) Identify the causes of problems and work to prevent recurrence as a part of correcting the problem.
(4) Review item characteristics, process implementation, and other quality-related information to identify items, services, and processes needing improvement.

Both the NRC and DOE have published materials in the past decade related to this problem. The DOE has made S/CI prevention mandatory for its contractors through Order 414.1D "Quality Assurance."

The EPRI's "Plant Support Engineering: Counterfeit and Fraudulent Items Mitigating the Increasing Risk, Revision 1 of 1019163" has been transmitted by the NEI to the NRC. The guide is intended to support, and encourage its use by, licensees and suppliers to enhance existing practices for prevention, detection, and control of CFI.

ASME NQA-1 does not directly address suspect items, but a broad range of QA principles apply, including:

Requirement 8: Identification and Control of Items
100 Basic: Controls shall be established to assure that only correct and accepted items are used or installed. Identification shall be maintained on the items or in documents traceable to the items, or in a manner that assures that identification is established and maintained.

Requirement 15: Control of Nonconforming Items
100 Basic: Items that do not conform to specified requirements shall be controlled to prevent inadvertent installation or use. Controls shall provide for identification, documentation, evaluation, segregation when practical, and disposition of nonconforming items, and for notification to affected organizations. (Sections 200, 300, and 400 refer to Identification, Segregation, and Disposition, respectively.)

Requirement 16: Corrective Action
100 Basic: Conditions adverse to quality shall be identified promptly and corrected as soon as practicable. In the case of a significant condition adverse to quality, the cause of the condition shall be determined, and corrective action taken to preclude recurrence. The identification, cause, and corrective action for significant conditions adverse to quality shall be documented and reported to appropriate levels of management. Completion of corrective actions shall be verified.

7.5.4 Impact of Counterfeit, Suspect, Fraudulent Items

Suspect items may include mechanical components such as bolts, valves, lifting devices; electronic components such as individual resistors and capacitors through circuit boards and control devices; and electrical components such as circuit breakers. Other issues may include plagiarism of documents, false brand names applied to items, and forgery. EPRI 1019163 Section 4 contains several examples of documented CSFI incidents.

The USS *Iwo Jima* steam line rupture of 1990 is a well-documented event with loss of life due to inadvertent use of counterfeit bolts, studs, and nuts during a high-pressure steam valve repair. Although a non-nuclear-powered ship, the implications of a similar incident at a nuclear power plant are significant. The valve failed catastrophically soon after the steam plant was brought online, and the resulting nonisolable high-pressure steam leak killed 10 sailors and endangered the ship.

A difficulty with detection of fraudulent or counterfeit items versus simply defective items is there was intent from some person or persons to purposely deceive a customer at some point in the supply chain. In the *Iwo Jima* example, a manufacturer intentionally made fasteners out of brass, and then applied a black coating. "Because those fasteners were covered with a manufacturer-applied black coating, at a glance, they could be mistaken for the correct grade 4 steel nuts." If the manufacturer had inadvertently supplied brass fasteners to fulfill and order for grade 4 steel, that would have been easily detected in a visual inspection. Instead, the intentional deception was not detected and led to 10 deaths.

NRC IN 2008-04 states:

> In recent years many vendors, including foreign companies, with little to no experience in the nuclear industry have entered the market to supply parts and components for both safety and non-safety applications to nuclear power plants. It remains the licensees' responsibility to ensure that all suppliers use standards and processes that conform to US standards. Effective oversight of suppliers becomes increasingly more important.

DOE O 414.1D includes a Contractor Requirements Document with the following purpose:

> To set forth requirements for DOE and its contractor organizations, as part of their QAPs [Quality Assurance Plan], to establish, document and implement effective controls and processes that will: (1) ensure items and services meet specified requirements; (2) prevent entry of Suspect/Counterfeit Items (S/CIs) into the DOE supply chain; and (3) ensure detection, control, reporting, and disposition of S/CIs.

7.5.5 Prevention, Detection, and Control

Detecting misrepresented products is difficult because most QA programs are not designed for detecting counterfeit or fraudulent practices. The criteria used to confirm the quality of products during receipt inspection and testing generally have assumed vendor integrity and are not focused on identifying an intent to deceive. Healthy skepticism and asking why "this is too good to be true" may need to be developed.

EPRI 1019163 does recommend three primary CSFI strategies:

1. Prevention—prevent a suspect item from entering the supply chain in the first place
2. Detection—develop the ability to detect incoming and existing CSFI in the supply chain. This is accomplished through inspection at the source, receipt, and pre-installation
3. Control—this includes quarantine and disposal of suspect items and communication the results internally and externally

DOE Order 414.1D relies upon the contractor's QA plan to "include a S/CI oversight and prevention process commensurate with the facility/activity hazards and mission impact."

7.5.6 Procurement

General indications may be found early in the procurement process, beginning with the price quote and scheduled delivery time requirements, according to the NRC. Some things that have been found to be present when misrepresented products were identified, and which can be found during the quoting process are:

1. The name of the vendor—several instances of apparent counterfeit and fraud involved vendors who were not authorized distributors for the products they supplied
2. The price—quoting of prices by the vendor that are significantly lower than those of the competition
3. Delivery schedule—a shorter delivery time than that of the competition
4. The source of the item—drop shipment of items has been noted in several cases of misrepresentation where the quoted supplier subcontracted the order to another company and then had the subcontractor ship the product directly to the purchaser. The quoted supplier never saw or verified the quality of the product which, in some cases, has been substandard.

NRC GL 89-02 talks about effective procurement and dedication programs. With engineering involvement, licensee engineering staff would be involved for effective controls in the (1) development of specifications to be used for the procurement of products to be used in the plant (2) determination of the critical characteristics of the selected products that are to be verified during product acceptance (3) determination of specific testing requirements applicable to the selected products (4) evaluation of test results.

NRC GL 89-02 also discusses for licensees with effective products acceptance programs have (1) included receipt/source inspection and appropriate testing criteria, effective vendor audits, special tests and inspections and post-installation tests in their programs (2) required identification and verification of product's critical characteristics (3) utilized sampling plans to perform the required inspection and tests (4) verified the traceability to the original manufacturers of procured materials, equipment, and components (5) included consideration of audit approach, depth of audit, and audit team composition and have included appropriate engineering/technical representatives.

DOE O 414.1D calls for prevention of introduction of S/CI in the procurement process through the involvement of engineering staff, and inclusion of technical and quality specifications in procurement specifications. The DOE S/CI handbook lists specific procurement practices in Subsection 7.1. These practices primarily relate to engineering development of specification requirements.

7.5.7 Inspection

From its inspections, the NRC has identified three characteristics of effective procurement and dedication programs, which it lists in GL 89-02:

1. The involvement of engineering staff in the procurement and product acceptance process
2. Effective source inspection, receipt inspection, and testing programs
3. Thorough, engineering-based programs for review, testing, and dedication of commercial-grade products for suitability of use in safety-related applications

As stated in NRC GL89-02, it is each licensee's responsibility to provide reasonable assurance that nonconforming products are not introduced into their plants. Dedication programs that ensure the adequacy of critical parameters of products used in safety-related applications can also contribute to the identification of counterfeit or fraudulently marketed vendor products. The licensees who use methods similar to those described in EPRI NP-5652 to verify the critical characteristics of commercial grade items intended for safety-related applications have the basis for effective dedication programs.

The NRC found that programs that embodied the above three characteristics generally were effective in providing enhanced capability to detect counterfeit or fraudulently marketed products and in assuring the quality of procured products, both in safety-related and other plant systems. Note the implied relationship between engineering staff, procurement, inspection and testing, and commercial grade dedication.

Section 7.1 of EPRI 1019163 discusses "vigilant inspection" to detect CSFI. EPRI NP-6629 "Guidelines for the Procurement and Receipt of Items for Nuclear Power Plants" is stated to be effective and should continue to be followed. Other inspection recommendations include the use of digital photographs of authentic items and verifying certification documentation and test results from sources independent of the supplier. Inspections should be performed at the source, pre-receipt, receipt, at the warehouse, and pre-installation.

Section 7.2 of EPRI 1019163 discusses modern methodologies for positive identification, similar in concept to methods to prevent counterfeiting of paper money and radio frequency identification (RFID) chips.

DOE O 414.1D also includes inspection for compliance with procurement specifications, consensus standards, and commonly accepted industry practices. Inspections of inventory and storage areas for S/CIs are also called for. Further details on inspections, sampling, and acceptance criteria are provided in Section 7.3 of the DOE S/CI handbook.

Both the DOE S/CI handbook and the DOE S/CI training manual, offer additional guidance.

7.5.8 Safety Culture

The NRC also has stressed the importance of the nuclear industry's vendors and suppliers establishing a positive nuclear safety culture. NRC policy statements related to safety culture identified, among other qualities, the need for continuous learning, effective safety communications, and employees with a questioning attitude as characteristics of a positive safety culture.

7.5.9 Training and Awareness

NRC documents also recommend the use of training. Training, including hands-on instruction, should be considered for all employees supporting the procurement process, including purchasing (materials and services), QA, product receiving, maintenance, and investigation personnel. Refresher training also may be regularly emphasized to update employees on new threats, identification techniques, and communication strategies. Although these are only recommendations from the NRC, CSFI auditors should be aware of these recommendations and question if the auditee has considered the recommendations. If the recommendations have not been followed, the auditee's rationale should be obtained.

NRC IN 2012-22 provides information about training, which comes with the following caveat:

> The NRC expects that recipients will review the list of available training resources listed in this [Information Notice] as it may be useful for educating personnel involved in NRC-regulated activities on current trends in CFSI, and techniques to prevent the use of CFSI parts. The suggestions contained within this IN are not NRC requirements; therefore, no specific action or written response is required. Addressees can review this information and consider actions, as appropriate.

The NRC believes that training and awareness is important for combating CSFI. NRC IN 2012-22 does include a table of available training courses as of the time of writing. It is stated that the NRC does not intend to maintain the list up to date, nor is it a "complete" listing of all available offerings. The DOE S/CI handbook also makes reference to this IN.

EPRI 1019163 contains a section on recommended training and scope. Similar to NRC Information Notice 2012-22, Section 6.5 states that "training on CFIs should be provided to everyone involved in the procurement process from the specification of items to installation." The section identifies more than 20 topics and targeted audiences that can provide a basis for training learning objectives. Interestingly, the EPRI 1019163 suggests providing CFI precautions during pre-job briefings. Also recommended is having actual examples of counterfeit fraudulent items to use during hands-on training.

The DOE S/CI handbook discusses definitions, the DOE S/CI process, DOE directives, the Government-Industry Data Exchange Program (GIDEP), and the DOE S/CI website. Appendices cover fasteners, components and product information, suspect indications list, S/CI found at DOE facilities, references, and resources.

The DOES/CI handbook also references GIDEP and states that the "DOE and its contractors should utilize GIDEP to report S/CI to organizations outside of DOE and to identify information from outside organizations to prevent S/CIs from entering their supply chain."

7.5.10 Identify Scope and At-Risk Components

EPRI 1019163 recommends that an "appropriate scope of concern" be communicated. CSFI affects a broad range of components, and this scope should be effectively communicated to appropriate individuals and departments. Consider the items in the "Reporting Databases" subsection below when assessing the scope of counterfeit items. EPRI 1019163 points out ammunition as a procurement that might be overlooked when considering CSFI.

Identification of at-risk components is covered in Section 6.4 of EPRI 1019163. Section 6.4.1 contains a list of risk factors, such as "the supplier is unknown or unverified (for example, Internet-based) supplier or broker."

7.5.11 Use Authorized Suppliers and Distributors

The NRC does require inspection and oversight of industry vendor activities. Its Enforcement Policy is applicable to nonlicensees, including contractors and subcontractors, applicants or holders of NRC approvals (e.g., certificates of compliance, early site permits, standard design certificates, QA program approvals), and employees of any of the foregoing who knowingly provide components, equipment, or other goods or services that relate to a licensee's activities subject to NRC regulation. A close relationship with suppliers and documentation in the Approved Supplier List (as required by other quality guidance) can prevent introduction of CSFI.

EPRI 1019163 points out that brokers and unauthorized distributors are more likely (than authorized distributors) to supply CSFI or used or refurbished parts. EPRI 1019163 also recommends that parts be procured directly from the original component manufacturer (ocm)/original equipment manufacturer (OEM) when possible. If not able to procure directly from the OCM/OEM, use an authorized distributor. As a distributor could make false statements about OCM/OEM status, it is worth confirming the authorization with the OCM/OEM. Many OEMs and OCMs provide information about authorized distributors on their websites.

Section 7.2.1 of the DOE S/CI handbook provides guidance on approved suppliers and the processes to approve suppliers.

7.5.12 Relationships with Suppliers

EPRI 1019163 recommends "enhanced supplier communication and interface." Establish expectations and identify concerns with suppliers. Close partnering with a supplier can result in a productive information exchange. Consider use of a document like Lockheed Martin's "Counterfeit Materials Prevention," which sets expectations for procurement with the company.

For DOE and its contractors, the DOE S/CI handbook states that "all contracts should contain the S/CI clauses prohibiting delivery of S/CIs." The handbook "highly recommends" making the clause a contract requirement, and an example clause is provided in Section 7.2.2.

7.5.13 Supplier Evaluation

EPRI 1019163 does recommend incorporation of CSFI criteria into supplier assessment checklists and questions to be asked by auditors. The Nuclear Industry Assessment Committee (NIAC)'s "Standard Checklist" includes assessment of a supplier's CSFI inspection and testing processes.

Section 6.3.2.3 of EPRI 1019163 provides a list of 13 questions to consider during supplier evaluation. Section 6.4.2 contains precautions to take when dealing with at-risk components, including inspection requirements and acceptance criteria to put in place.

The DOE S/CI handbook states that supplier QA "should be sufficient to provide the requisite level of assurance that the supplier or distributor has the capability to comply with purchase order requirements" and lists five specific criteria. Further, if there are multiple suppliers in the supply chain, "each step in the supply chain process should be validated by audit, source inspection, or other methods as appropriate."

7.5.14 Control

EPRI 1019163 lists "control" as one of the primary three methods for combating CSFI. The organization should have a defined and documented method for responding to discovery of a suspect item. A "generic process for Controlling and Reporting Suspect Items" is provided in Section 8.2. Primary actions described include quarantine and labeling of the item, investigation, internal and external reporting, notifying of law enforcement where appropriate, and physical disposition of the item. Reporting should include documentation in the corrective action management system.

DOE Order 414.1D requires inspection, identification, evaluation, and disposition of S/CIs that have been installed in safety applications. Engineering evaluations are required for S/CIs discovered in nonsafety applications to determine if they may be used as is. Marking to prevent future reuse is also required. Further guidance is provided in Section 7.5 of the DOE S/CI handbook. In addition, Section 7.6 of the DOE S/CI handbook contains additional actions to be taken if the SC/I is installed in lifting equipment, "including both fixed and mobile cranes and other devices (e.g., forklifts, scissor lifts, man lifts, balers, truck and dock lifts, elevators, conveyors, and slings)."

Both Section 9 of the DOE S/CI handbook and the DOE Office of Health, Safety and Security S/CI awareness training manual contain detailed information, tables, and photos to help identify S/CI during inspections.

7.5.15 Reporting Databases

EPRI 1019163 advises that commercial nuclear operators in the United States have established protocols for the use of two data-sharing tools:

- INPO [Institute of Nuclear Power Operations] has requested that all licensees report incidents of CFIs to INPO as operating or construction experience.
- EPRI has established a website (scfi.epri.com) that can be used by EPRI members to report and search for incidents of suspected CFIs.

DOE Order 414.1D also contains reporting requirements for S/CI discoveries. S/CI are required to be reported in accordance with Occurrence Reporting and Processing System (ORPS) requirements. In addition, trend analyses for use in improving the S/CI prevention process are required. The DOE S/CI handbook calls for timely processing of a nonconformance report (NCR) and determination of status to meet reporting timeliness.

There are several reporting databases available to find, track, and report instances of CSFI. Use of these databases can help prevent procuring items from known CSFI sources and share knowledge with others. This listing is not meant to be all-inclusive, nor should a listing be considered an endorsement of these data services. Nuclear and nonnuclear examples include the following:

Suspect/Counterfeit and Defective Items Database

For DOE employees and contractors only, this database is maintained by the DOE's Office of Environment, Health, Safety & Security.
https://energy.gov/ehss/policy-guidance-reports/databases/suspectcounterfeit-and-defective-items

GIDEP (Government-Industry Data Exchange Program)

GIDEP is a cooperative activity between government and industry. Proper utilization of GIDEP data can materially improve the total quality and reliability of systems and components during the acquisition and logistics phases of the life cycle. Membership is available to US and Canadian government entities and their suppliers.
http://www.gidep.org/

National Intellectual Property Rights Coordination Center

Manages and supports the US Immigration and Customs Enforcement commercial fraud program. Its website includes consumer alerts documenting cases of fraud, counterfeiting, and piracy.
https://www.iprcenter.gov/

International Anti-Counterfeiting Coalition

Washington, DC-based nonprofit organization devoted solely to combating product counterfeiting and piracy. It offers the "IACC Market Safe Program," which is a strategic collaboration to create a cross-industry alliance to combat counterfeit products online.
http://www.iacc.org/

International Chamber of Commerce

The ICC includes documentation on counterfeiting and fraud, including "Anti-Counterfeiting 2015: A Global Guide."
https://iccwbo.org/

The Counterfeit Report

Mostly consumer goods-oriented; offers a "free search before you buy" and product alerts.
http://www.thecounterfeitreport.com/

"Fake It 'Til We Make It: Regulating Dangerous Counterfeit Goods," *Journal of Intellectual Property Law & Practice* **10, no. 4 (2015): 246–254.**

This article by James L. Bikoff, David K. Heasley, Valeriya Sherman, and Jared Stipelman uses survey to broadly characterize anti-dangerous-counterfeiting legal regimes in the United States, European Union, China, and India. It analyses certain best practices including consumer education on the public health impact of dangerous counterfeits (particularly food and medicine), integrated product tracing systems, and greater international coordination in enforcement efforts.
https://academic.oup.com/jiplp/article-abstract/10/4/246/809270/Fake-it-til-we-make-it-regulating-dangerous?rss=1

ERAI

A global information services organization that monitors, investigates, and reports issues affecting the global electronics supply chain, which includes a database of suspect counterfeit and nonconforming electronic parts. https://www.erai.com/Counterfeit_Part_Reporting_and_Alerts

Section 7.6 Control of Electronic Records
Code of Federal Regulations

https://www.govinfo.gov/content/pkg/cfr-2018-title10-vol1.pdf
    10 CFR Appendix B To Part 50—Quality Assurance Criteria For Nuclear Power Plants And Fuel Reprocessing Plants. Note: Though not dealing with electronic records specifically, NRC documents refer back to this as the primary requirements for records.

Nuclear Regulatory Commission Documents

NQA-1-2008/2009, Part III, Subpart 3.1, Nonmandatory Appendix 17A-2, "Guidance for Electronic Records"; NQA-1-2008/2009, Part III, Subpart 3.1, Nonmandatory

Appendix 17A-1, "Guidance on Quality Assurance Records"; and NQA-1-2008/2009, Part I, Requirement 17, "Quality Assurance Records."
https://www.nrc.gov/docs/ML1503/ML15037A441.pdf NUREG-0800 17.5

Quality Assurance Program Description—Design Certification, Early Site Permit and New License Applicants

https://www.nrc.gov/reading-rm/doc-collections/gen-comm/gen-letters/1988/gl88018.html
Plant Record Storage on Optical Disks (Generic Letter No. 88-18)
https://www.nrc.gov/reading-rm/doc-collections/gen-comm/reg-issues/2000/ri00018.html
RIS 00-018: Guidance on Managing Quality Assurance Records in Electronic Media
https://www.nrc.gov/docs/ML1509/ML15099A561.pdf
Safety Evaluation Of Duke Energy Carolinas, Llc Amendment 40 To The Quality Assurance Topical Report, (TAC Nos. MF5055, MF5056, MF5057, MF5058, MF5059, MF5060, and MF5061)
https://www.nrc.gov/docs/ML1430/ML14300A011.pdf
Change to Quality Assurance Topical Report, Amendment 40 [letter from Duke related to above document]
https://www.nrc.gov/docs/ML1120/ML11200A122.pdf
Subject: Regulatory Information Summary 00-18, "Guidance on the Management of Quality Assurance Records on Electronic Media" [Letter from NIIRMA related to above document]. This NIRMA letter contains an important table at the end showing the difference between the 1998 versions and 2011 versions of the four NIRMA Technical Guidance documents referred to here.
Inspection procedure https://www.nrc.gov/docs/ML0605/ML060530433.pdf
Inspection Procedure 88113 Control Of The Electronic Management Of Data
https://www.nrc.gov/docs/ML1125/ML11256A069.pdf
Electronic Signatures talking points
https://www.nrc.gov/docs/ML1303/ML13031A056.pdf
Guidance for Electronic Submissions to the NRC

Nuclear Information and Records Management Association

https://www.nirmashop.com/product-category/e-books/
 NIRMA TG-11—"Authentication of Records and Media"
 NIRMA TG-15—"Management of Electronic Records"
 NIRMA TG-16—"Software Configuration Management and Quality Assurance "
 NIRMA TG-21—"Electronic Records Protection and Restoration"

Institute of Electrical and Electronics Engineers

http://www.ieee.org/index.html
 IEEE Std. 730-2014, "Standard for Software Engineering Quality Assurance Plans"
 IEEE Std. 828- 2012, "Standard for Software Configuration Management Plans"
 IEEE Std. 1012-2016 (R1992), "Standard for Software Verification and Validation Plans"
 IEEE Std. 1028-2008 (R1993), "Standard for Software Reviews and Audits"
 IEEE Std. 1062-2015, "Recommended Practice for Software Acquisitions"

IEEE Std. 14764-2006, "Standard for Software Maintenance"
IEEE Std. 1228-1994, "Standard for Software Safety Plans"

US Department of Energy (US DOE) Documents

https://energy.gov/cio/office-chief-information-officer/services/guidance/records-management
US DOE Records Management home page
https://www.energy.gov/sites/prod/files/cioprod/documents/DOD5015.2Standard.pdf
Electronic Records Management Software Applications Design Criteria Standard [A DOD standard, but has been reissued by DOE] OTHER SOURCES
https://www.accessdata.fda.gov/scripts/cdrh/cfdocs/cfcfr/CFRSearch.cfm?CFRPart=11
[US Food and Drug Administration]
http://www-pub.iaea.org/MTCD/publications/PDF/trs467_web.pdf
Long Term Preservation of Information for Decommissioning Projects https://www.nitsl.org/default.aspx
The Nuclear Information Technology Strategic Leadership (NITSL) group is a nuclear industry group of all nuclear generation utilities that exchange information related to information technology management and quality issues.

From CFR—Code of Federal Regulations Title 21 (Food and Drugs) Part 11.3.

(5) Digital signature means an electronic signature based upon cryptographic methods of originator authentication, computed by using a set of rules and a set of parameters such that the identity of the signer and the integrity of the data can be verified.
(6) Electronic record means any combination of text, graphics, data, audio, pictorial, or other information representation in digital form that is created, modified, maintained, archived, retrieved, or distributed by a computer system.
(7) Electronic signature means a computer data compilation of any symbol or series of symbols executed, adopted, or authorized by an individual to be the legally binding equivalent of the individual's handwritten signature.

Electronic Records

Requirements to keep records pertaining to quality issues have been around for years. Only in the past few decades have we gained the ability to move from paper records in mass warehouses (perhaps similar to the scene at the end of *Raiders of the Lost Ark*) to having quickly retrievable, compact electronic storage. Even with all of the advantages of electronic records, we are faced with the challenge of how to maintain the electronic records for the long durations required. Mission tapes from the 1970 Apollo missions are nearly unreadable 40 years later. Will pdf files on hard drives be readable 40 years from now even if the hardware is?

Primary issues to consider with electronic records are:

• Verification
• Validation
• Authentication (especially control of digital signatures)
• Storage management

- Standards applied to the digital and physical environment
- Security
- Access control
- Records management programs (application and infrastructure)
- Disaster recovery methods

Regulatory Requirements from 10 CFR 50 Part B for Records

The following section from 10 CFR 50 serves as the foundation for the requirements for maintenance of records, whether hard copy, microfiche, or electronic.

XVII. Quality Assurance Records

Sufficient records shall be maintained to furnish evidence of activities affecting quality. The records shall include at least the following: operating logs and the results of reviews, inspections, tests, audits, monitoring of work performance, and materials analyses. The records shall also include closely related data such as qualifications of personnel, procedures, and equipment. Inspection and test records shall, at a minimum, identify the inspector or data recorder, the type of observation, the results, the acceptability, and the action taken in connection with any deficiencies noted. Records shall be identifiable and retrievable. Consistent with applicable regulatory requirements, the applicant shall establish requirements concerning record retention, such as duration, location, and assigned responsibility.

NRC Requirements

A primary current document for records requirements is NUREG-0800 17.5 Quality Assurance Program Description—Design Certification, Early Site Permit And New License Applicants Section Q, Quality Assurance Records (Criterion XVII). Salient points include "measures are required to be established that ensure that sufficient records of completed items and activities affecting quality are appropriately stored (ANSI/ANS 3.2)." The standard further specifies the types of information that should be treated as records. "Records shall be identifiable and retrievable" is listed as a requirement. The applicant is also expected to establish requirements for retention duration, location, and protecting records "from destruction by fire, flooding, tornadoes, insects, and rodents and from deterioration by extremes in temperature and humidity."

"Plant Record Storage on Optical Disks (Generic Letter No. 88-18)" was published by the NRC in 1988 in order to "approve the use of optical disk document imaging systems for the storage and retrieval of record copies of quality assurance records." "RIS 00-018: Guidance on Managing Quality Assurance Records in Electronic Media" was published soon after GL 88-18 in order to provide "additional guidance on the acceptability of new information management technologies." This document referenced four 1998 Nuclear Information and Records Management Association (NIRMA) Technical Guides (TG) for use. Nine Institute of Electrical and Electronics Engineers (IEEE) documents were listed that nuclear facilities "may use" to supplement the NIRMA guidelines.

In May 2015, the NRC Office of New Reactors published the "Evaluation Of Duke Energy Carolinas, Llc Amendment 40 To The Quality Assurance Topical Report." This letter approved a requested change to the subject document to reference the 2011 Nuclear Information and Records Management Association (NIRMA) technical guides rather than the1998 version of the guides referenced in Regulatory Issue Summary 2000-018, "Guidance on the Management of Quality Assurance Records on Electronic Media." The letter states:

> The newer 2011 NIRMA . . . changes are based on the development and implementation of enterprise content management systems, web-based technologies, and higher capacity LAN/WAN networks. The key difference between the 1998 and 2011 NIRMA technical guides is that the newer technical guides provide better understanding and controls for an integrated approach to the creation, capture, and maintenance of records using electronic tools.

The letter listed authorized the following newer versions of the NIRMA Technical Guides listed in RIS 00-018 for use at the subject plant locations. One could assume that this letter is a precedent for future NRC direction, and perhaps permission for others to use will be forthcoming. However, the older versions from RIS-0018 are still official NRC policy at the time of this writing:

> TG 11-2011 "Authentication of Records and Media"
> TG 15-2011 "Management of Electronic Records"
> TG 16-2011 "Software Quality Assurance Documentation and Records"
> TG 21-2011 "Required Records Protection, Disaster Recovery and Business Continuation"

Information from these documents will be included in the requirement/subject list below.

The following are specific requirements for electronic records that the program must address:

USAGE NUREG-0800 17.5 contains provisions for the generation, distribution, use, maintenance, storage, and disposition of electronic records, as well as administration, receipt, retrieval capabilities for all records.

NIRMA TG15-98 states that "due to the unique vulnerabilities of electronic records, special measures should be taken to ensure their usability. The document states electronic records must be retrievable, intelligible, understandable and reliable, and requirements are listed for each of these four terms.

Original records/media should not be used for work purposes or maintained online. Refer to Guidance for Electronic Submissions to the NRC May 18, 2017, Revision 8 (see Reference list for URL) when sending electronic reports/records to the NRC.

Procedures

NIRMA TG16-98 contains requirements for a Software Quality Assurance Plan (SQAP), a Software Configuration Management Plan (SCMP), a Software Quality Assurance (SQA) Policy, and an SQA Program. The SQA Policy should consider interfaces with:

- Information services/information technology
- Regulatory compliance
- Engineering management
- Configuration management
- Information and records management
- Site corrective

NRC Inspection Procedure 88113 states the following:

> If the licensee intends to rely on the electronic record as its official record, it is of the utmost importance that a statement of intent to rely on the electronic record exists. . . . The official record, once designated by the licensee, must be subject to rigorous procedures for creation, modification, and destruction under a records-management program.

A statement designating the electronic record as the official record must exist as part of the licensee's overall records-management program.

Media

NUREG-0800 17.5 includes guidance on acceptable media on which electronic records are created and stored. Provisions to verify that the media is appropriate, suitable for the capture or storage of records, and error/defect free are also listed.

NIRMA TG11-1998 provides a detailed listing of types of media and storage requirements. Microform and magnetic media requirements are provided. A general guidance in the document is that the media should outlive the required retention period or be able to be regenerated or migrated to other media before the end of life of the media.

Software

NIRMA TG15-1998 provides a listing of "several existing and de facto standards" that should be used. This includes (but is not limited to) JPEG, MPEG, AVI, HTML, RTF, and PDF formats.

NRC Inspection Procedure 88113 points out that most file formats are patented by owning companies, and those companies may go out of business and/or stop supporting the format. As a result, the licensee may be unable to access and view their electronic records. "There is no guaranteed way to avoid this, but if the format adopted is widely used, it is more likely to be supported for years to come." Also, "the licensee should adopt media that are mainstream, widely-used devices that comply with industry standards—avoid both cutting-edge and obsolete technologies."

The software itself used to manage electronic records should meet software QA requirements. NIRMA TG16 calls for several Software Quality Assurance documents, a graded approach and classification of software and lifecycle development practices. The TG does reference to NITSL-SQA-2005-02. Further discussion of software QA is contained in Section 7.3.

Hardware

NUREG-0800 17.5 lists requirements to safeguard against equipment malfunction or human error related to electronic records storage.

Access/Security

NUREG-0800 17.5 requires that access controls, user privileges, and other appropriate security controls be established.

NIRMA TG15-1998 states that "physical security is required for designated electronic data (i.e., limiting physical access to the hardware, assuring fire protection, maintaining an inventory, maintaining data security)." Also, sensitive data should not be stored on unsecured systems, and "special measures" should be taken for removable media.

NIRMA TG15-1998 contains the following specific security requirements:

- When a master list of access identifiers is maintained in a text file, it should be encrypted
- Access rights should be revoked on transfer, retirement, resignation, or termination of the employees to whom they were assigned
- Access identifiers should be associated with specific privileges, such as the ability to retrieve records or to add records to a file
- Whenever a predefined number of consecutive invalid attempts to access the system by a single user are made, the system should invalidate that access identifier
- Continuing need for specific access privileges should be verified at regular intervals
- Additional security measures may be applied to certain specific records or quality data (i.e., proprietary, safeguards, or confidential) as deemed appropriate
- Four types of document access controls or levels of permission are used by systems: read (browse), write (update), delete, and approve permissions

Audits/Inspections

NUREG-0800 17.5 states that "magnetic and optical media should be tested periodically to identify any loss of data, to ensure that they are free of permanent errors, and that the record system hardware/software still supports the retrieval of the records." NIRMA TG11-1998 also lists specific testing for magnetic media, including cleaning requirements, inspections every three years, and limitations on the number of errors found on the media.

NIRMA TG15-1998 calls for performing and documenting audits and inspections of systems, applications, media, and processes used in the generation of electronic records to ensure electronic record integrity. "A statistical sample of media records should be read each year to identify any loss of data and to discover and correct the causes of data loss. If errors are discovered, other media which might have been affected by the same cause (i.e., poor-quality media, high usage, poor environment, improper handling) should be read and corrected as appropriate." "Magnetic computer tapes should be tested no more than 6 months prior to using them to store electronic records that are scheduled for permanent or long-term retention."

Review NRC Inspection Procedure 88113 when developing inspection criteria.

Training

NUREG-0800 17.5. Training should be provided for individuals or organizations in charge of electronic records. NRIMA TG15-1998 provides specific training requirements and roles and responsibilities of managers of electronic records.

Labels/Retention/Retrievability

NUREG-0800 17.5. In addition to indexing information requirements, the software name, version, and equipment (hardware) used to produce and maintain the electronic media must be recorded.

NIRMA TG11-1998. Labels for electronic media should include the originating office, title, data begin and end dates, software version used, record density, type of internal labels and system on which it was produced.

NIRMA TG15-1998 contains extensive requirements for record retention schedules and retention system requirements.

Authentication

NUREG-0800 17.5 contains a number of authentication requirements and states that "authentication is accomplished by manually affixing seal, signature, an electronic representation (user ID/password combination, digital signature) or other acceptable process control that ensures genuineness, validity, or reliability." Users should have a unique user ID/password for access. Controls to ensure data integrity and prevent unauthorized alteration or erasure are required.

NIRMA TG11-1998 states that electronic media are allowed to be treated as "record copies" after proper certification as an exact duplicate of the original record.

NIRMA TG15-1998 states that "electronic records and media should be turned over to the authorized storage organization/facility as soon as the document has been authenticated."

Correction

NUREG-0800 17.5 records are corrected in accordance with procedures that provide for appropriate review or approval by the originating organization. The correction includes the date and the identification of the person authorized to issue such correction. For records stored in electronic media, a new record is to be generated when substantial corrections or changes to previous electronic records are required.

NIRMA TG11-1998, which provides guidance for how to correct electronic media, states that "corrections, changes or supplements to records should have the same review and authentication requirements as the original record."

Copying/Migration

NUREG-0800 17.5. An electronic record migration/regeneration program is implemented for electronic records stored in media with a standard life expectancy that fails to meet the specific retention period. This program is implemented in accordance with documented procedures that provide for appropriate record authentication, quality verification of the completion, and accuracy of the data transferred. NIRMA TG11-1998 also provides similar controls.

Storage/Disaster Planning

NUREG-0800 17.5. Electronic media should be stored in a dust-free environment, away from electronic devices and demagnetizing equipment. Media should be maintained at the constant temperature of 40–80°F, with a constant relative humidity of 30–50%.

The applicant's program must implement Generic Letter (GL) 88-18, "Plant Record Storage on Optical Disks" (Appendix B/RIS 2000-18) NUREG-0800 17.5.

NIRMA TG11-1998 provides temperature and humidity specifications for optical media (such as CD-ROM).

NIRMA TG15-1998 requires maintaining a duplicate copy of designated data as a backup in case recovery is needed: "Backup copies should be stored in a different area from the on-line copy to prevent possible destruction by the same source that destroyed the on-line copy." The original hard copy record is allowed to be destroyed if the electronic record has been approved and indexed, as long as this meets other regulatory, business, or insurance requirements. It is "strongly recommend[ed]" that draft documents of records should not be retained unless necessary for a business need.

NIRMA TG15-1998 states the following requirements for storage facilities. All electronic records storage should be conducted inside the storage facility. Electronic devices or demagnetizing equipment are not allowed in the facility. All media and containers should be examined on entry or exit from the facility. Electronic media should be shielded from electronic signals.

NIRMA TG 21 Required Records Protection, Disaster Recovery, And Business Continuation contains full information on emergency planning and response for electronic records. The document includes the following sections:

- Section 4—Disaster Response Team Responsibilities
- Section 5—Disaster Response Plan Development
- Section 6—Prevention Planning
- Section 7—Response and Recovery Planning
- Section 8—Post-Disaster Planning
- Section 9—Testing and Maintenance

Appendix A is a table of "Recovery Options for Water-Damaged Collections and Records." For example, the options for CD-ROMs are air dry and "dehumidification-dry."

Destruction

NIRMA TG15-1998 contains the following requirements for destruction of electronic records:

- Electronic records scheduled for destruction are reviewed electronically on-screen to facilitate disposition action decisions
- Electronic records scheduled for destruction are disposed of in a manner that ensures protection of sensitive, proprietary, or confidential information
- Computer media previously used for electronic records containing sensitive, proprietary, confidential, or security information are not reused
- The records destruction process is suspended in the case of foreseeable, pending, or actual litigation or government investigation
- The responsible party assigned to destroy the records should decide the appropriate method of destruction for the media contained on the Destroyed Records Inventory Form. Burning, shredding, disposal in an on-site landfill, or electronic erasure are approved methods for the destruction of records. For security, proprietary, or confidential electronic records, electronic erasure SHOULD NOT be used as the means of destruction.
- Only by degaussing, or by using a program that writes an alternating pattern of zeros and ones over the data to be erased can destruction be ensured.

Section 7.7 Suspect/Counterfeit Items

Appendix A—Reference Documents (S/CI)

Nuclear Regulatory Commission Documents

https://www.nrc.gov/about-nrc/cfsi.html,https://www.nrc.gov/about-nrc/cfsi/guidance.html#policy-issues
NRC Main Page and Library of CSFI documents
https://www.nrc.gov/docs/ML1500/ML15008A191.pdf
NRC Regulatory Issue Summary 2015-08oversight Of Counterfeit, Fraudulent, And Suspect Items In The Nuclear Industry
https://www.nrc.gov/docs/ML1122/ML112200150.pdfNRC SECY-11-0154
"An Agency-wide Approach to Counterfeit, Fraudulent and Suspect Items"
https://www.nrc.gov/reading-rm/doc-collections/gen-comm/gen-letters/1989/gl89002.html
US Nuclear Regulatory Commission (NRC) Generic Letter (GL) 89-02, "Actions to Improve the Detection of Counterfeit and Fraudulently Marked Products"
https://www.nrc.gov/docs/ML0936/ML093620098.pdfNRC
Information Notice 2008-04, "Counterfeit Parts Supplied to Nuclear Power Plants"
https://www.nrc.gov/reading-rm/doc-collections/gen-comm/info-notices/1989/in89070.html
NRC Information Notice No. 89-70: "Possible Indications of Misrepresented Vendor Products"
https://www.nrc.gov/docs/ML1314/ML13142A437.pdf
NRC Information Notice 2013-15: Willful Misconduct/Record Falsification And Nuclear Safety Culture. Includes descriptions of willful record falsification and counterfeit parts.
https://www.nrc.gov/docs/ML1507/ML15075A434.pdf
Guidelines For The Use Of Accreditation In Lieu Of Commercial Grade Surveys For Procurement Of Laboratory Calibration And Test Services. Primarily CGD, but does contain information on CSFI on pages 18 and A-1.

Electric Power Research Institute (EPRI) Documents

https://www.epri.com/#/pages/product/000000003002002276/
"Plant Support Engineering: Counterfeit and Fraudulent Items Mitigating the Increasing Risk, Revision 1 of 1019163." See also https://www.nrc.gov/docs/ML1424/ML14245A078.pdf.
http://www.nuclear-exchange.com/pdf/tp_counterfeit_tannenbaum.pdf
"Keeping counterfeit and fraudulent items out of the nuclear supply chain" an article by an EPRI author overviewing EPRI SFCI efforts.

US Department of Energy Documents

https://www.directives.doe.gov/directives-documents/400-series/0414.1-EGuide-2b-admchg2DOE G 414.1-2B
 Chg 2 5-8-2013 Quality Assurance Guide
https://www.directives.doe.gov/directives-documents/400-series/0414.1-BOrder-d-admchg1DOE O 414.1D
 Chg 1 5-8-2013 Quality Assurance
https://www.standards.doe.gov/standards-documents/1200/1221-BHdbk-2016-CN1-2017DOE-HDBK-1221-2016
 Chg Notice 1, Suspect/Counterfeit Items Resource Handbook

https://energy.gov/ehss/downloads/suspectcounterfeit-items-awareness-training
-manual
DOE Office of Health Safety and Security "Suspect/Counterfeit Items Awareness Training"

Other Sources

The American Society of Mechanical Engineers (ASME) NQA-1
http://www.gidep.org/GIDEP
Government-Industry Data Exchange Program is a cooperative activity between government and industry. Does include a reporting database as well as product information, metrology, engineering, and reliability reports and documentation.
https://dap.dau.mil/acquipedia/Pages/ArticleDetails.aspx?aid=5ea0eba7-13f0-40be
-9ec7-0e1fa52934ad
 DOD Counterfeit Part information, published by the Defense Acquisition University (DAU). Several references to other documents and websites.
http://www.gao.gov/assets/680/675227.pdf
 GAO "DOD Needs to Improve Reporting and Oversight to Reduce Supply Chain Risk"
http://www.lockheedmartin.com/content/dam/lockheed/data/corporate/documents
/suppliers/FAQs-Counterfeits-122016.pdf
A Lockheed Martin document titled "Counterfeits Prevention" which is a listing of expectations for suppliers to Lockheed Martin. Focused on DOD; however, contains several valid principles and is a good example of documenting procurement expectations.

GLOSSARY

Definitions—10 CFR Part 1 Section 200
Basic Component
(Use same definition as in CGD reference)

http://www.upi.com/Archives/1990/10/30/Scalding-steam-from-ships-boiler-kills
-7-US-sailors/3273657262800/
http://www.nationalboard.org/index.aspx?pageID=164&ID=226
http://www.jag.navy.mil/library/investigations/IWO%20JIMA%2090.pdf
https://timothycummings.wordpress.com/2012/12/03/35/

Defect. Defect means:

(1) A deviation in a basic component delivered to a purchaser for use in a facility or an activity subject to the regulations in this part if, on the basis of an evaluation, the deviation could create a substantial safety hazard;
(2) The installation, use, or operation of a basic component containing a defect as defined in this section;
(3) A deviation in a portion of a facility subject to the early site permit, standard design certification, standard design approval, construction permit, combined license or manufacturing licensing requirements of Part 50 or Part 52 of this chapter, provided the deviation could, on the basis of an evaluation, create a substantial safety hazard and the portion of the facility containing the deviation has been offered to the purchaser for acceptance;
(4) A condition or circumstance involving a basic component that could contribute to the exceeding of a safety limit, as defined in the technical specifications of a license for operation issued under Part 50 or Part 52 of this chapter; or

(5) An error, omission, or other circumstance in a design certification, or standard design approval that, on the basis of an evaluation, could create a substantial safety hazard.

Defective Item. A defective item or material is any item or material that does not meet the commercial standard or procurement requirements as defined by catalogues, proposals, procurement specifications, design specifications, testing requirements, contacts or the like. It does not include parts or services that fail or are otherwise found to be inadequate because of random failures or errors within the accepted reliability level. Manufacturers generally notify their customers when defective items are identified through such mechanisms as recall notices. Such notices may be directly sent to customers or may appear in a federal agency or industry.

Definitions—US DOE S/CI Awareness Training

Counterfeit Item. A counterfeit item is a suspect item that is a copy or substitute without legal right or authority to do so or one whose materials, performance, or characteristics are knowingly misrepresented by the vendor, supplier, distributor, or manufacturer.

Deviation. Deviation means a departure from the technical requirements included in a procurement document, or specified in early site permit information, a standard design certification or standard design approval.

Nonconformance. A deficiency in characteristic, documentation, or procedure that renders the quality of an item or activity unacceptable or indeterminate.

Suspect Item. A suspect item is one in which there is an indication by visual inspection, testing or other information that it may not conform to established government—or industry—accepted specifications or national consensus standards.

Definitions—EPRI 1019163

Counterfeit. Counterfeit items are items that are intentionally manufactured or altered to imitate a legitimate product without the legal right to do so. An example of a counterfeit item is one that has been fabricated in imitation of something else with the purpose of defrauding by passing the false copy for genuine or original or an item copied without the legal right or authority to do so.

Enhanced inspection/testing. Inspection/testing performed in addition to the standard receiving inspection/testing process in order to reasonably ensure that the items received are authentic.

Fraudulent Item. Fraudulent items are items that are intentionally misrepresented as something other than they actually are, with intent to deceive. Fraudulent items include items with falsified or inaccurate trademarks, manufacturer names, markings, test results and/or certifications. Fraudulent items also include used items sold as new as well as manufacturing overages sold by entities that have acquired the legal right to manufacture a specified quantity of an item (such as an integrated circuit) but produce a larger quantity than authorized and sell the overage as legitimate inventory.

Counterfeit Suspect Fraudulent Items

Counterfeit, suspect, fraudulent items (SFI or CSFI in NRC parlance) or suspect/counterfeit items (S/CI in US DOE parlance) are a significant quality threat.

Although not specifically called out in 10 CFR Energy laws, quality requirements of 10 CFR 50 Appendix B and 10 CFR 830.122(c) apply as follows:

From 10 CFR 50 Appendix B

Criterion VII—"Control of Purchased Material, Equipment, and Services"

Criterion VIII—"Identification and Control of Material, Parts, and Components"

Criterion X—"Inspection"
Criterion XV—"Nonconforming Materials, Parts, or Components"
Criterion XVI—"Corrective Action"
From 10 CFR 830.122(c) Criterion 3—Management/Quality Improvement.

(1) Establish and implement processes to detect and prevent quality problems.
(2) Identify, control, and correct items, services, and processes that do not meet established requirements.
(3) Identify the causes of problems and work to prevent recurrence as a part of correcting the problem.
(4) Review item characteristics, process implementation, and other quality-related information to identify items, services, and processes needing improvement.

Both the Nuclear Regulatory Commission (NRC) and the US Department of Energy (DOE) have published materials in the past decade related to this problem. The US DOE has made S/CI prevention mandatory for its contractors through Order 414.1D "Quality Assurance."

The Electrical Power Research Institute has published "Plant Support Engineering: Counterfeit and Fraudulent Items Mitigating the Increasing Risk, Revision 1 of 1019163." This document has been transmitted by the Nuclear Energy Institute to the NRC. This guide is intended to be used by licensees and suppliers to enhance existing practices for prevention, detection, and control of CFI.

The American Society of Mechanical Engineers (ASME) NQA-1 does not directly address suspect items, but a broad range of QA principles apply, including:

Requirement 8, Identification and Control of Items

100 BASIC

Controls shall be established to ensure that only correct and accepted items are used or installed. Identification shall be maintained on the items or in documents traceable to the items, or in a manner that ensures that identification is established and maintained.

Requirement 15, Control of Nonconforming Items

100 BASIC

Items that do not conform to specified requirements shall be controlled to prevent inadvertent installation or use. Controls shall provide for identification, documentation, evaluation, segregation when practical, and disposition of nonconforming items, and for notification to affected organizations. (Sections 200, 300, and 400 refer to Identification, Segregation, and Disposition, respectively.)

Requirement 16, Corrective Action

100 BASIC

Conditions adverse to quality shall be identified promptly and corrected as soon as practicable. In the case of a significant condition adverse to quality, the cause of the condition shall be determined, and corrective action taken to preclude recurrence. The identification, cause, and corrective action for significant conditions adverse to quality shall be documented and reported to appropriate levels of management. Completion of corrective actions shall be verified.

Impact of Suspect Fraudulent Counterfeit Items

Suspect items may include mechanical components such as bolts, valves, lifting devices; electronic components such as individual resistors and capacitors through circuit boards and control devices; and electrical components such as circuit breakers. Other issues may include plagiarism of documents, false brand names applied to items, and forgery. EPRI 1019163 Section 4 contains several examples of documented SFCI incidents. The USS *Iwo Jima* Steam Line Rupture of 1990 is a well-documented event with loss of life due to inadvertent use of counterfeit bolts, studs, and nuts during a high-pressure steam valve repair. Although a non-nuclear-powered ship, the implications of a similar incident at a nuclear power plant are significant. The valve failed catastrophically soon after the steam plant was brought online, the resulting nonisolable high-pressure steam leak killed 10 sailors and endangered the ship.

http://www.upi.com/Archives/1990/10/30/Scalding-steam-from-ships-boiler-kills-7-US-sailors/3273657262800/
http://www.nationalboard.org/index.aspx?pageID=164&ID=226
http://www.jag.navy.mil/library/investigations/IWO%20JIMA%2090.pdf
https://timothycummings.wordpress.com/2012/12/03/35/

A difficulty with detection of fraudulent or counterfeit items versus simply defective items is there was intent from some person or persons to purposely deceive a customer at some point in the supply chain. In the *Iwo Jima* example, a manufacturer intentionally made fasteners out of brass, and then applied a black coating. "Because those fasteners were covered with a manufacturer-applied black coating, at a glance, they could be mistaken for the correct grade 4 steel nuts." If the manufacturer had inadvertently supplied brass fasteners to fulfill and order for grade 4 steel, that would have been easily detected in a visual inspection. Instead, the intentional deception was not detected and led to 10 deaths.
NRC Information Notice 2008-04 states:

> In recent years many vendors, including foreign companies, with little to no experience in the nuclear industry have entered the market to supply parts and components for both safety and nonsafety applications to nuclear power plants. It remains the licensees' responsibility to ensure that all suppliers use standards and processes that conform to US standards. Effective oversight of suppliers becomes increasingly more important.

US DOE Order 414.1D includes a contractor requirements document with the following purpose:

> To set forth requirements for DOE and its contractor organizations, as part of their QAPs [Quality Assurance Plan], to establish, document and implement effective controls and processes that will: (1) ensure items and services meet specified requirements; (2) prevent entry of Suspect/Counterfeit Items (S/CIs) into the DOE supply chain; and (3) ensure detection, control, reporting, and disposition of S/CIs.

Prevention, Detection and Control

Detecting misrepresented products is difficult because most QA programs are not designed for detecting counterfeit or fraudulent practices. The criteria used to confirm the quality of products during receipt inspection and testing generally have assumed vendor integrity and are not focused on identifying an intent to deceive. Healthy skepticism and asking why "this is too good to be true" may need to be developed.

EPRI 1019163 does recommend three primary CFSI strategies. First, is Prevention. Prevent a suspect item from entering the supply chain in the first place. Second is Detection. Develop the ability to detect incoming and existing CFSI in the supply chain. This is accomplished through inspection at the source, receipt, and pre-installation. Third is Control. This includes quarantine and disposal of suspect items and communication that results internally and externally. US DOE Order 414.1D relies upon the contractor's QA plan to "include a S/CI oversight and prevention process commensurate with the facility/activity hazards and mission impact."

Procurement

General indications may be found early in the procurement process, beginning with the price quote and scheduled delivery time requirements, according to the NRC. Some things that have been found to be present when misrepresented products were identified, and which can be found during the quoting process are:

(1) The name of the vendor—several instances of apparent counterfeit and fraud involved vendors who were not authorized distributors for the products they supplied
(2) The price—quoting of prices by the vendor that are significantly lower than those of the competition
(3) Delivery schedule—a shorter delivery time than that of the competition
(4) The source of the item—drop shipment of items has been noted in several cases of misrepresentation where the quoted supplier subcontracted the order to another company and then had the subcontractor ship the product directly to the purchaser. The quoted supplier never saw or verified the quality of the product which, in some cases, has been substandard.

NRC GL89-02 talks about effective procurement and dedication programs. With engineering involvement, licensee engineering staff would be involved for effective controls in the (1) development of specifications to be used for the procurement of products to be used in the plant; (2) determination of the critical characteristics of the selected products that are to be verified during product acceptance; (3) determination of specific testing requirements applicable to the selected products; and (4) evaluation of test results.

NRC GL89-02 also discusses that licensees with effective products acceptance programs have (1) included receipt/source inspection and appropriate testing criteria, effective vendor audits, special tests and inspections, and post-installation tests in their programs; (2) required identification and verification of product's critical characteristics; (3) utilized sampling plans to perform the required inspection and tests; (4) verified the traceability to the original manufacturers of procured materials, equipment, and components; and (5) included consideration of audit approach, depth of audit, and audit team composition and have included appropriate engineering/technical representatives.

US DOE Order 414.1D calls for prevention of introduction of S/CI in the procurement process through the involvement of engineering, and inclusion of technical and quality specifications in procurement specifications. The DOE S/CI Handbook lists specific procurement practices in section 7.1. These practices are primarily related to engineering development of specification requirements.

Inspection

In Generic Letter GL89-02, the NRC identified three characteristics of effective procurement and dedication programs. These characteristics are

(1) The involvement of engineering staff in the procurement and product acceptance process
(2) Effective source inspection, receipt inspection, and testing programs
(3) Thorough, engineering-based programs for review, testing, and dedication of commercial-grade products for suitability of use in safety-related applications

As stated in NRC GL89-02, it is each licensee's responsibility to provide reasonable assurance that nonconforming products are not introduced into their plants. Dedication programs that ensure the adequacy of critical parameters of products used in safety-related applications can also contribute to the identification of counterfeit or fraudulently marketed vendor products. The licensees who use methods similar to those described in EPRI NP-5652 to verify the critical characteristics of commercial-grade items intended for safety-related applications have the basis for effective dedication programs. The NRC found that programs that embodied the above three characteristics generally were effective in providing enhanced capability to detect counterfeit or fraudulently marketed products and in assuring the quality of procured products, both in safety-related and other plant systems. Note the implied relationship between engineering staff, procurement, inspection and testing, and commercial grade dedication.

Section 7.1 of EPRI 1019163 discusses "vigilant inspection" to detect CFSI. The EPRI document *Guidelines for the Procurement and Receipt of Items for Nuclear Power Plants.* EPRI, Palo Alto, CA: 1990. NP-6629 is stated to be effective and should continue to be followed. Other inspection recommendations include the use of digital photographs of authentic items and verifying certification documentation and test results from sources independent of the supplier. Inspections should be performed at the source, pre-receipt, receipt, at the warehouse, and pre-installation.

Section 7.2 discusses modern methodologies for positive identification, similar in concept to methods to prevent counterfeiting of paper money and radio frequency identification (RFID) chips.

DOE Order 414.1D also includes inspection for compliance with procurement specifications, consensus standards, and commonly accepted industry practices. Inspections of inventory and storage areas for S/Cis are also called for. Further details on inspections, sampling, and acceptance criteria are provided in section 7.3 of the DOE S/CI handbook.

Both the DOE S/CI handbook and the DOE S/CI training manual address this practice.

Safety Culture

The NRC also has stressed the importance of the nuclear industry's vendors and suppliers establishing a positive nuclear safety culture. NRC policy statements related to safety culture identified, among other qualities, the need for continuous learning, effective safety communications, and employees with a questioning attitude as characteristics of a positive safety culture.

Training and Awareness

NRC documents also recommend the use of training. Training, including hands-on instruction, should be considered for all employees supporting the procurement process, including purchasing (materials and services), QA, product receiving, maintenance, and investigation personnel. Refresher training also may be regularly emphasized to update employees on new threats, identification techniques, and communication strategies.[†] Although these are only recommendations from the NRC, CFSI auditors should be aware of these recommendations and question if the auditee has considered the recommendations, and if not followed, what the auditee's rationale is.

NRC INFORMATION NOTICE 2012-22 does provide information about training. It does come with the caveat that:

> The NRC expects that recipients will review the list of available training resources listed in this [Information Notice] as it may be useful for educating personnel involved in NRC-regulated activities on current trends in CFSI, and techniques to prevent the use of CFSI parts. The suggestions contained within this IN are not NRC requirements; therefore, no specific action or written response is required. Addressees can review this information and consider actions, as appropriate. The NRC believes that training and awareness is important for combatting CFSI. The NRC Information Notice does include a table of available training courses as of the time of publishing. It is stated that the NRC does not intend to maintain the list up to date, nor is it a "complete" listing of all available offerings. The DOE S/CI Handbook also makes reference to NRC Information Notice 2012-22.

The EPRI 1019163 also contains a section on recommended training and scope. Similar to the NRC Information Notice, section 6.5 states that "training on CFIs should be provided to everyone involved in the procurement process from the specification of items to installation." The section identifies more than 20 topics and targeted audiences that can provide a basis for training learning objectives. Interestingly, the EPRI 1019163 suggests providing CFI precautions during pre-job briefings. Also recommended is having actual examples of counterfeit fraudulent items to use during hands-on training.

The US DOE provides a *Suspect/Counterfeit Items Resource Handbook* that discusses definitions, the DOE suspect/counterfeit items (S/CI) process, DOE directives and Government-Industry Data Exchange Program (GIDEP), and the DOE S/CI website. Appendices cover fasteners, components and product information, suspect indications list, S/CI found at DOE facilities, references, and resources.

The DOE's handbook also references GIDEP and states that the "DOE and its contractors should utilize GIDEP to report S/CI to organizations outside of DOE and to identify information from outside organizations to prevent S/CIs from entering their supply chain."

Identify Scope and At Risk Components

EPRI 1019163 recommends that an appropriate scope of concern be communicated. CSFI affects a broad range of components, and this scope should be effectively communicated to appropriate individuals and departments. Consider the items in the "Reporting Databases" section when assessing the scope of counterfeit items.

[†] NRC INFORMATION NOTICE 2012-22, REV. 1: COUNTERFEIT, FRAUDULENT, SUSPECT ITEM TRAINING OFFERINGS, November 20, 2019.

EPRI 1019163 points out ammunition as a procurement that might be overlooked when considering CSFI.

Identification of "At Risk Components" is covered in section 6.4 of the EPRI 1019163 document. Section 6.4.1 contains a list of risk factors, such as "The supplier is unknown or unverified (for example, Internet-based) supplier or broker."

Use Authorized Suppliers and Distributors

The NRC does require inspection and oversight of industry vendor activities. NRC Enforcement Policy is applicable to nonlicensees, including contractors and subcontractors, applicants or holders of NRC approvals (e.g., certificates of compliance, early site permits, standard design certificates, QA program approvals, and employees of any of the foregoing, who knowingly provide components, equipment, or other goods or services that relate to a licensee's activities subject to NRC regulation. A close relationship with suppliers and documentation in the Approved Supplier List (as required by other quality guidance) can prevent introduction of CSFI. EPRI 1019163 points out that brokers and unauthorized distributors are more likely (than authorized distributors) to supply CFIs or used or refurbished parts.

EPRI 1019163 also recommends that parts be procured directly from the original component manufacturer (OCM)/original equipment manufacturer (OEM) when possible. If not able to procure directly from the OCM/OEM, use an authorized distributor. As a distributor could make false statements about OCM/OEM status, it is worth confirming the authorization with the OCM/OEM. Many OEMs and OCMs do provide information about authorized distributors on their websites.

Section 7.2.1 of the DOE S/CI handbook provides guidance on approved suppliers and the processes to approve suppliers.

Relationships with Suppliers

EPRI 1019163 recommends "enhanced supplier communication and interface." Establish expectations and identify concerns with suppliers. Close partnering with a supplier can result in a productive information exchange.

Consider use of a document such as the Lockheed Martin reference document (link provided in reference list), which sets expectations for procurement with the company.

For DOE and its contractors, the DOE S/CI handbook states that "all contracts should contain the S/CI clauses prohibiting delivery of S/CIs." The handbook "highly recommends" making the clause a contract requirement, and an example clause is provided in section 7.2.2.

Supplier Evaluation

EPRI 1019163 does recommend incorporation of CSFI criteria into supplier assessment checklists and questions to be asked by auditors. The Nuclear Industry Assessment Committee (NIAC) "Standard Checklist" includes assessment of a supplier's CSFI inspection and testing processes.

Section 6.3.2.3 of EPRI 1019163 provides a list of 13 questions to consider during supplier evaluation. Also, section 6.4.2 of EPRI 1019163 contains precautions to take when dealing with at risk components, including inspection requirements and acceptance criteria to put in place.

The DOE S/CI handbook states supplier QA "should be sufficient to provide the requisite level of assurance that the supplier or distributor has the capability to comply with purchase order requirements" and lists five specific criteria. Further, if there are multiple suppliers in the supply chain, "each step in the supply chain process should be validated by audit, source inspection, or other methods as appropriate."

Control

EPRI 1019163 lists "control" as one of the primary three methods for combating CFSI. The organization should have a defined and documented method for responding to discovery of a suspect item. A "generic process for Controlling and Reporting Suspect Items" is provided in section 8.2. Primary actions described include quarantine and labeling of the item, investigation, internal and external reporting, notifying of law enforcement where appropriate, and physical disposition of the item. Reporting should include documentation in the corrective action management system.

DOE Order 414.1D requires inspection, identification, evaluation, and disposition of S/CIs that have been installed in safety applications. Engineering evaluations are required for S/CIs discovered in nonsafety applications to determine if they may be used as is. Marking to prevent future re-use is also required. Further guidance is provided in section 7.5 of the DOE S/CI handbook. In addition, section 7.6 of the handbook contains additional actions to be taken if the S/CI is installed in lifting equipment "including both fixed and mobile cranes and other devices (e.g., forklifts, scissor lifts, man lifts, balers, truck and dock lifts, elevators, conveyors, and slings)."

Both section 9 of the DOE S/CI handbook and the DOE HSS S/CI Awareness Training publications contain detailed information, tables, and photos to help identify S/CI during inspections.

Reporting Databases

EPRI 1019163 does advise that commercial nuclear operators in the United States have established protocols for the use of two data sharing tools:

- INPO [Institute of Nuclear Power Operations] has requested that all licensees report incidents of CFIs to INPO as operating or construction experience.
- EPRI has established a website (scfi.epri.com) that can be used by EPRI members to report and search for incidents of suspected CFIs.

DOE Order 414.1D also contains reporting requirements for S/CI discoveries. S/CI are required to be reported in accordance with Occurrence Reporting and Processing System (ORPS) requirements. In addition, trend analyses for use in improving the S/CI prevention process are required. The DOE S/CI handbook calls for timely processing of a Non-Conformance Report (NCR) and determination of status to meet reporting timeliness. There are several reporting databases available to find, track, and report instances of CSFI. Use of these databases can help prevent procuring items from known CSFI sources and share knowledge with others. This listing is not meant to be all-inclusive, nor should a listing be considered an endorsement of these data services. Nuclear and nonnuclear examples include the following:

https://energy.gov/ehss/policy-guidance-reports/databases/suspectcounterfeit-and-defective-items

Database of Suspect and Defective Items for US DOE and contractors maintained by the DOE Office of ES&H Reporting and Analysis (AU-23).

http://www.gidep.org/

GIDEP (Government-Industry Data Exchange Program) is a cooperative activity between government and industry. Proper utilization of GIDEP data can materially improve the total quality and reliability of systems and components during the acquisition and logistics phases of the life cycle. Membership is available to US and Canadian government entities and their suppliers.

https://www.iprcenter.gov/

National Intellectual Property Rights (IPR) Coordination manages and supports the US Immigration and Customs Enforcement (ICE) commercial fraud program. The website includes consumer alerts documenting cases of fraud, counterfeiting, and piracy.

http://www.iacc.org/

International Anti-Counterfeiting Coalition. The International Anti-Counterfeiting Coalition (IACC) is a Washington, DC-based nonprofit organization devoted solely to combating product counterfeiting and piracy. The IACC believes that acts of counterfeiting create severe public health and safety hazards, as well as economic harm. The IACC does offer the "IACC Market Safe Program," which is a strategic collaboration to create a cross-industry alliance to combat counterfeit products online.

https://iccwbo.org/

International Chamber of Commerce. The ICC does include documentation of counterfeiting and fraud, including "Anti-counterfeiting 2015 A Global Guide."

http://www.thecounterfeitreport.com/

The Counterfeit Report. Mostly consumer goods oriented, offers a "free search before you buy" and product alerts.

https://academic.oup.com/jiplp/article-abstract/10/4/246/809270/Fake-it-til-we -make-it-regulating-dangerous?rss=1

"Fake it 'til we make it: regulating dangerous counterfeit goods" *Journal of Intellectual Property Law & Practice* (2015) 10 (4): 246–254. This article uses survey to broadly characterize anti-dangerous-counterfeiting legal regimes in the US, EU, China and India. This article analyses certain "best practices," including consumer education on the public health impact of dangerous counterfeits (particularly food and medicine), integrated product tracing systems and greater international coordination in enforcement efforts.

https://www.erai.com/Counterfeit_Part_Reporting_and_Alerts

ERAI, Inc. is a global information services organization that monitors, investigates, and reports issues affecting the global electronics supply chain, which includes a database of suspect counterfeit and nonconforming electronic parts.

Appendix A
Reference Documents

ANSI/ANS-3.2-2012 (R2017), "Managerial, Administrative, and Quality Assurance Controls for the Operational Phase of Nuclear Power Plants"

ANSI/ASME NQA-1-2019, "Quality Assurance Requirements for Nuclear Facility Applications"

DOE 10 CFR 830, "Nuclear Safety Management"

DOE 10 CFR 830.120, "Quality Assurance Requirements"

DOE Order 414.1, "Quality Assurance"

INPO 12-013, Performance Objectives and Criteria: PM.1, "Projects are selected, planned and implemented with predictable quality and resources that improve material condition to maintain safe and reliable plant operation."

ISO 9001, "Quality Management Systems"

NRC 10 CFR 50 Appendix B, "Quality Assurance Criteria for Nuclear Power Plants and Fuel Reprocessing Plants"

NRC NUREG-0800, "Standard Review Plan for the Review of Safety Analysis Reports for Nuclear Power Plants"

NRC RG 1.28, "Quality Assurance Program Criteria—Design and Construction"

NRC RG 1.33, "Quality Assurance Program Requirements—Operations"

COMPARISON OF STANDARDS AMONG COUNTRIES

Country	Regulatory Authority	Standards Development Organization	Codes and Standards/Regulations
United States	NRC	ASME	ASME BPVC (III, V, IX, XI), ASME NQA-1, 10 CFR 50 App. B, 10 CFR 50.55a, 10 CFR 71, 72, ANSI B31.1, B31.7, ANS 3.2
Brazil	CNEN	CNEN, ABNT	CNEN, safety guides, NUREG, ASME, ISO, ABNT NBR
Canada	CNSC	CSA	CSA (N285, N286-12, CSA Z299, N299, N286) ASME, ISO 9001:2015
China	NNSA	SAC, MEE, NIM, IAEA	HAF series, HAD, ASME, RCC-M, Decree 500, 666
Finland	STUK	STUK	ASME, RCC-M, YVL guides
France	ASN	AFCEN	RCC-M, RCC-C, RCC-E, ETC-C, RCC-C, RSE-M
Japan	NRA	JNES, JSME	JSME S NAI-2008, ASME
South Korea	MEST/NNSC	KEA	ASME, CSA, RCC-M, KEPIC
Russia	Rostekhnadzor	Rosatom, REA	PNAE G-7, SPIR-BN, SPIR-WWER, HU-090-11, HU-001-15, HU-010-16
South Africa	NNR		RCC-M, ASME, PER
UK	ONR		ASME, RCC-M, SAP, TAG, T/AST
UAE	FANR		KEPC, ASME, RCC-M, ISO 9001:2015
India	AEC/AERB	AERB	AERB/SC/G safety guides and manual

AEC (India) = Atomic Energy Commission

AERB (India) = Atomic Energy Regulatory Board

ASME = American Society for Mechanical Engineers

BPV = Boiler and Pressure Vessel Code

CNSC = Canadian Nuclear Safety Commission

CAEA = China Atomic Energy Authority

CFR = Code of Federal Regulations

IAEA = International Atomic Energy Agency

JSME = Japanese Society of Mechanical Engineers

KEPIC = Korean Electric Power Industry Code

MEE = Ministry of Ecology and Environment (China)

NNSA = National Nuclear Safety Energy Administration (China)

NEA = National Energy Administration (China)

NIKIET = Scientific Research and Design Institute of Energy Technologies (Russia)

NIM = National Institute of Metrology (China)

NRC = Nuclear Regulatory Commission (USA)

NRA = Nuclear Regulatory Authority (Japan)

ONR = Office for Nuclear Regulation (UK)

STUK = Radiation and Nuclear Safety Authority of Finland

FANR = Federal Authority for Nuclear Regulation

SAC (China) = Standards Administration of China

CNEN (Brazil) = Nuclear Energy National Commission

ABNT (Brazil) = Technical Standards Brazilian Association

Appendix B
Case Studies

CASE STUDY 1—INTERNAL AUDIT OF NUCLEAR UTILITY

APPLICATION

Internal (utility) audit

SCOPE

Inspector certification

SETTING

A meeting held at an operating nuclear plant, in the office of the QC Supervisor. The Lead Auditor from the utility's QA Department opens the meeting by specifying that questions shall be asked on inspector certifications in accordance with 10 CFR 50 Appendix B, Criterion II, and ANSI N45.2.6. A checklist will be used by the lead auditor.

CHARACTERS

Walt Door—Lead Auditor
Nat Epstein—Nondestructive Examination (NDE) Specialist
Abel Crank—Inspector Supervisor
Terry Borkowski—Records Center Clerk
Diane Muff—NDE Inspector

(Walt Door and Nat Epstein arrived at the office of the Inspection Supervisor, Abel Crank, at 8:30 a.m. Since this is an internal audit, introductions were not required. Walt went over the scope of the audit with Abel and gave a portion of the checklist to Nat for his part of the audit. Nat has left and Walt now begins his questioning of Abel.)

Walt—   How are your inspectors certified?

Abel—   All inspectors are certified in accordance with our Quality Instruction titled "Inspector Certification."

Walt—   I have reviewed that instruction at my office, and noted you referenced the requirements of ANSI N45.2.6, "Qualification of Inspection, Examination and Trusting Personnel for Nuclear Facilities," and SNT-TC-lA, "Recommended Practice." In my review, your instruction appears to meet the requirements of both documents. Are there any exceptions to them you have taken?

Abel—	No. We satisfy both completely, and since your audit of last year on this subject, we have revised our instruction to consolidate certification of NDE and quality control inspectors into one procedure, rather than the two you saw last year. Of course, while consolidating the procedures, we made some minor revisions to streamline our methodology.
Walt—	Nat and I reviewed the instruction online and it appears to be compliant. Is Revision 4 the current revision?
Abel—	Yes, Revision 4 is the current revision.
Walt—	Should your inspectors all be certified to Revision 4?
Abel—	No. As you will see in the instruction, I certify all inspectors annually, during their birthday month. I believe there are two inspectors to be certified next month and that will complete all inspector certification to Revision 4.
Walt—	How do you know when it is time to recertify an inspector?
Abel—	The clerk in the Records Center maintains a spreadsheet file on that for me, and on the first of each month he sends me a note listing those inspectors required to be recertified that month. It is then up to me to take action, in accordance with the instruction, to get the appropriate documentation back to the records center for filing that month.
Walt—	Does the Records Center maintain a database of all the documentation required for each individual inspector certification, such as activities he/she is qualified to perform, record of education and experience, test results, physical examination results, or eye tests?
Abel—	Yes. Each inspector has an electronic file in the database with his/her name on it. All the documentation you mentioned, as well as other required papers such as the annual recertification, are filed in the record center under the inspector's name.
Walt—	That should be all the information I need at this time, Abel. I want to see how Nat is doing. He is talking to the maintenance superintendent to find out if any NDE inspections will be required today. I'll then go over to the Records Center to start my review of the inspectors' files. Do you want to come along?
Abel—	No. I'll call the clerk to let him know you're coming and that he is to give you any assistance necessary. By the way, the new clerk's name is Terry Borkowski. I would request though, Walt, that if you have any problems to let me know immediately.
Walt—	Oh sure, Abel, I'll keep you informed as I go along. You know it's not my style to pull an "I gotcha!" out of my pocket at the exit.
	(Walt then leaves Able's office and meets up with Nat at the maintenance superintendent's office. Nat is discussing an NDE job to be done later that morning on the safety system. Walt gives Nat a copy of the Quality Instruction titled "Inspector Certification.")
Nat—	I am going to stay here, as they have just called for an NDE inspector to come and do a dye penetrant examination or inspection on a safety injection weld. I am going to observe the inspector's technique and extent of knowledge for that method.

Walt—   Fine. What is the inspector's name and I'll include that name as part of my audit of the certification files.

Nat—   The inspector is Diane Muff. The superintendent told me she is certified as a Level II Dye Penetrant Inspector.

Walt—   OK. As soon as you're finished with this part of the audit, meet me in the Records Center.

(Walt then walks into the Records Center where Terry greets him and Walt starts his investigation of the certification files.)

Walt—   I would like to review your file of inspection reports completed by plant inspectors for the last six months.

Terry—   Which discipline do you want? We have them filed by Mechanical, Electrical, Operation, Instruction & Control, or NDE.

Walt—   I want to see all the disciplines.

(Walt randomly selects inspection reports from each discipline. He then lists these report numbers on his tablet along with the inspector's name, date, and inspection discipline.)

Walt—   Now Terry, I would like to see the certification files for your inspectors.

Terry—   Over here in this cabinet, Walt, where they are arranged alphabetically.

Walt—   How do you know what information to keep in these files, Terry?

Terry—   I get all the records from Abel that go in here, but I follow our Inspector Certification Instruction.

Walt—   May I see your copy of that instruction? Terry gets a book and opens it and then hands it to Walt.

Terry—   Yes. All instructions in there are the latest revisions. I am on direct distribution from the print room.

Walt—   I see this is Revision 3.

Terry—   That is the latest one I have received.

Walt—   You haven't seen this Revision 4 then?

Terry—   No I haven't.

Walt—   OK, let's start through the individual's files according to this list of inspection reports.

Terry—   Here are the ones from your list of operational inspection reports.

Walt—   These are fine, now let me see these people's files from the I&C reports. . . . I see this one inspector has not had an eye exam in 19 months, and the Quality Instruction requires an annual eye exam.

(Walt then reviews the dates on 13 additional eye exams and finds five of those out of date.)

Terry—   I know Revision 3 required a biannual eye exam. Except for NDE inspectors. That has always been an annual requirement.

Walt— See here on page 4? It requires this annually during the birthday month.

Walt— OK. Now let me see the files on these NDE inspectors and also the file on Diane Muff. . . . Is this all you have on Muff?

Terry— Yes. All mail that came in today has been sorted and there was nothing for the certification files in it.

Walt— I do not find any certification for Muff being a Level II Dye Penetrant Inspector.

Terry— Then she is only a Level I, as far as I know.

Walt— Would you call the maintenance superintendent's office for me and see if Nat Epstein is there?

Terry— He left there about three hours ago to watch Diane Muff do a PT on a safety injection weld.

Walt— Thanks for your help, Terry. I'll stop over and see Abel to tell him what I have, but first I want to see what is taking Nat so long.

(Walt then leaves the Records Center and goes into the Auxiliary Building where he finds Nat busily involved in performing a PT on a weld. The inspector, Diane, is watching Nat work.)

Walt— Hi, Nat. Are you finished with the performance portion of the audit?

Nat— No. Matter of fact, Diane here was having some difficulty with the weld being too hot, so I have been helping her cool off the surface and then there were some surface indications that were questionable, so I told her I would try it. After all, I have been doing NDE for 13 years and Diane has only been at it for 11 months.

Walt— Diane, does your supervisor know of your difficulties with this PT?

Diane— Yes. I talked to him on the phone but he is tied up in the Containment and can't get here for another 20 minutes. I suggested to Nat that we wait for him.

Walt— What level of NDE certification are you, Diane?

Diane— I'm Level II in PT. I took the exam and was certified Level II over 3 weeks ago.

Walt— Fine, Diane. Nat, are you finished here?

Nat— Not yet. I want to wait until Diane does this final area, then I'll help her evaluate it.

Walt— I don't think we have time for that, Nat. We have to talk to Abel before he leaves for the day, and it is 4 o'clock now.

(Walt and Nat then walk over to Abel's office. This walk took about 10 minutes during which time Walt discusses Nat's role in the audit with him.)

Abel— Walt, before you start, I got a call from Terry who told me you were looking for a Level II PT Certification for Diane Muff. I have her current certification right here in my file cabinet. By the way, I also got a call from Diane who was complaining about your auditor and the way he was interfering with her job.

Walt— Yes, I know about the problem, and I'll handle that within my department. OK now, I see this is a fire-resistant file cabinet, which is good. However, your Quality Instruction says that certification files are required to be maintained in the Records Center.

Abel— That is true enough; however, I just finished going over her exams, and it will be in the Records Center by tomorrow.

Walt— That takes care of the deficiency then. Now, my other deficiency is your program for the control of Quality Instructions in that the Quality Instruction your records clerk is using is outdated. Therefore, I am going to make a finding against 10 CFR 50 Appendix B, Criterion VI.

Abel— I really do not feel one copy of an instruction being out of control means the entire program for Controlled Instructions is *ineffective*. But I really appreciate the finding. This should help me justify the additional print room clerk I have requested.

Walt— My last item is that out of 14 inspectors' eye exams reviewed, I found six did not meet the time interval you have established for reexamination. This will be my last finding.

Abel— What do you think happened to allow that?

Walt— I feel it is a result of the revision you made to the Instruction for Certification last year. You did not ensure that the more stringent time intervals would not require a review of your certification files at that time to ensure this did not happen.

Abel— I see what you mean, Walt. I certainly appreciate your help in pointing out these items, and by the time I get your report, all the corrective action required here will have been completed. I should be able to respond to your letter within seven days after I receive it, telling you all action has been completed.

CASE STUDY 2—UTILITY AUDIT OF MANUFACTURING SUPPLIER

APPLICATION

External (supplier) audit; internal (manufacturing) audit

SCOPE

Document control (drawings)

SETTING

Manufacturing plant (pressure vessels). A pre-audit meeting has been held in the auditee's conference room at 9:00 a.m. with responsible personnel. During the meeting, the Auditor specified what questions will be asked on the drawing control system prior to a shop evaluation. A checklist will be used by the Auditor.

CHARACTERS

Bob Long—Auditor
Pete Young—QA Engineering Guide (auditee most familiar with the drawing system)
Ray Smith—Shop Clerk (auditee crib attendant)

(The pre-audit meeting ends and all personnel leave except Bob Long and Pete Young, the QA engineer who was most familiar with the drawing control system. Long asks the following questions from his checklist.)

Long— Are written procedures available for the control of drawings?

Young— Yes, Administrative Procedure MV-0309 titled "Drawing Flow and Control." Would you like to see it?

Long— Yes, I would. Further, I would like a copy for my use during the entire audit.

(Young proceeds to obtain a copy for Long and remains silent while Long is reading the procedure.)

Long— I have noticed that this procedure has not been revised for the last four years. Does this imply that there have been no changes in your drawing system during this period?

Young— There have been no major changes. Therefore, the procedure has not been revised.

Long— I see. Are drawings approved by the customer?

Young— Yes, the Contract Administrative Department informs manufacturing sections that drawings are approved by a formal release system. You will note this is further defined in paragraph 25 of our procedure.

Long— Is a system in effect for control of customer furnished drawings? As you know, the above questions were related to your own company's manufacturing drawings. Do you receive contracts from a customer who demands that your company use his detailed manufacturing drawings?

Young— Normally we do not release the customer's drawing to the shops, reason being that manufacturing personnel are only familiar with one drawing format, notes, symbols, etc. By having only one format to interpret, this helps to eliminate manufacturing errors. I would answer your question by saying no, we do not use customer's drawings for manufacturing purposes. We do use them for engineering purposes.

Long— Is there a formal review and approval system in effect?

Young— Yes.

Long— Are drawings formally released and revision numbers published so that shops and sections can verify that correct revisions are used on the job?

Young— Yes, we use a computerized drawing list.

Long— Are the latest computerized drawings lists maintained on file?

Young— Yes.

Long— Are the latest approved drawings on file?

Young— Yes.

Long— Are obsolete, illegible, or unauthorized drawings in use?

Young— No.

Long— Are old revisions accounted for and destroyed by responsible personnel?

Young— Yes.

Long— Are missing drawings properly signed out?

Young— Yes.

Long— I see. Well, after reading your procedure and having you answer my questions, I am somewhat familiar with your drawing flow and control system. I would like to continue my evaluation by using your answers against actual implementation during a shop evaluation.

Young— Fine, let's get our hard hats and safety glasses on and go down to the shop floor and see the shop clerk who is the crib attendant in Bay 5.

(As they walk through the manufacturing shops, Long notices several drawings lying on workbenches near the machining area. This would be a good time for him to record the drawing numbers on his checklist and verify if these were current with the latest computerized list in the possession of the shop clerk, he thinks. Long points to drawings laying on workbenches.)

Long— May we stop a few minutes until I record these drawing numbers?

Young— Sure, no problem.

(Upon arriving at the shop crib, Long proceeds to ask questions of the shop clerk.)

Long— May I see the latest computerized drawing list?

Smith— Yes.

(Smith pulls the record book from the drawing file and opens it to Section 1, which includes a copy of the computerized drawing list, and hands it to Long.)

Long— I noticed earlier today by reading the administrative procedure that the computerized drawing list is revised and updated at least once a week to keep the drawing revisions current for shop use. Please explain to me why this list is three weeks old?

Smith— I am familiar with the procedure of receiving a revised computer list each week; however, I cannot explain why we have not received a revised printout from the Computer Center.

Long— Is this not an important item that you should have called the Computer Center to find out why you had not received a copy each week?

Smith— Well, I guess that is what I should have done, but I am so busy with other duties that it just slipped my mind. I will call right now and get the latest list.

(Long proceeds to check the drawings and their revisions from his checklist that were obtained from the shop tour against the computerized drawing list. Out of seven drawings, three are found to be obsolete. There may be more, but Long cannot determine this due to the three-week-old computerized drawing list.)

Long— May I see your drawing files?

Smith— Yes.

Long— What are these drawings doing on top of the filing cabinet? Shouldn't these be filed inside the cabinet in their proper position? The Administrative Procedure, paragraph 38, specifies that the shop clerk crib attendant shall file all drawings by contract number in numerical order inside the cabinet. Are these obsolete or unauthorized drawings? If so, these should be destroyed.

Young— This is very embarrassing. I will talk to the area foreman about the problem.

Long— I noticed that the Administrative Procedure, paragraph 40, specifies that before the shop clerk assigns any drawing to the shop floor, a check must be made against the computerized drawing to assure that the latest revision is in the crib files. If drawing list and shop files do not agree, the drawing shall not be issued until resolved. Because of lack of concern in this area as indicated in my findings, I find this area in violation of your procedure and totally out of control. Pete, when was the last time you performed an internal audit in this area on drawing control?

Young— I cannot give you the date until I call my office; it will only take me a minute to call. . . . My office has informed me that this area was audited 12 months ago. There is no question in my mind that another internal audit is needed immediately based on your findings today. We must get this area cleaned up of deficiencies.

Long— I have seen enough in this area. Let us check other responsible sections in regard to the drawing approval cycle prior to manufacturing release. The Administrative Procedure specifies that Graphic Design Engineering shall be responsible and specify the final review distribution on Approval Form No. PDS-22510-1. Let us proceed to Graphic Design Engineering.

Young— OK.

(Long's concern is over the fact that the administrative procedure has not been revised for the last four years. Upon arriving at Graphic Design Engineering, Long requests a copy of the latest example of Approval Form No. PDS-22510-1.)

Long— This is not the same revision number as referenced in your procedure. I have noticed also that the format and the responsible organizations have changed for the approval cycle; therefore, not in accordance with the procedure. Why was this condition overlooked 12 months ago when the last internal audit of drawings was performed?

Young— I do not know. I will have to check the audit records.

Long— Pete, I am very much concerned over the lack of interest and concern your plant has involving the drawing flow and control program. I have seen enough; let us return to the conference room.

Long completes his draft of findings and recommendations and leaves a copy with Young. Long informs the auditee that a formal audit report shall be completed and mailed to his attention within the next few days. Long will ask for a reply of corrective action and, sometime thereafter, a follow-up audit shall be performed to ensure that the corrective action has been implemented.

CASE STUDY 3—INTERNAL AUDIT OF NUCLEAR UTILITY (CONSTRUCTION/CIVIL)

APPLICATION

Internal (utility) audit (construction/civil)

SCOPE

Compliance to 10 CFR 50 Appendix B

SETTING

Nuclear construction site. The Auditor and the Engineer, who will be his guide, are meeting in the main conference room at 8:00 a.m. on the second day of the audit. The Auditor tells the representative, who will be his guide, that he would like to begin the day's activities by examining design drawings that pertain to cable tray supports.

CHARACTERS

Jerry Neal—Auditor
Bob Blankenship—Engineer assigned by the Construction Engineer as a guide
Paul Horn—Print Room Supervisor
Wayne Thorne— Civil Engineering Unit
Sam Hogin—Shop Inspector
Doug Wallace—Foreman
Art Davis—Receiving Clerk
Bill Roberts—Welder
Susan Smith—Records Clerk

The men arrived at the print room, and Bob introduced Jerry to the supervisor, Paul. Jerry then asked Paul if he could see the design drawings for cable tray supports.

"Sure," said Paul. "We keep them here with the structural drawings. This set here is for supports on the 737.0 elevation in the Auxiliary Building."

"Fine," said Jerry. "I see here in the notes on the drawing that cable tray supports are Quality Level II. Could you tell me exactly what that means?"

"It simply means that only the Certificate of Compliance (COC) is needed from the manufacturer of the steel tubing. However, when the contract is written, we often ask for more information than is actually required. An example of the information would be the Certified Material Test Report (CMTR)."

"I see. Could you tell me what these red markings on the drawing represent?"

"One of the engineers put that change there in order to indicate a change in the dimensions of one of the supports."

"Shouldn't there be a new revision to the drawing showing this?"

"There will be later on, but as long as there is a FCR [field change request] we are authorized to go ahead and make the necessary changes before the next revision is actually issued. That is, as soon as the FCR is approved."

"Then it isn't approved at this time?"

"Well, the design engineers have agreed to the change over the phone, but not all of the appropriate signatures have been obtained."

Jerry made notes of his conversation with Paul and then asked Bob if he could see some of the structural tubing contracts.

"We will have to step across the hall to where those documents are kept," Bob said.

Bob took a file out of the cabinet of the R&T Structural Steel Company and handed it to Jerry.

"I see here," Jerry said, "that a CMTR [certified mill test report] was required as well as the COC [certificate of compliance], but I can't find the CMTR in this folder."

"That's because the CMTR is one of the documents that is required to be kept in the fireproof vault. I'll get Susan Smith, our records clerk, to retrieve the document for you."

Bob asked Susan to get the CMTR for material received from the R&T Structural Steel Company. She returned in a few minutes and said that that particular document had never been received.

"That's really OK," Bob said to Jerry, "since the COC is all that was actually required by the drawing."

"Can I see another contract?"

"Sure, here's one on Johnson Steel."

"I see this contract also calls for a CMTR as well as the COC."

Jerry finished his notes on his observation and then asked if he could take a look at some of the field fabrication orders. Bob then took him to the Civil Engineering Unit and introduced him to Wayne Thorne, the supervisor.

"Hello Wayne, I would like to see some of your field fabrication orders and have you tell me something about the way your unit handles them," said Jerry.

"Well, they are made up by the office engineers and then copies are sent to the construction engineer for his approval and to us as well. We then make sure that our representative, the shop inspector, gets a copy of it."

"What does he do with it?"

"He is responsible for determining how much material the fab shop can handle and then he requisitions the material from the warehouse. When the material arrives, he inspects it to make sure that it is exactly what is specified by the applicable drawing or bill of material. For example, he makes sure that if he asked for 8" x 8" x .5" tubes they didn't send him 8" x 8" x .625" tubes. He also makes sure that the craftsmen who fabricate the supports use the right size material and that all dimensions are in accordance with the design drawings."

"Is the inspector certified to perform these activities?"

"He has been with us only for about three weeks, but according to his resume he has had ample experience in this type of work. Because of this we decided that he wouldn't have to undergo the normal process of certification."

"It's almost time for lunch now," said Jerry. "Bob, I would like to talk to the inspector, so I will meet you here in an hour."

After lunch, Bob took Jerry to meet Sam Hogin, the shop inspector.

"Hello Sam," Jerry said, "could you describe to me some of your duties here after material has arrived from the warehouse?"

"Sure. My job is to inspect the supports as they are being fabricated, so I generally take a pretty close look at the materials the men are using."

"By this, do you mean that you don't always examine each piece of tubing?"

"Well, like I said, I check most of it, but I have always felt that you have to put a certain degree of faith in the men doing the work."

"I see here on the form that releases the finished product back to the warehouse that you have signed off as having checked the supports. Wouldn't this indicate that you have checked each and every piece of material going into the makeup of the supports?"

"Well, I don't intend it to mean anything other than what I have already indicated."

"OK, thanks for your time, Sam. Bob, could I take a look at the area for nonconforming materials?"

"It's just outside, follow me."

"It sure looks like you have things pretty much in order here, Bob, but what's this material over here outside the fence?"

"Oh, that's some of the material I heard talk about yesterday. It should be inside the fenced area, but they have only left it here temporarily."

"Don't you identify or tag items of that type to prevent their inadvertent use?"

"No," said Bob, "since that is only a temporary storage."

Jerry finished up all his notes to this point and then asked to be taken to the warehouse. Once they were there, Jerry looked around and noticed that some of the supports that were there didn't have the welding inspector's stamp on them. He then asked to talk to the individual who receives the supports from the fab shop.

Bob introduced Jerry to Art Davis and then excused himself for a few minutes.

"Art, what procedures do you normally use in receiving these supports?"

"Well, there are two main procedures. The first one is for all items in general and the other is specifically for cable tray supports."

Noticing that Bob wasn't around, Art said, "I am careful to use the general procedure correctly, but sometimes it seems just a little bit silly to do all the things stated in the other procedure. Many times we just ignore it."

Bob returned and Jerry then asked to go to the place where they were welding the supports to the embedments.

The men arrived inside the Auxiliary Building, and Jerry met Doug Wallace, the foreman. "Doug," asked Jerry, "I'd like to talk a few minutes with one of your men."

"All right, how about John? He's probably our most experienced welder."

"If you don't mind, I would like to talk to someone with a little less experience. What about this man over here?"

"OK, but he has only been with us about a month."

"That will be fine," Jerry indicated.

Doug then took Jerry to Bill Roberts.

"Bill," Jerry said, "could you tell me which procedures you are using in order to perform this welding?"

"I don't actually work from any written procedures. Whenever I come across something that I'm not sure about, I just ask John and he generally can give me some advice."

"What kind of on-the-job training have you received?"

"Mr. Wallace worked pretty closely with me for the first couple of days that I worked for him."

Jerry then finished up his notes and indicated to Bob that he had seen all he needed to see. He thanked Bob for his cooperation and concluded his reviews and observations for the day. He then left to go back to the conference room where he would write up the deficiencies that he had seen. He told Bob he would tell him what he found after he had finished reviewing his notes, and this would be before he left for the day.

CASE STUDY 4—INTERNAL AUDIT OF NUCLEAR UTILITY (CONSTRUCTION/MECHANICAL)

APPLICATION

Internal (utility) audit (construction/mechanical)

SCOPE

Compliance to 10 CFR 50 Appendix B

SETTING

Nuclear construction site. The auditors have completed their pre-audit meeting with construction management and are beginning their general evaluation of construction activities. The Lead Auditor tells the Engineer, who will be his guide, that they would like to begin the day's activities with the Mechanical Engineering Unit.

CHARACTERS

Jim Conner—Audit Team Leader
Phil Fain—Auditor
Joe Haver—Engineer assigned by the construction engineer as a guide
John Keen—Supervisor, Mechanical Engineering Unit
Max Smiddy—Craft Foreman
Ann Willis—Supervisor, QA Records
Jane Iddins—QA Records Clerk
Olen Jones—Welder
Gary Anson—Supervisor, QA Engineering Unit
Ron Abel—Supervisor, Hanger Engineering Unit

Jim Conner—	Please describe to us the duties and activities of the Mechanical Engineering Unit. We are particularly interested how you handle systems.
	(John Keen briefly describes the responsibilities of his organization.)
John Keen—	In the past there have been problems in installing piping. My unit is now developing a new procedure which will be used to verify pipe locations.
Phil Fain—	John, what type of testing do you conduct after a piping assembly is installed?
John Keen—	We do many different types of nondestructive testing as specified in our company's engineering standards. These procedures are listed in the work order package prepared by unit for each job. These packages are our method of giving specific installation instructions to the craft.
Jim Conner—	May we see some of the work order packages that you just talked about?

(The Audit Team randomly reviews five packages and makes notes relative to each.)

Jim Conner— In the package we just reviewed, we noted that several of the referenced nondestructive test procedures do not contain acceptance criteria or an approval signature. . . .

John, I want to thank you for your cooperation. I believe we are through here. Joe, I would like you to take us to the Auxiliary Building. When we get to there, we would like to talk to the craft that is installing the piping listed in the work order packages we just reviewed.

(The Audit Team arrives at the Auxiliary Building.)

Joe Haler— Gentlemen, this is Max Smiddy, the craft foreman responsible for the installation of the piping systems you have been evaluating.

Phil Fain— [*to Max Smiddy*] Please show me the procedures you use to control your group's activities.

Max Smiddy— They are in the Construction Craft Office, and you can go and see them there. We do not have them down here in the work area, as they will get dirty and greasy here.

Phil Fain— How are your welders certified?

Max Smiddy— Each welder has to successfully attend the site's welding school. The school certifies the welders.

Phil Fain— What welding procedures are the four welders in your group certified to perform?

Max Smiddy— I don't have this information. There is a list of welders' qualifications in the Records Vault. But each of my welders can stick-weld, and if some other procedure is needed, I send a man back to school for certification.

(The Audit Team observes the work area.)

Jim Conner— Phil, do you see that six-inch diameter spool piece being positioned with a hoist attached to that small diameter pipe? Joe, is that small pipe part of a safety-related system?

Joe Haler— I believe it is.

Jim Conner— Max, can you tell me which welder made the weld on this section of installed piping?

Max Smiddy— You can identify the welder from the weld history records.

Jim Conner— We have completed our observation of your work area, Max. We find several items that we need to bring to your attention. First, we have identified over 35 examples of pipes, flanges, and fittings that are not protected. Also, many stainless-steel valves for safety-related systems that are in temporary storage do not have their internal surfaces and weld preps protected from contamination and damage. And lastly, unused low hydrogen electrodes—Type E-7018—are stored in an open bin in the weld issue area. The material issue card next to the bin indicated the electrodes had been issued at the beginning of the previous shift.

Phil Fain— Max, I would like to talk to one of your welders.

Max Smiddy— Olen, will you come over here for a few minutes?

Phil Fain— We are conducting a quality audit in this area and would like to ask you a question.

Olen Jones— OK.

Phil Fain— What acceptance criteria do you use for welds you are making?

Olen Jones— I use the work package, and knowledge gained from over 20 years of welding experience.

Jim Conner— Max, I want to thank you and Olen for your cooperation. I guess you know our concerns. If you have no questions, I will now have Joe take us to the QA Records Vault.

(Joe introduces the Audit Team to the QA Records Supervisor.)

Ann Wallis— I am responsible for all QA records received or generated on site. The site people or our vendors make them, and we file them.

Jim Conner— We have been following some work order packages. Can we see some of the records generated as a result of these packages?

Ann Willis— Sure, just go into the vault and look in the file cabinet marked "Auxiliary Building Piping."

(The auditors enter the vault and locate the files they are interested in.)

Phil Fain— Ann, most of these inspection records are signed by the lead piping inspector instead of the actual inspector.

Ann Willis— I don't see how that can happen. All records are reviewed before they go into the vault.

The auditors return to the record administration area and are told by Ann Willis that the nonconformance reports (NCRs) are maintained by the QA Records Clerk, who is present.

Jane Iddins— All NCRs are numbered and filed sequentially.

Phil Fain— How many are still active?

Jane Iddins— All open NCRs are maintained in a separate file until closed.

Phil Fain— May we see the file?

Jim Conner— Phil, did you make note of the considerable length of time many of these NCRs have been open?

Phil Fain— Yes, I also noted that 14 of them concern significant conditions and no corrective action to prevent recurrence was taken or planned.

Jim Conner— Let's review some more of these NCRs—both open and closed.

Phil Fain— Jim, I notice there are many reports concerning missing or bent rebar.

Jim Conner— Yes, they have been written during the past seven months, and it does not appear the condition is being eliminated. In fact, I see that 12 NCRs on the same subject have been written during the past 30 days. I think we are through here at the vault. Let's get Joe to take us to the QA Engineering Unit.

(Joe Haver introduces the team to the supervisor of the QA Engineering Unit.)

Jim Conner— Gary, will you tell us what are the duties of your unit?

Gary Anson— We review field purchase requests for QA requirements, prepare trend analysis reports, review and approve site-generated QA procedures, and approve letters that the site prepares in response to NRC violations and 50.55(e) items.

Jim Conner— How are purchase requests (P/Rs) reviewed?

Gary Anson— We just read them over quickly and, if they appear satisfactory, we sign them and send them on for further processing.

Phil Fain— Do you check the P/Rs against applicable specifications, codes, and drawings?

Gary Anson— No, that is very time-consuming, and it has already been done by the preparer.

Jim Conner— What about those letters that go to the NRC? What do you do with them?

Gary Anson— These letters have a very short period of time for review and as deadlines must be met, our review is very brief. If we do see something that is not in the best interest of quality, we bring it to the attention of the project manager, but as he has the final say, we believe this act fulfills our responsibility.

(The Audit Team moves on to the Hanger Engineering Unit.)

Joe Haler— Ron, these gentlemen are conducting an audit, and I have been asked to bring them to you, as they have some questions about hangers.

Ron Abel— We see that all hangers and supports are fabricated and installed in accordance with approved engineering requirements.

Phil Fain— What happens when one of your engineers finds an installed and inspected hanger that he does not believe meets approved requirements?

Ron Abel— I personally inspect the hanger in question, and if I agree with my engineer, I have him prepare a field change request (FCR). I also discuss the situation with the responsible design engineer to get his concurrence on the recommended corrective action, which is usually use-as-is. I get a verbal approval so the work can continue and this is followed up later with the completed FCR. This method is a lot quicker than initiating a noncompliance report (NCR) and holding up the job until the NCR is completely processed.

Jim Conner— We thank you, Ron, for your cooperation and being so candid with us. Joe, I think we will make a general tour of the construction site before we finish our auditing for the day.

(The Audit Team goes on tour of the site.)

Phil Fain— Did you notice that all cable reels are stacked on end and are not protected from the weather?

Jim Conner— Yes, and in the same storage yard there are some spool pieces that did not have end caps in place.

(The tour continues in the warehousing area.)

Phil Fain— This warehouse is supposed to be environmentally controlled, but there seems to be a lot of dust on the instrumentation stored in here.

Jim Conner— I think I have seen enough. Let's go back to the Administration Building and discuss what we found out during today's evaluation.

(The Audit Team has a meeting.)

Jim Conner— Joe, I think we are through for the day. I am going now to see the project manager to tell him what we found today. We will see you tomorrow morning at 8 o'clock when we will continue our audit investigations.

CASE STUDY 5—EXTERNAL SUBCONTRACTOR READINESS AUDIT (TECHNICAL/LABORATORY)

APPLICATION

External subcontractor readiness audit (technical/laboratory)

SCOPE

General analytical laboratory operations

SETTING

The laboratory, which is a potential subcontractor to a larger firm, performs preparation and analysis of samples for possible radioactivity determinations. The larger firm has sent the Auditor to determine if the laboratory is capable and ready to receive and analyze samplers prior to providing a subcontract.

CHARACTERS

Loman—Lab Manager
Harry D—Lab QA Manager
S. Elmore—Lab Sales Manager
Audrey Q—Auditor
Subina—Sample Prep Manager

	Audrey Q enters the lab building, finds no receptionist, waits until someone stops by, calls Loman, who comes out with his team to greet her.
Audrey—	Hi, my name is Audrey Q. I'm pleased you were able to agree to this audit on such short notice. My boss thought that since I had just finished helping to write a proposal in our West Coast office that listed your lab as a subcontractor, that I should do an audit on you here in the Midwest, on my way home for my vacation on the East Coast. I got a good flight for the holidays. I understand another office in our company has used your services before, and liked your low prices. Unfortunately, I didn't bring my notes or checklists, but I do have the sales literature that S. Elmore, your Sales Manager, sent us. I've used it to outline what I would like to see today. I think if we work through lunch, we can get it all done today.
Loman—	We'll do our best to help you see that you made the right decision to use our lab. Some of our technical staff are away because of the holiday, but I'm sure I can answer your questions. I'd like you to meet S. Elmore, our Sales Manager, and Harry D, our QA Manager.
S. Elmore—	I have to apologize, I have been late in getting out our newest brochure describing the lab's expansion. You have the old materials, and since then we have added several new instruments, hired over 20 new employees, and expanded into three new workrooms. Our customers have really liked the look of our remodeled facility, too. You can set up in the nice new conference room, and we'll bring you whatever you would like to see.

Harry D—	Loman and S. Elmore can give you a quick tour of the lab, but I have to finish analyzing our PE [performance evaluation] samples and some top-priority client samples, then send the results out today. I'll leave my QA manual and SOPs [standard operating procedures] in the conference room for your inspection. I'll be back in a couple of hours, I hope, to answer any questions you may have about our quality program.
Loman—	That Harry D, he is always busy. If he isn't analyzing samples, he is QC-ing somebody else's results. That is why he is so valuable to us, does the work of two people. Well, have you had any coffee yet? We have a nice little kitchen and break room, and there should be some donuts, too. Why don't you grab a cup, and we'll go to the conference room. You tell us just what you want to see.
Audrey—	I'll skip the coffee. I'd prefer to take a tour of the lab first, to see what might be different than the promotional materials we used in our proposal.
S. Elmore—	OK, let's go! I know all about the new equipment and can tell you our customers really like our service.
Loman—	If you don't mind, I'll lead the tour. Samples sent to us by overnight air express should be arriving now. We can show you our state-of-the-art receiving center, and our brand new Laboratory Information Management System—we call it LIMS.
	(They leave the reception area. Audrey did not sign a visitor log, showed no identification, was not provided with a visitor's badge, safety glasses, or a lab coat.)
Loman—	This is the Sample Receiving area. To expedite the receipt of samples at odd hours and on the weekends, we give our customers keys to this area. They can open the back door and bring their samples into the walk-in refrigerator if no one is here to log them in. We get lots of samples from local industry at odd times, and can't get our staff to work weekends—no one wants to give up their time anymore. Not like the old days, when people jumped at the chance to pitch in.
S. Elmore—	This is one of the selling points we made since the old brochures were printed. We emphasize customer service. We make it easy for you to get the work to us so we can get started sooner!
Audrey—	I'd like to speak to the Receiving Clerk.
Loman—	Oh, Reese Eving is not here today, looks like I'll have to ask Subina to fill in. Fortunately, we help each other out all the time; there's plenty of work to go around. Subina from Sample Prep has seen samples logged in before, so she can do it today. She can take the samples with her when she is done.
Audrey—	May I see the SOP for receiving samples? And the training records that show Subina is qualified to perform the SOP?
Loman—	Here is the SOP, on the shelf.

Audrey—	The date on this SOP is three years ago. Do you have a policy for regular review and revision of your lab procedures?
Loman—	Yes, Harry reissues them each year. I guess Reese didn't pick up his new copies. But we can get one from Harry, he always carries his SOPs with him in case somebody asks what the latest requirements are.
	(Loman leaves and returns in a few minutes with an SOP for Sample Receiving. He hands it to Audrey.)
Audrey—	Your SOP is current, but I don't see your signature on it.
Loman—	Oh, I'm too busy to review and sign them all. Harry writes up each procedure, describing exactly what we are supposed to do, and prints up copies for each lab area. He sends an email so the managers in each area know when they can pick up new ones. We get new ones all the time.
Audrey—	What happens to the old procedures?
S. Elmore—	Oh, we ask each manager to recycle them. We encourage paper and can recycling at the lab.
Loman—	Here is Subina, ready to get those new samples into the LIMS!
Audrey—	Subina, can you please show me your training records for the sample receiving procedure? Or does Harry D. keep them in a main file?
Subina—	Oh, I haven't had any formal training, but I used to watch and help in my old job at a biomedical lab. I've worked with Reese when we were backlogged from installing the new LIMS, and had to do things manually. You just unpack the ice chests, set up the bottles on the table, get the LIMS computer to print out labels with the lab numbers on them, stick them on, and they are ready for me to start processing in the Sample Prep room.
Audrey—	Do you check the temperature of samples and screen the bottles for radiation before logging in?
Subina—	Reese does, but I don't know where he moved the thermometer and Geiger counter. Anyway, these samples are in the ice chests of a customer we have served before. They always ask for the same tests, and they never have any counts above background.
Audrey—	Where are your gloves and safety glasses?
Subina—	Oh, I was in such a hurry to get here that I must have left them in my Sample Prep office. I'll use some paper towels from this roll to remove the samples from the ice chest, so I don't get my hands wet.
Audrey—	How are the samples identified?
S. Elmore—	Our LIMS has a record of the customer's shipments. They email what they are sending. Saves us paperwork when we get the samples, and we have the information right in the computer. We give them our own Lab ID number too, uniquely, consecutively, chronologically, and by the type of analysis requested. We can print barcodes soon. We don't have any hard-copy logbook for the samples; it's all on the computer. We email

our managers when samples are here, and they come pick them up, or send someone. State-of-the-art here!

Audrey— So you check the LIMS computer to verify you received what they told you to expect?

Subina— Well, I don't know how to use the LIMS to do that. For these new arrivals, I'll just assign them today's date and use the client's name and consecutive numbers for their Lab ID. I'll leave a written list for Reese to enter into the LIMS when he returns. Since I'll be working on them right away, I know which ones they are.

Audrey— Do analysts sign custody records for transfer of samples?

Subina— Reese tells the computer to keep track of who has them.

Audrey— What about those ice chests of samples over there by the door? Will you log those in?

Subina— I don't know who brought them in, there's no paperwork or message about them. Must have been dropped off last night by one of our local clients with a key. I'll put them into the walk-in refrigerator, and Reese can log them in tomorrow.

(Audrey looks around, sees no hood, no shower or eyewash station. There are no temperature logs available for the sample refrigerators.)

Audrey— OK, I've seen enough here. Let's go to Sample Prep.

Loman— It is time for lunch, we made reservations at a nice place only a 30-minute drive away. They have a great buffet, you'll want to get seconds. If we leave now we can avoid the crowd and a 15-minute wait in line. Our employees are looking forward to joining us there. We don't want to disappoint them, do we?

Audrey— I'm sorry, I'll have to keep going here to see as much as possible in the lab in my short time here.

Loman— I understand, but you don't know what you are missing. I'll order a sandwich for carryout, and you can have it later today. It will be our treat!

Subina— I've finished here. We can start on these samples right away. I'll carry them over with us.

(Loman and S. Elmore carry several bottles each and accompany Audrey and Subina to the Sample Prep room.)

S. Elmore— It may look like a mess here, but they know where everything is.

Audrey— May I please see your SOPs?

Subina— Oh, I took them home to read the latest ones from Harry D.

Audrey— Who will do the work on these samples?

Loman— We are short on staff and long on samples these days. I've had to hire some temporary chemists to help out while we recruit for permanent positions. We tell the temp service what skills we need, and they send over their best employees. If they work out, maybe we can offer them a real job.

Audrey— Do they bring records of their qualifications, or do you train them on your own procedures?

Subina— Oh, the temp agency can't release those records unless we pay extra. They wouldn't send us chemists who don't know how to do the work, though, would they?

Audrey— We seem to be running late. I'll need to go to the counting rooms if you don't mind.

(They leave Subina to process samples, and move to the Instrument Lab. Harry D is there, recording counts and calculating efficiencies, entering data into the LIMS computer.)

Audrey— Loman, where does the lab buy its standards?

Loman— You'll have to ask Harry, he knows the best places. Hey, Harry, where do you get the standards?

Harry D— I have some friends at the university. They order a lot for their classes and research, and they always have extra. We get it cheap.

Audrey— Do you have certificates that show the source, counts, date, how it was measured, etc.?

Harry D— I can get a copy of the certificate from my friends when we need them.

Audrey— May I see the calibration records for this instrument you have been using?

Harry D— I'm using last week's calibration information, since it doesn't change much from week to week. I don't have time to recalibrate and still run these samples today. The response from my check standard this morning is about what I remember it should be.

Audrey— May I please see the SOP you use for this test?

Harry D— I left it in the conference room for you. I know it pretty well myself. After all, I wrote it.

Audrey— Then your training records will show you have passed a qualifying test for this analytical procedure, you are familiar with the instrument configuration, and know how to operate it?

Harry D— I don't have this in my file because I don't do this test on a regular basis. But the results have to go out today.

Audrey— May I please see your records of instrument maintenance?

Harry D— This is a rental instrument; the rental company hasn't given us a maintenance logbook. I don't know of anything that has needed repair in the three weeks we have used it.

Audrey— Loman, if Harry is conducting this analysis, who reviews the work for its quality?

Loman— Oh, I look at it before it goes out. After all, I'm the one the customer sends the checks!

S. Elmore— That's right, we don't want any delays in reporting. We have streamlined our review process.

Audrey— Well, it looks like this is all I'll have time for today. I'll send you my report within two weeks. I appreciate the time you have taken to show me your operations.

S. Elmore— But we didn't even get to show you our conference room! Here is the sandwich we got for you. At least take these souvenirs of your visit— a nice walnut pen and pencil set for your desk, this walnut clock with our lab's name on it, and this crystal paperweight.

Loman— We look forward to hearing from you and working with your firm when you win the proposal. Have a safe trip!

CASE STUDY 6—COMMERCIAL GRADE DEDICATION OF ITEM

APPLICATION

Source verification for Commercial Grade Dedication item Method 3 (see Figure 7.2)

SCOPE

Compliance to ASME NQA-1, Part I, Requirement 7, "Control of Purchased Items and Services," Section 700, "Commercial Grade Items and Services"; and Part II, Subpart 2.14, "Quality Assurance Requirements for Commercial Grade Items and Services," Section 604, "Source Verification"

SETTING

NuFab has a current spent nuclear fuel cask fabrication supplier with fully equipped inspection capability whose QA program has been approved with subsequent inclusion on the NuFab Qualified Supplier List. Increased customer orders indicate this may be insufficient and an alternate supplier is desired, rather than maintaining a large inventory. NuFab desires to procure only a limited fabrication/inspection service for a targeted evaluation of an alternate supplier's program with subsequent consideration of capability, rather than initially expending resources to perform a more extensive commercial grade survey. The audit begins in the conference room of Hanover Forge. Following a presentation of Hanover Forge's history, manufacturing capabilities, and industries served by the QA Manager, the NuFab Auditor/Source Inspector, Hanover Quality Engineer, and QA Manager proceed to the QC Department, where the Quality Engineer initiates the tour of Manufacturing. The QA Manager departs, requesting that she is informed when NuFab is concluding the source verification, and will join them later the same afternoon.

CHARACTERS

James T. Randall—NuFab Auditor/Source Inspector
Jeanette Finlay—QA Manager, Hanover Forge
Mark Sanders—Quality Engineer assigned by Hanover Forge as a guide

Mark— Hanover has a long history dating back to 1974 with customers in the Defense industry, automotive industry, farm equipment manufacturing, and energy producers. Although this is our first item produced for NuFab, we anticipate additional orders from nuclear power plants in the future. Defense industries were our initial customer base and our QA program has been audited annually for compliance to Defense standards. We expect you will be pleased with our personnel qualification, measurement capabilities, and records retention.

James— NuFab reviewed some of Hanover's records, including prior products, to ensure manufacturability as the component you are processing for NuFab, the nuclear fuel shipping cask inner shield lid, is both expensive and requires compliance to rigorous nuclear safety provisions specified in the Code of

Federal Regulations. Please include the equipment used to finish the inner shield lid during Hanover Forge tour.

Mark— You just viewed the fabrication equipment used to finish the NuFab cask lid, and these are the training records for Jay Watson, indicating he was initially qualified to operate this equipment in March 2011 and requalified to production using current Hanover Procedure #HF-M13 Rev B on 10/12/16.

James— "Polish Surface Finish to #7" is among the critical characteristics specified by NuFab on NuFab Drawing #9235-423G Rev C 3/17/09, and contributes to the seal required by this lid for this safety application. Could you please show me the method you are using to verify surface finish?

Mark— Yes, Hanover Forge measures surface finish using visual examination of surface roughness comparator blocks as specified in MIL-STD-120 "Gage Inspection." This provides accuracy to microns and has been employed reliably since Hanover began production in 1974.

James— I'll review the MIL-STD after lunch, Mark, to ensure I understand the basis for your statements. Now I would like to see the 12/4/16 records for inspection instrument calibration. I would like to understand the measurement system capability vs. tolerances specified in NuFab Drawing #9235-423G Rev C 3/17/09.

Mark— These are the records of our calibration service provider, Votive Instruments, for Hanover Asset # G23, our height gage used during the thickness measurement of the cask inner lid.

James— The NuFab drawing callout for the lid thickness is 9.000" +/− 0.125" required, and Hanover recorded 8.946" actual. However, review of Votive Instruments' calibration records indicated tolerance should be less than 30% of measurement system capability, and Hanover Asset #G23 does not meet this requirement. I will need to observe an alternate measurement of thickness before NuFab can accept this product.

Mark— This will require additional time for me to select an appropriate instrument with current calibration records. I'll take you to the cafeteria and then you can return to the QC lab after you have finished lunch. I should be ready then for the thickness measurement of the lid and will also have the surface finish standard for you to review.

(After lunch James returns to QC lab, joins Mark and observes a second Hanover measurement of lid thickness, reviews instrument calibration records, and accepts results.)

Mark— This is a copy of the MIL-STD-120 "Gage Inspection" you requested, which is referenced in Hanover Inspection Procedure #HF-M13 Rev B 10/14/12.

James— According to the section of this standard addressing surface finish, surface roughness comparator blocks should be used for tactile (touch) rather than visual comparison as sight is so unreliable and varies more between individuals. In addition, I checked the website during lunch and found that MIL-STD-120 was canceled 5/15/96. Hanover will need to identify an alternate standard specifying applicability of surface roughness comparator blocks and remeasure using the appropriate technique. Do you expect to complete this today?

Mark— I'll contact Votive Instruments now, and we can take care of this today, James.

(Mark places a call to learn that portable surface finish gages are now available and typically used for automotive, aeronautical, heavy machinery manufacturing, among other applications.)

Mark— Votive will send Hanover the product information so that I can review and possibly order this more reliable technique for future applications. In the meantime, they referred me to ASME B46.1 2009 "Surface Finish, Surface Roughness, Waviness, and Lay," which I can purchase online and use today. I will also prepare a Revision C to #HF-M13 Rev B 10/14/12, amending visual examination of surface roughness comparator blocks to use more reliable touch comparison. What time did you need to finish today, James?

CASE STUDY 7—SUSPECT/COUNTERFEIT ITEMS

APPLICATION

Independent review, in preparation for follow-on external reviews.

SCOPE

NRC and DOE requirements for suspect/counterfeit items (S/CI).

SETTING

The Auditor has been hired by Behling Electronics to review their program for supply of electrical switchgear to commercial nuclear and US Department of Energy (DOE) facilities. The Auditor is performing an independent program review, to be followed by a random sample of in-use materials stocked for fabrication into breakers and isolation devices.

PROCEDURES

BE-Proc-05 Procurement
BE-Train-01 Training Documentation and Records
BE-QA-20 Receipt Inspection
BE-QA-18 Control of Counterfeit Parts

CHARACTERS

Jennie Spear—Auditor
Charles Grey—Manager, Electrical Fabrication Facility
Paul Metcalf—Chief Engineer
Adam Svensen—Quality Control Manager

Spear— Good morning, Behling Electronics has hired me to provide an independent audit of your programs to prevent the use and distribution of S/CI. As you supply to organizations that fall under NRC and DOE requirements, I will be checking against both sets of requirements and guidelines. Fortunately, there is much similarity between the two, but we will keep track of any differences in requirements as they arise.

Grey— Thank you for your visit and your assistance. We have assembled our documents pertaining to procurement, training, and inspections. Paul Metcalf and Adam Svensen are available to provide further information, and also will accompany you on your plant visit and inspection.

Spear— Very good. Let us start with the training records and required training related for S/CI. How did you develop your training requirements and materials?

Svensen— We chose a vendor referenced in the table provided with NRC Information Notice 2012–22, and they provided our engineers, managers, and procurement specialists the recommended training for identification and control of S/CI. The training records for these personnel are available in our training records database, which we may pull up on the computer in this meeting room. We did the training last year and do intend to have a three-year requirement for refresher training. Those dates are tracked in the database here. For example, here is the record for one of our purchasers showing when they took the training and the required retraining date.

Spear— Thank you. The training records do look to be complete. However, I would like to later compare your current staffing records against the training database.

Svensen— Certainly. We'll pull that together for tomorrow's review.

Spear— One question, however. If you look at EPRI 1019163, which is referenced by both the NRC and DOE, it states that production and craftspeople should receive training on S/CI, as well as have the opportunity to see and handle actual S/CI. Do you provide training to these workers?

Metcalf— No we have not considered that. We believe that our engineers and procurement personnel will prevent any such parts from reaching fabrication.

Spear— Still, this is called out in the training documentation. I'd at least like to see your justification for not requiring such training, and this may need to be an opportunity for improvement. The topics that you have provided for the managers, engineers, and procurement specialists do appear to address current issues in S/CI, and cover EPRI 1019163 scope as well as the DOE S/CI training materials. I do hope to see pictures and posters in the plant on identification of S/CI parts.

Svensen— Yes, we will point out examples in the inspection areas this afternoon. Perhaps indeed it would be a good idea to post those in the assembly areas as well.

Spear— OK, let's move on with our overview. I do see that you recently completed a review of your Commercial Grade Dedication process, and I see it was noted that S/CI prevention was included and reviewed as effective, so we will move on to procurement. Could you please run through the applicable procedures with me?

Svensen— The procedures are here on the table. We do limit the number of suppliers we use, and definitely include a full life-cycle cost analysis rather than going with lowest bidder. We do maintain a close relationship with our suppliers, and do send our quality engineers out to visit the suppliers on a rotating basis. We have the results of the most recent reviews here in our corrective action database. Also, here is the approved supplier list.

Spear— Could you tell me about your maintenance of the approved list? Have you had to remove any suppliers from the list?

Svensen— Yes, unfortunately so. Here are the metrics we keep on receipt inspection results and timeliness from our suppliers. As you can see from last year's metrics analysis, this supplier (we'd prefer not to name their name at this time) was behind in order delivery dates and also had a high failure rate for performance against specifications. Although we did not find that they used any S/CI, we nonetheless removed them from the list and have found a better replacement.

Metcalf—   Speaking of metrics, we also do keep a set of metrics here for our S/CI program. I see you had asked in your pre-visit paperwork to provide any metrics related to S/CI. We had noted the DOE requires trending of S/CI prevention at their facilities, and some of their facilities have asked to see our metrics in order to support their programs, so here are our metrics, with their trend analyses results. We would appreciate if you could take a look at the metrics and provide any recommendations. This includes training completion rates, receipt inspection timeliness, and effectiveness, and assessments completed on schedule.

Spear—   Let me take a little while to review those metrics and I will get back with you. Where is your procedure for segregation of S/CI components when they are found?

Metcalf—   Our employees are diligent about setting any parts aside, and we collect them at the end of the week for disposal.

Spear—   So, if a S/CI is found on Monday, it could be on the shop floor for the rest of the week?

Metcalf—   Well, yes, but everyone is notified when we find an S/CI item, which maybe is only a few times per year.

Spear—   Still there needs to be a process to ensure someone does not retrieve one of these parts and install them in a product. We will need to look at this closer.

Spear—   Do you have contract requirements for S/CI?

Grey—   Yes, most of our DOE contracts contain S/CI clauses. We follow those requirements and will point out examples during the plant tour. Also, we flow down the requirements to the suppliers we purchase from.

Spear—   Very good. Do you participate in any reporting databases for S/CI?

Grey—   Of course. We are, as an electrical manufacturer, a member of EPRI and participate in their database and review the latest information and precautions from there. Since we supply to government entities, including DOE, we do also participate in the GIDEP (Government-Industry Data Exchange Program) database. We did have an event come up with a DOE facility two years ago where we did help them with reporting of a S/CI event in the Occurrence Reporting and Processing System. Fortunately, the installation did not turn out to be one of ours, and we did help the facility meet the required reporting requirements. We also pass on DOE S/CI reports from their Lessons Learned program.

Spear—   What are the bases for your inspection program? And I would like to visit the inspection stations this afternoon.

Metcalf—   We do coordinate with Quality Control with establishment of inspection criteria. We do perform a 100% inspection of incoming items that have been determined to be of risk for S/CI. You may see that list in Appendix B of Procedure BE-QA-20 here. We also perform quarterly assessments where a QA engineer performs a random sample of 29 items each month. We track and trend those results for both S/CI concerns and for other contract specifications. The most recent quarterly report is available here in the Assessment system database.

Spear—   Thank you. All appears to be in order here. I would like to meet a few inspectors on our tour and ask them some knowledge questions I have prepared. Here are the questions so you may see what I will be asking.

Grey—   This looks good. I am sure our employees will be able to answer these questions. Well, let's take a break and get ready for the plant tour. Jennie—you will need to take a brief computer training here, should only take about a half hour. We will make sure you have the appropriate personnel protective equipment provided, and we will start in on the tour once you are ready to go.

CASE STUDY 8—SOFTWARE USE IN NUCLEAR APPLICATIONS

APPLICATION

Internal (utility) audit; analysis

SCOPE

Software use

SETTING

The auditors have completed their pre-audit meeting with utility management and are beginning their general evaluation of design and analysis activities. The Auditor responsible for the software portion of the audit tells the Nuclear Analysis Manager that they would like to begin with looking at one of the organization's analyses that employed software.

CHARACTERS

David Trotter—Auditor
Bret Archer—Nuclear Analysis Manager
Hannah Sound—Engineer

Trotter— I'm David Trotter and I am the software specialist on the audit team. I'll be looking at software that was used in safety-related engineering analysis and design to ensure conformance with NQA-1-2008/2009. From the list of documents you provided prior to the audit, I have selected the Loss of Coolant Accident (LOCA) analysis that you completed recently. I believe a number of different programs were used in that analysis: MARTHA for steady-state analysis, GALILEO for transient analysis, and ERLAP for system modeling. And I understand that all three are run on standard Windows desktop machines.

Sound— That's correct. There were also a few small utilities for things like plotting and, of course, standard Office products to prepare the report.

Trotter— According to the cover sheet of the report, you determined this analysis to be safety-related. Why is that?

Sound— It just seemed reasonable that analyzing loss of coolant in a nuclear reactor would be a safety-related activity.

Archer— While that's true, Hannah, there are three specific criteria for defining an analysis as safety-related. They come from 10 CFR 21, Section 21.3, which lists them as:
- The integrity of the reactor coolant pressure boundary;
- The capability to shut down the reactor and maintain it in a safe shutdown condition; or

- The capability to prevent or mitigate the consequences of accidents which could result in potential offsite exposures comparable to those referred to in § 50.34(a)(1), § 50.67(b)(2), or § 100.11 of this chapter, as applicable.

Obviously, a LOCA would meet those criteria.

Trotter— Let's begin with the code MARTHA. Was MARTHA pre-verified?

Sound— No, it was verified within the analysis itself.

Trotter— About how long did the analysis take, and were you using MARTHA for the entire time period?

Sound— It took about three weeks and, yes, we did use MARTHA the entire time.

Trotter— So, what can you tell me about how your computers are updated? I know from my own experience Microsoft issues a lot of updates—or at least it seems like a lot—to their operating systems. I understand that many corporate IT departments "push" those vendor updates to all networked computers. Is that the case here?

Sound— Yes. We are *constantly* being notified that an update is pending and given the opportunity to save our work before the update is applied to our machine.

Trotter— So, is it likely that one or more updates were loaded on your computer while you were doing the analysis?

Sound— Definitely! I was quickly approaching a deadline but still had to stop work to allow the update to load and then restart my computer.

Trotter— What sort of testing do you do after a system update?

Sound— None. IT is responsible for installing the update and we assume that they are certain the update is necessary. We can find the Knowledge Base article that describes the update but, generally, it does not mean anything to us.

Trotter— But you don't actually rerun any tests for any engineering design or analysis programs after a system update?

Sound— No.

Trotter— OK. Let's look at how you documented the use of MARTHA within your analysis.

Sound— We always have a section for computer programs. We can go to that section, and I will point out to you where we met the documentation requirements.
- We begin by documenting the name and revision number of the computer program. In this case, it is MARTHA revision 2.3.
- We include the inventory control number of the computer that was used for the analysis; in this case it was my Lenovo laptop, control number HS00001. While not specifically required, we also include the version of the operating system; in this case, the program was run under Windows 10.
- Turning to the section of the analysis where we document the use of MARTHA, you can see that we list all of the inputs for the program as well as the outputs that are generated as a result of executing MARTHA.

- In this same section, you will find the information on how we verified MARTHA. We ran a set of sample problems that are documented in Leonardo and Donatello 2010, which is generally accepted as the standard for steady-state analysis. The ranges of inputs in the sample problems included all of the inputs for our analysis. As you can see, our results are within a rounding error of those stated in Leonardo and Donatello.

Trotter— NQA-1-2008/2009, Requirement 3, Section 401(a) requires that the program be verified to show that it produces correct solutions for the encoded mathematical model within defined limits for each parameter employed. How did you make certain that the parameters you used were within the defined limits?

Sound— Of course we knew what parameters we were using in this analysis. We then compared that list to the validation documentation we had for MARTHA to ensure that all parameters we were using were within the bounds of the software validation.

Trotter— That's great. Now, where do you explain why MARTHA is the proper program to use for this analysis?

Sound— We don't state that specifically in the analysis, but MARTHA and other programs like it are generally considered the appropriate calculation tools for steady-state analysis.

Trotter— I think that's enough for this morning. Let's resume after lunch with a look at the program GALILEO, which I understand was developed under NQA-1, Part II, Subpart 2.7, and is managed within your configuration management system.

Archer— That's correct. We'll make sure our Software Configuration Manager is here for that part of the audit as well.

CASE STUDY 9—SOFTWARE
VERIFICATION AND VALIDATION

APPLICATION

Internal (utility) audit; analysis

SCOPE

Software development (verification and validation)

SETTING

The Auditor spent the morning reviewing how software was used in one of the organization's analyses (see Case Study 8). They left the morning part of the audit planning to resume after lunch to review the program GALILEO, which was developed under NQA-1-2008/2009, Part II, Subpart 2.7. The entire development process will, of course, be reviewed, but the emphasis here is on how the organization validated GALILEO for use in safety-related calculations.

PROCEDURES

QP 3-1 Design Control
QP 3-2 Control of Computer Software and Error Control
QP 11-1 Test Control

CHARACTERS

David Trotter—Auditor
Bret Archer—Manager, Nuclear Analysis
Tracy Street—Software Configuration Manager
Hannah Sound—Engineer

Trotter— Good afternoon, everyone. I hope everyone enjoyed their lunch. This afternoon I would like to focus on the development process used to design, implement, and test the program GALILEO. I understand that the current version of GALILEO is 1.0 and that it is maintained within your configuration management system. I will be using the industry standard software development checklist for the audit. The checklist covers the design of the program as defined in NQA-1-2008/2009, Part I, Requirement 3; testing of the program as defined in Requirement 11; and configuration management and development and implementation activities as defined in Subpart 2.7. During the audit we will be looking at each checklist item in two different ways. First, we want to ensure that your quality program contains requirements that reflect the requirements in NQA-1, and, second, we want to ensure that you actually implement the program in accordance with your own program. NQA-1-2008/2009, Part II, Subpart 2.7, Section 400, requires that the software engineering method being used is documented to ensure that software life-cycle activities are planned and performed in a traceable and orderly manner. Please show me how the engineering method is defined for GALILEO.

Archer— QP 3-1 prescribes a general approach to software engineering. In general, it specifies a modified waterfall life-cycle method that uses the waterfall model but allows each major component of the program—like user interface, model, input, etc.—to have its own path. Of course, the engineering approach requires that the entire code must be tested as an integrated unit before being used in production. QP 3-1 allows each project to use the general approach or define a unique approach that meets all requirements. In the case of GALILEO, we use the QP 3-1 approach as is. The GALILEO software development plan incorporates QP 3-1 and then specifies which engineering organization will accomplish each part, an overall schedule, and an allocation of functions to various parts of the code.

Sound— And you will see, as we proceed through the development process, that we have followed that process. You'll see the requirements document, the design, the design verification, etc.

Trotter— OK. Let's take a look at your software design requirements for GALILEO.

Sound— OK. Here's the document. The table of contents pretty well lists the requirements that are in the document. This document was created under the requirements of QP 3-2. QP 3-2 requires that if a particular section is required but not applicable, we will include the section and just mark it "N/A." The first section of the requirements document describes the functional requirements which, of course, must be validated. The second section of the document includes:
- Operating system
- Interfaces
- Performance requirements
- Installation considerations
- Design inputs
- Design constraints
- Reference drawings
- Codes
- Standards
- Regulations
- Procedures or instructions that establish software design requirements, test, inspection, and acceptance criteria

Each requirement is assigned a unique identifier that can be traced throughout all the life-cycle documents from requirements through design, implementation, and test. The software design requirements document was written by me, reviewed by one of the other engineers, and approved by Bret Archer.

Trotter— OK, let's take a look at the design document for GALILEO.

Sound— Here's our design document, and again, our procedure requires that we include every required section even if it is marked "N/A." The design document for GALIELO has the following sections:
- Numerical methods
- Mathematical models
- Physical models
- Control flow
- Control logic

- Data flow
- Process flow
- Data structures
- Process structures
- Applicable relationships between data structures and process structures

In addition, we have a section that addresses the computer-program operating environment and an appendix that postulates what problems might occur during use of the program and what we have done and what we can do to mitigate the effects of those problems. There is a second appendix that correlates functional requirements with design elements to ensure that all functional requirements were addressed.

Trotter— As you know, most of the verification activities required by NQA-1-1994 have been eliminated in the 2008 edition. But the standard still requires a verification of the design. Does your GALIELO software development plan define the process for design verification?

Sound— No, it does not. But QP 3-1 meets all of the requirements for defining a software design verification. QP 3-1 outlines the design verification process and, in the case of GALIELO, we use the procedurally required process rather than developing a unique design verification method just for this program. QP 3-1 requires that the design verification evaluates the technical adequacy of the design approach, including:
- Ensuring internal completeness, consistency, clarity, and correctness of the software design
- Ensuring software design traceability back to the software design requirements

Typically, our software design verifications are accomplished by a detailed review of the design document, but we do allow the verifier to complete all or parts of the verification using alternate calculations or, in rare cases, even tests. QP 3-1 requires that the software design verification be completed and documented prior to approval of the computer program for use. We have a standard design verification checklist that helps the verifier ensure that all required design activities have been completed. The design verification is always completed by an engineer with at least the same qualifications as the developer and totally independent of the development process. The design verification checklist is then reviewed and approved by the manager. In the case of GALILEO, Mary Dodd completed the design verification and it was approved by Bret Archer.

Trotter— What are Mary Dodd's qualifications for completing the design verification?

Sound— Mary is an Engineer II like me. She has been working in our department for two years but has not been involved in the development of GALILEO. She has completed all company training on software development.

Trotter— Did the design verification include the first required software review?

Sound— Yes, it did. Mary Dodd did that as well. As you can see, when you look at the design verification checklist, Mary was tasked to do the entire review.

Trotter— Did Mary have any comments on the design?

Sound— Yes, she did. She had a number of comments. All of them were incorporated, and again, as you can see on the design verification checklist, Mary approved the second revision without comment.

Trotter— Do you have a programming standards document?

Archer— We do. It is a desktop guide that we use to define general requirements for developing engineering applications software. We use a desktop guide rather than a procedure because programming is somewhat of an art and it's difficult to be too prescriptive. For example, we say what a program header should contain, but sometimes the developer uses a compiler that provides a template that is slightly different. Or we might say how many comments per how many lines of code. But we might have 500 or more lines of code that do exactly the same thing, and it makes no sense to break it up every 10 lines or so to add a comment. We allow the developers a reasonable amount of freedom within a broad set of guidelines.

Trotter— Besides the software executable, what other outputs do you generate formally during the software implementation process?

Sound— Well, we no longer create paper listings of the software. All the code is stored in protected and controlled areas of the engineering server.

Trotter— We'll look at that some more when we talk about software configuration management. How about instructions for use of the software?

Sound— It depends. In some cases we actually produce a user's manual that includes instructions on how to use the program, but, most often, we develop extensive help files that are accessible to the user during operation that provide all the instructions necessary to run the program and, in some cases, interpret the results.

Trotter— OK, let's move on to acceptance testing. May I see your test procedure, please?

Sound— Here you go. As you can see, the document has not been finalized. We usually leave our test procedures fluid so that we can adjust them as we go through the test process.

Trotter— Well, that's actually not permitted by the standard. Test procedures must be complete and approved before they are used. They are then placed under change control. Change control and configuration management, in general, is especially important during test. Test discrepancies can lead back to requirements changes or design changes or implementation changes or all three, so it is extremely important to ensure that the software baseline remains in sync. But let's take a look at your test procedure to see what you've got in there.

Archer— Thanks for that explanation. We'll have to check and make sure that any other software that might be in development uses only formally approved test procedures.

Trotter— Bret, your checking of other software is what we call in the corrective action process an extent of condition determination.

Sound— Well, of course, the most important criterion for our test procedures is that they are comprehensive enough to ensure that the software produces the correct results. Before writing the test procedures, we determine what the range of parameters is for the code so that we test the complete range and actually beyond, to give us good confidence that the program works correctly all the way to the limits. And naturally we test the unusual situations, zero, negative measurements, etc. We always publish the range of parameters that we use for test in either the test planning document, the test report, or the user's manual. This way, our engineers know what range of parameters was tested so that if they need to use the program outside of that range they can follow the QP 3-2 process to extend the validation range. As you noticed in the design document, we trace our requirements through. We note the requirement number in the design document, in the code itself, and in the test procedure. This way we ensure that all functional requirements are addressed. We'll also have a general section of the test procedure to capture the nonfunctional requirements, not with the same rigor, of course, but we do want to make sure all nonfunctional requirements are met as well.

Trotter— What do you compare your test results to so you are certain that the program is producing the correct results?

Sound— It depends. Typically we will use one of three benchmarks, if you will:

- The first is a published document such as a textbook, or a juried article, or another generally accepted tome.

- The second is to compare the results with a computer program that was approved earlier. Sometimes we update the user interface or something but the model is the same as we used before. So, we can use that program to provide us with a standard to compare results to.

- And finally, and least desirable, is to use hand calculations. This is a labor-intensive, long process, but, sometimes, it is the only way to produce a standard for the program we are developing.

Fortunately, for GALILEO we had another program we used to use that implements the same model and we were able to use it as our standard.

Trotter— OK, let's take a look at your GALILEO test report and see what you've got in there.

Sound— Again, QP 3-2 requires us to include every required section, even if it is not applicable. This way we can be sure we capture each of the required elements of the test report. In our test report, we have:
- The name, version, and operating system of the program being tested
- The specific computer hardware on which the test was run
- Test equipment with calibration records if appropriate
- The date(s) of the test
- The name of the individual(s) who conducted the test and/or recorded the data
- A description of any simulation models used
- A description of test problems to include inputs, expected results, and the requirement with which they are associated

- The results of the test and applicability of the results to the problem being solved by the program
- Actions taken as a result of any test deviations noted
- The name of the individual evaluating the results

Trotter— How is the test report processed?

Sound— As with all our controlled documents, the report is reviewed by an engineer equally qualified in both programming and the science being modeled, and then approved by the manager.

Trotter— Well Hannah, Bret, and Tracy, thank you very much for your time and your candor. Tracy, I'm sorry we did not get to configuration management today but, hopefully, you will be available tomorrow to address that subject.

CASE STUDY 10—CONTROL OF ELECTRONIC RECORDS

APPLICATION

Independent review, in preparation for follow-on external reviews

SCOPE

Electronic records storage requirements for NRC compliance
Edison-PRO-081 Software Quality Assurance

SETTING

The Auditor has been hired by Edison Plant 3 to review their program for storage of electronic records for their commercial nuclear plant. The auditor is performing an independent program review, to be followed by a physical walkthrough of the media storage facility and a random sample of electronic documents for verification to storage, access, and inspection requirements.

PROCEDURES

Edison-PRO-067 Records Management
Edison-PRO-4294 Training Documentation and Records
Edison-PRO-003 Quality Assurance

CHARACTERS

Jennie Spear—Auditor
Virgil Tracy—Information Technology Manager and Chief Information Officer (CIO)
Jeremy Wilkin—Quality Control Manager for Plant 3

Spear—   Good afternoon. I have been assigned to conduct an independent audit of your processes for storage and control of electronics records. The audit will be conducted in accordance with NRC requirements for records management and, specifically, electronic records. We will review your documentation, software controls, and physical storage during my visit. This afternoon's meeting is to do an overview of your documentation and to prepare for the visit to the records storage facility tomorrow morning.

Wilkin—   We appreciate your assistance in this manner. Electronic records is a constantly evolving field, with new media and software encoding, and we want to ensure we are current with NRC requirements. Virgil Tracy, our CIO, is here to offer assistance from his department.

Spear—   Very good. Let's go ahead and start with your reference material. I see you invoke NIRMA documents for the basis of your program.

Tracy—   Yes, that's true. The NIRMA documents TG-11, 15, 16, and 21 have been listed in NRC letters as good basis documents for electronics records management.

Spear—   One problem though—you are referencing the 2011 versions. You are not owned by Duke Power, correct?

Tracy— No, we are not owned by Duke. Why do you ask?

Spear— The NRC has only granted permission to Duke Energy to use the 2011 versions. The current direction from the NRC is in RIS-00-018, which specifically lists the 1998 versions. Fortunately, there is a cross-reference between the 1998 to 2011 versions listing the differences that we may consult to see if there are any issues there as we proceed with the audit. Let's move on to a few specific NIRMA requirements from 1998. What are your access control precautions for being able to gain access to the records facility?

Tracy— Here is our listing of personnel who are allowed access to the records. We do separate their access into the required four types: read, write, delete, and approve. We do review this list twice per year for the need to have this access.

Spear— That appears to be appropriate. However, could you get for me a current plant employee list so we may spot-check if anyone who has left the facility recently is still on the access list?

Wilkin— Yes, we will provide tomorrow morning.

Spear— This computer over here—can it access records?

Wilkin— Yes, and it is secured with encryption and user controls.

Spear— [*notices a yellow sticky under the keyboard*] Hmm, looks like a password written here under the keyboard—this might present a problem.

Tracy— This certainly goes against what we have told the employees, but with the large number of passwords some of our engineers must maintain, we've found previous instances of this and will add this to the corrective action we have on security requirements. We will get to the bottom of this one!

Spear— Yes. Now, how do you handle modifications to records?

Tracy— That ability is limited to a small number of personnel as noted on the access listing. We do keep track of the date and who has made changes to the records. We do have a procedural guidance that after five corrections or a change of more than 40 words then we generate a new record. That seems to work for us.

Spear— Glad you have defined what you consider "substantial corrections" to be. I see we are visiting the storage facility tomorrow—what sort of environmental controls do you have in place?

Wilkin— We do have temperature and humidity controls, and do keep a strip chart to record those levels. We do control at 65° Fahrenheit and 40% humidity, which is a good center range for magnetic tapes, which we still do hold, and newer CDs.

Spear— Yes, that is a good range to meet requirements for multiple media. I would like to review the strip chart data to see how well that temperature and humidity is controlled. What is your program for periodic verification of the data stored?

Wilkin— In PRO-067, we do specify a schedule and minimum sample size for random sampling of media. We do track and trend any flaws found, and do identify if a given item (CD or tape) has an unusual number of flaws found, and rewrite and verify that record if needed.

Spear— Very good. [*noticing a shelf with several binders labeled as record copies of procedures*] Let's choose one of these binders here. What is the record retention date for this first procedure in this binder? I do not see the retention date on this.

Tracy— [*examines the binder*] Unfortunately you are correct, there is no retention date listed. We will remove this binder and have it verified and document the retention date and owner of the record.

Spear— One last thing before we go to the facility—what is your training program and who is trained?

Tracy— That is contained in our training manual, PRO-4294. We do identify, by their responsibilities, what training requirements are needed. We also provide training to all employees on awareness of records in general and specific items about electronic records during annual refresher training. I will admit there was an initial reluctance to declare an item as a record, but we have an efficient process for storage and have gotten much better awareness and compliance this past year.

Spear— Thank you for your time. Let's meet back in 15 minutes to head to the storage facility.

CASE STUDY SOLUTIONS

CASE STUDY 1—INTERNAL AUDIT OF NUCLEAR UTILITY

WORKSHEET—AUDITOR TECHNIQUES

ITEM NO.	PAGE NO.	TECHNIQUE USED	GOOD OR INADEQUATE	COMMENT
1		Not using audit technique in this instance	Inadequate	The auditor is working the job rather than auditing. The instructor should lead a discussion on the problems with Nat's method of performance.
2		Audit of instructions for current revision level	Good	The lead auditor exercises good judgment here by not making this a finding based on review of a single instruction.

CASE STUDY 2—UTILITY AUDIT OF MANUFACTURING SUPPLIER

WORKSHEET—AUDIT DEFICIENCIES

ITEM NO.	PAGE NO.	OBSERVATION (STATE TEXT THAT CONTAINS DEFICIENCY)	REASON OBSERVATION IS A DEFICIENCY	VIOLATION OF 10 CFR 50 APP. B CRITERION NO.
1		Computerized drawing list was not current (3 weeks old)	Ineffective document control	VI
2		3 drawings were found obsolete	Poor document control	VI
3		Several drawings not filed in proper location	Poor document control Poor housekeeping	VI
4		Latest computerized drawing list not checked against the drawings on file; violation on internal procedure	Poor document control	VI
5		Internal audit program weak in the area of drawing control	Ineffective audit program	XVIII
6		Administrative procedure on flow and control of drawings not current; had not been revised for 4 years; Approval Form No. PDS-22510-1 has been revised	Ineffective procedure	VI
7		Organizational changes were made for the approval cycle of drawings; procedure had not been revised	Ineffective procedure; organizations participating not clearly defined	XVIII

WORKSHEET—AUDITOR TECHNIQUES

ITEM NO.	PAGE NO.	TECHNIQUE USED	GOOD OR INADEQUATE	COMMENT
1		Audited actual condition	Good	
2		Audited drawings found on shop floor against computerized list of drawings; computerized list is the authorized document specifying drawings to be used during manufacturing	Good	
3		Audited actual condition against governing procedure	Good	
4		Audited actual condition against governing procedure	Good	
5		Lack of concern in the drawing control program by the auditee apparent to the auditor	Good	
6		Audited actual condition against governing procedure	Good	
7		Audited actual condition against governing procedure	Good	

CASE STUDY 3—INTERNAL AUDIT OF NUCLEAR UTILITY (CONSTRUCTION/CIVIL)

WORKSHEET—AUDIT DEFICIENCIES

ITEM NO.	PAGE NO.	OBSERVATION (STATE TEXT THAT CONTAINS DEFICIENCY)	REASON OBSERVATION IS A DEFICIENCY	VIOLATION OF 10 CFR 50 APP. B CRITERION NO.
1		"I see. Could you tell me what these red markings on the drawings represent?" "One of the engineers put that change there in order to indicate a change in the dimensions of one of the supports."	Design changes, including field changes, shall be subject to design control measures commensurate with those applied to the original design and be approved by the organization that performed the original design.	III
2		Bob asked Susan to get the CMTR for material received from the R&T Structural Steel Company. She returned in a few minutes and said that particular document had never been received.	Purchased materials required to conform to procurement account CMTR required by contract were not available at site.	VII
3		"He has been with us only about three weeks. Because of this, we decided that he wouldn't have to undergo the normal process of certification."	Personnel performing activities affecting quality shall be indoctrinated and trained to assure that proficiency is achieved and maintained.	II
4		"By this, do you mean that you don't always examine each piece of tubing?"	(1) No evidence that a program for inspection of activities affecting quality has been established and is being executed. (2) No evidence that instructions which include appropriate quantitative or qualitative acceptance criteria are being utilized.	X & V

ITEM NO.	PAGE NO.	OBSERVATION (STATE TEXT THAT CONTAINS DEFICIENCY)	REASON OBSERVATION IS A DEFICIENCY	VIOLATION OF 10 CFR 50 APP. B CRITERION NO.
5		"I see here on the form that releases the finished product. Wouldn't this indicate that you have checked each and every piece of material going into the makeup of the supports?"	(1) No evidence that instructions which include appropriate quantitative or qualitative acceptance criteria are being utilized. (2) Measures shall be established to assure that purchased material, equipment, and services, whether purchased directly or through contractors and subcontractors, conform to the procurement documents.	V & VII
6		"Oh, that's some of the material I heard talked about yesterday. It should be inside the fenced area but they have left it here temporarily."	Measures shall be established to segregate material which does not meet requirements to prevent its inadvertent use.	XV
7		"Once they were there Jerry looked around and noticed that some of the supports which were there didn't have the welding inspection stamp on them."	Measures shall provide for the identification of items which have satisfactorily passed required inspections and tests.	XIV
8		"I am careful to use the general procedure correctly but sometimes it seems just a little silly to do all . . ."	Activities affecting quality shall be accomplished in accordance with procedures.	V
9		"I don't actually work from any written procedure."	Activities affecting quality shall be indoctrinated and trained to assure that proficiency is achieved and maintained.	II

ITEM NO.	PAGE NO.	OBSERVATION (STATE TEXT THAT CONTAINS DEFICIENCY)	REASON OBSERVATION IS A DEFICIENCY	VIOLATION OF 10 CFR 50 APP. B CRITERION NO.
10		"What kind of on-the-job training have you received?"	Personnel performing activities affecting quality shall be indoctrinated and trained to assure that proficiency is achieved and maintained.	II
11		"That's really OK," Bob said to Jerry, "since the COC is all that was actually required by the drawing."	Measures shall be established to assure that materials, items, and services conform to the requirements or procurement documents.	VII

WORKSHEET—AUDITOR TECHNIQUES

ITEM NO.	PAGE NO.	TECHNIQUE USED	GOOD OR INADEQUATE	COMMENT
1		Audited design drawings for cable supports against actual condition	Inadequate	Auditor should have reviewed sufficient no. of drawings to determine whether identified discrepancies represented isolated cases or were generic.
2		Audited contracts for cable tray supports against actual condition	Inadequate	Auditor should have reviewed additional contracts to determine whether identified discrepancies represented an isolated case or were generic.
3		Audited orders for cable tray additional supports against actual condition	Inadequate	Auditors should have interviewed inspectors to determine if the qualification of other inspectors was similar to one interviewed and to see if all used same inspection technique.
4		Observations of auditor relative to conditions of material that should have been nonconforming and supports which lacked welding inspector's stamp; apparent lack of concern on part of auditee noticed by auditor	Good	
5		Audited procedures for cable tray supports against actual conditions	Good	

CASE STUDY 4—INTERNAL AUDIT OF NUCLEAR UTILITY (CONSTRUCTION/MECHANICAL)

WORKSHEET—AUDIT DEFICIENCIES

ITEM NO.	PAGE NO.	OBSERVATION (STATE TEXT THAT CONTAINS DEFICIENCY)	REASON OBSERVATION IS A DEFICIENCY	VIOLATION OF NQA-1 SECTION
1		NDE procedures did not identify acceptance criteria	Procedures shall include acceptance criteria for determining that important activities have been satisfactorily accomplished.	V
2		NDE procedures did not indicate approval authority	Procedures shall be performed by authorized personnel.	VI
3		Procedure in Construction Craft Office	Documents shall be distributed to and used at the location where the prescribed activity is performed.	VI
4		Foreman did not have documentation to indicate qualification of welders	Management should have documentation which indicates qualifications of personnel under their supervision.	II & IX
5		Hoist was attached to safety-related pipe	Activities affecting quality must be accomplished under controlled conditions and proper handling equipment utilized.	II & XIII
6		Pipes, flanges, & fittings for safety system were unprotected	Measures shall be established to control and preserve material and equipment.	XIII
7		SS valves in storage internal surfaces unprotected	Measures shall be established to control and preserve material and equipment.	XIII
8		Low hydrogen electrodes stored in open bins	Measures shall be established to control and preserve material and equipment.	XIII

ITEM NO.	PAGE NO.	OBSERVATION (STATE TEXT THAT CONTAINS DEFICIENCY)	REASON OBSERVATION IS A DEFICIENCY	VIOLATION OF NQA-1 SECTION
9		No acceptance criteria	Procedures containing criteria must be available at workstation.	V & IX
10		Auditors permitted free access to record vault without escort	Responsibility for records cannot be enforced when anyone can enter records vault unescorted.	XVII
11		Most inspection records signed by lead piping inspector	Records must identify the inspector who did the inspection.	XVII
12		Many hold or witness points were not signed off and dated	Inspection activities shall be established and executed to verify conformance with instructions, procedures, and drawings for accomplishing the activity. Inspection hold points where work shall not proceed without the consent of its designated representative shall be indicated in appropriate documents.	X & XVIII
13		A number of NCRs were open for considerable length of time	Conditions adverse to quality must be promptly identified and corrected. (This maybe an audit finding depending on the circumstances involved.)	XVI
14		For 14 NCRs concerning significant conditions, corrective action to prevent recurrence not taken or planned	The cause of significant conditions adverse to quality shall be determined and corrective action taken to preclude repetition.	XVI
15		Many reports on missing or bent rebar reported over 7 months	Corrective action(s) not effective.	XVI

ITEM NO.	PAGE NO.	OBSERVATION (STATE TEXT THAT CONTAINS DEFICIENCY)	REASON OBSERVATION IS A DEFICIENCY	VIOLATION OF NQA-1 SECTION
16		P/R not checked against specs, codes, and/or drawing as it is time-consuming	Measures shall be established to assure appropriate quality requirements are included in purchase documents.	IV
17		This type of letter has a very short review time; his reviews are very brief	Inadequate document review.	II
18		Installed hangers that do not meet requirements documented on FCR instead of an NCR as required by the quality program	Nonconforming items shall be reviewed and accepted, rejected, repaired, or reworked in accordance with documented procedures. This use of an FCR is not appropriate as the work had already been accomplished and inspected.	XV
19		Cable reels stacked on end and not protected from the weather	Measures must be established to control the storage of material.	XIII
20		Some of the stored spool pieces had missing end caps	Measures must be established to control the storage of material.	XIII
21		Considerable dust in environmentally controlled warehouse	When necessary for particular products, special protection environments must be specified and provided.	XIII

CASE STUDY 5—EXTERNAL SUBCONTRACTOR READINESS AUDIT (TECHNICAL/LABORATORY)

WORKSHEET—AUDITOR TECHNIQUES

ITEM NO.	PAGE NO.	TECHNIQUE USED	GOOD OR INADEQUATE	COMMENT
1	1	Short notice for audit; no time to prepare plan or checklists; key lab staff not present; not enough hours to do thorough job	Inadequate	5.4, Scheduling and Notification; 5.6, Identification of Documents Required to Conduct an Audit; 5.7, Development of Audit Checklists
2	1	No real pre-audit conference	Inadequate	5.8, Pre-Audit Conference Agenda
3	1	Skipped coffee, kept to schedule	Good	5.10, Adjustment of Audit Progress
4	1	Didn't look at QA manual, SOPs	Inadequate	5.9, Examination of Evidence; 6.4, Review of Quality Assurance Manual
5	2	Asked to see SOPs in lab areas	Good	5.9, Examination of Evidence; 6.11, Fact Finding and Verification
6	2	Followed up on disposition of old SOPs	Good	5.9, Examination of Evidence; 6.11, Fact Finding and Verification
7	2	Asked to see training records	Good	5.9, Examination of Evidence; 6.11, Fact Finding and Verification
8	2	Asked to see temperature/rad screen records	Good	5.9, Examination of Evidence; 6.11, Fact Finding and Verification
9	3	Asked about safety equipment	Good	5.9, Examination of Evidence; 6.11, Fact Finding and Verification
10	3	Declined lunch	Good	5.10, Adjustment of Audit Progress; 6.10, Handling Diversion
11	4	Asked for qualifications of temp staff	Good	5.9, Examination of Evidence; 6.11, Fact Finding and Verification

ITEM NO.	PAGE NO.	TECHNIQUE USED	GOOD OR INADEQUATE	COMMENT
12	4	Asked for calibration and maintenance SOPs, and Harry D's training records	Good	5.9, Examination of Evidence; 6.11, Fact Finding and Verification
13	4	Asked about potential conflict of interest with QA Manager reviewing own work, or reviewed by Lab Manager as a conflict	Good	6.11, Fact Finding and Verification
14	5	No post audit conference	Inadequate	5.13, Post-Audit Conference
15	5	Accepted sandwich and gifts	Inadequate	6.30, Audit Ethics

CASE STUDY 6—COMMERCIAL GRADE DEDICATION OF ITEM

WORKSHEET—AUDIT DEFICIENCIES

ITEM NO.	PAGE NO.	OBSERVATION (STATE TEXT THAT CONTAINS DEFICIENCY)	REASON OBSERVATION IS A DEFICIENCY Y/N	VIOLATION OF 10 CFR 50 APP. B CRITERION NO.
1		"However, review of Votive Instruments' calibration records indicated tolerance should be less than 30% of measurement system capability and Hanover Asset #G23 does not meet this requirement. I will need to observe an alternate measurement of thickness before NuFab can accept this product."	1. Y—Inspection/test instrument/method used inadequate to verify dimension/characteristic specified 2. N—Independence of inspection personnel	1. XII, 200: "Selection of measuring and test equipment shall be based on the type, range, accuracy and tolerance needed to accomplish the required measurements for determining conformance to specified requirements. A program for inspection of activities affecting quality shall be established and executed by or for the organization performing the activity to verify conformance with the documented instructions, procedures, and drawings for accomplishing the activity." 10 CFR 50 Requirement XI, Test Control: "A test program shall be established to assure that all testing required to demonstrate that structures, systems, and components will perform satisfactorily in service is identified and performed in accordance with written test procedures which incorporate the requirements and acceptance limits contained in applicable design documents. The test program shall include, as appropriate, proof tests prior to installation, preoperational tests, and operational tests during nuclear power plant or fuel reprocessing plant operation of structures, systems, and components. Test procedures shall include provisions for assuring that all prerequisites for the given test have been met, that adequate test instrumentation is available and used."

	"You just viewed the fabrication equipment used to finish the NuFab cask lid, and these are the training records for Jay Watson, indicating he was initially qualified to operate this equipment in March 2011 and requalified to production using current Hanover Procedure #HF-M13 Rev B on 10/12/16."		Requirement X, Section 100: "Inspection for acceptance shall be performed by qualified persons other than those who performed or directly supervised the work being inspected." 10 CFR 72.144B(d): "The licensee, applicant for a license, certificate holder, and applicant for a CoC shall provide for indoctrination and training of personnel performing activities affecting quality as necessary to ensure that suitable proficiency is achieved and maintained.
2	"The section of this standard addressing surface finish, surface roughness comparator blocks should be used for tactile (touch) rather than visual comparison as sight is so unreliable and varies more between individuals. In addition, I checked the website during lunch and found that MIL-STD-120 was canceled 5/15/96. Hanover will need to identify an alternate standard specifying applicability of surface roughness comparator blocks and remeasure using appropriate technique."	10. Inspection	Activities affecting quality shall be prescribed by documented instructions, procedures, or drawings, of a type appropriate to the circumstances and shall be accomplished in accordance with these instructions, procedures, or drawings. Instructions, procedures, or drawings shall include appropriate quantitative or qualitative acceptance criteria for determining that important activities have been satisfactorily accomplished."

CASE STUDY 7—SUSPECT/COUNTERFEIT ITEMS

WORKSHEET—AUDIT DEFICIENCIES

ITEM NO.	PAGE NO.	OBSERVATION (STATE TEXT THAT CONTAINS DEFICIENCY)	REASON OBSERVATION IS A DEFICIENCY	REFERENCE
1		"We believe that our engineers and procurement personnel will prevent any such parts from reaching fabrication."	These individuals [Maintenance, Production, Assembly, and Craftspeople] should attend periodic training in which OE along with examples of CFIs specific to their discipline are presented for hands-on examination along with their genuine counterparts.	EPRI 1019163 6.5.3
2		"Our employees are diligent about setting any parts aside and we collect them at the end of the week for disposal."	Measures shall be established to control materials, parts, or components which do not conform to requirements in order to prevent their inadvertent use or installation.	10 CFR 50 Appendix B, "Quality Assurance Criteria for Nuclear Power Plants and Fuel Reprocessing Plants," Section XV; 10 CFR 830 Subpart A, Element 3, "Management/ Quality Improvement"

CASE STUDY 8—SOFTWARE USE IN NUCLEAR APPLICATIONS

WORKSHEET—AUDIT DEFICIENCIES

ITEM NO.	PAGE NO.	OBSERVATION (STATE TEXT THAT CONTAINS DEFICIENCY)	REASON OBSERVATION IS A DEFICIENCY	VIOLATION OF NQA-1 SECTION
1	2	"None [speaking of testing after a system update]. IT is responsible for installing the update and we assume that they are certain the update is necessary. We can find the Knowledge Base article that describes the update but, generally, it does not mean anything to us."	NQA-1 states, "In-use test procedures shall be performed after the computer program is installed on a different computer, or when there are significant changes in the operating system." Auditee admitted she did not do any testing and did not know if the change was significant or not.	NQA-1-2008/2009, Part I, Requirement 11, Section 400(b)
2	3	"We don't state that [why MARTHA is the correct program to use for this analysis] specifically in the analysis but, MARTHA and other programs like it are considered the appropriate calculation tools for steady state analysis."	NQA-1 states, "Identification of any computer calculation, including . . . the basis (or reference thereto) supporting application of the computer program to the specific physical problem."	NQA-1-2008/2009, Part I, Requirement 3, Section 402(e).

CASE STUDY 9—SOFTWARE DEVELOPMENT (VERIFICATION AND VALIDATION)

WORKSHEET—AUDIT DEFICIENCIES

ITEM NO.	PAGE NO.	OBSERVATION (STATE TEXT THAT CONTAINS DEFICIENCY)	REASON OBSERVATION IS A DEFICIENCY	VIOLATION OF 10 CFR 50 APP B CRITERION NO.
1	2	"The second section of the document includes . . ."	NQA-1 states, "Software design requirements shall specify . . . requirements, including security features (e.g., vulnerability protection, and cyber security)."	NQA-1-2008/2009, Part II, Subpart 2.7, Section 401.
2	5	"We usually leave our test procedures fluid so that we can adjust them as we go through the test process."	NQA-1 states, "The preparation, issue, and change of documents that specify quality requirements or prescribe activities affecting quality such as instructions, procedures, and drawings shall be controlled to ensure that correct documents are being employed. Such documents, including changes thereto, shall be reviewed for adequacy and approved for release by authorized personnel."	NQA-1-2008/2009, Part I, Requirement 6, Section 100.

CASE STUDY 10—CONTROL OF ELECTRONIC RECORDS

WORKSHEET—AUDIT DEFICIENCIES

ITEM NO.	PAGE NO.	OBSERVATION (STATE TEXT THAT CONTAINS DEFICIENCY)	REASON OBSERVATION IS A DEFICIENCY	REFERENCE
1		"One problem though—you are referencing the [NIRMA] 2011 versions. You are not owned by Duke Power, correct?"	The NRC has only granted permission to Duke Energy LLC to use the newer 2011 versions.	NRC RIS-00-018
2		"Looks like a password written here under the keyboard—this might present a problem."	Users should have a unique user ID/password for access. Controls to ensure data integrity and prevent unauthorized alteration or erasure are required.	NUREG-0800 17.5
3		"I do not see the retention date on this."	The applicant shall establish requirements concerning record retention, such as duration, location, and assigned responsibility.	10 CFR 50 Appendix B, Section XVII

Appendix C
Examination Questions

INTRODUCTION

The following multiple choice questions have been developed to aid in preparing a written examination to measure the student's comprehension of the Handbook text and course instruction. Each question has one *best* answer; each question should be reviewed carefully before selecting the best answer.

It is recommended that the written examination contain a minimum of fifty (50) questions with a proportionate number covering each aspect of auditing. The examination should be administered without access to reference material. A passing grade of eighty percent (80%) is recommended.

Previous editions had only 94 exam questions from which to select. For this edition, the authors have included an additional set of exam questions to the original 94 exam questions for testing purposes.

The instructor is encouraged to include any questions that may be pertinent to the auditor's responsibilities/functions.

The solution keys to questions 1–94 and to the additional questions are located at the end of this handbook.

EXAMINATION

1. QA program audits are used to verify:
   a. the number of employees working on a job
   b. the measurements that are being taken on a product
   c. the degree to which a formal quality assurance program conforms with established requirements
   d. that inspections are performed by qualified personnel

2. The results of quality systems audits are intended to be used by:
   a. company management
   b. quality control supervisors
   c. quality control inspectors
   d. the auditor

3. Quality system surveys generally occur:
   a. prior to contract award
   b. after contract award
   c. during the contract
   d. all of the above

4. The quality system survey is used to evaluate the overall capability of a prospective supplier/contractor, including the _____ of his quality assurance program.
   a. adequacy
   b. implementation
   c. adequacy and implementation
   d. degree of sophistication

5. A quality systems audit is a detailed evaluation of _____ quality assurance program for its conformance to company policies, contract commitments, and regulatory requirements.
   a. a proposed
   b. a revised
   c. a utility's
   d. an existing

6. Two generic types of quality systems audits are those outside the company and:
   a. product audits
   b. internal audits
   c. process audits
   d. vendor audits

7. A Product Audit is the examination, inspection or testing of a product which has:
   a. been put into service
   b. not been previously evaluated and accepted for the characteristics being audited
   c. been audited
   d. been previously accepted for the characteristics being audited

8. A Process Audit is the evaluation of a manufacturing or test operation against documented instructions and standards to measure the _____ these standards and the effectiveness of the instructions.
   a. conformance of
   b. results of
   c. deviations from
   d. all of the above

9. The Owner of a nuclear facility is concerned with the performance of:
   a. the architect/engineer and the prime contractor
   b. vendors providing safety-related materials and services
   c. each participating organization
   d. activities related to the design of nuclear items

10. The Owner's concern relative to the performance of each participating organization stems from two major interests:
    a. scheduled completion dates and the cost of schedule
    b. public reactions and increasing costs of electric power
    c. assessment of efforts by the Nuclear Regulatory Commission and the Authorized Nuclear Inspection Agency
    d. records control mandated by federal regulations and economic interests assuring results from his quality program

11. To insure a nuclear facility is constructed efficiently and effectively, the Owner should:
    a. impose a penalty clause in his contract to collect losses due to slips in schedules
    b. impose an effective quality program and appraise conformance to controls
    c. purchase safety-related material from approved vendors
    d. engage consultants to review all nuclear designs

12. An Owner may, by necessity or option, delegate to other organizations some work scope, but must:
    a. assure compliance with his objectives related to cost and schedule
    b. also delegate overall administrative responsibility
    c. retain overall administrative responsibility to assure compliance
    d. not permit final inspection activities to be conducted unless a plant representative participates in the inspection

13. How does an Owner, either through his organization or by contractual requirements with others, assure his quality objectives are met?
    a. By establishing a comprehensive quality program covering all phases of plant design, procurement, construction and operation
    b. By assuring that all technical requirements are specified in appropriate detailed plans and specifications
    c. By having responsible parties submit progress reports on a scheduled basis
    d. By withholding payment to vendors and contractors who have not complied with contractual requirements and paying a premium to those who have

14. The Owner is ultimately responsible for every aspect of a nuclear facility because the person is the applicant and licensee. The quality assurance program must provide:
    a. safety analysis report (SAR) commitments to numerous federal codes and regulations
    b. direct control under its organizational structure
    c. a method that assures that suppliers of material, equipment and services have established and implemented effective quality assurance programs
    d. documented evidence that his program encompasses every aspect of these activities

15. If, in the Owner's evaluation of audit efforts by his prime organization, he concludes that their results are inadequate, the Owner may see fit to:
    a. issue a stop work order on the questionable activities
    b. have the prime organization submit a periodic report on its findings, showing what corrective action has been taken on the questionable activities
    c. perform unannounced audits in order to have proof for actions he plans to take against the prime organization
    d. conduct audits of a sampling of sub-tier organizations to provide assurance that the audit results reflected in the prime organization's audit reports are factual and effective

16. Because of contractual arrangements with Owners, the participating organization's audit concerns are similar to generic objectives of the Owner. How do they differ?
    a. They are emphasized in areas connected with their particular scope of contracted services.

b. They differ by their organization and the procedures in their respective quality assurance program

c. They do not differ as they both must meet all of the requirements of 10 CFR 50 Appendix B and ANSI N45.2/NQA-1.

d. Some organizations do not have a quality assurance program; therefore, the auditor must be sufficiently versed in quality requirements to perform his audit without benefit of a program.

17. Audits conducted by participating organizations assess conformance to:
    a. prevent or eliminate nonconforming equipment from being shipped
    b. determine product acceptance recognizing the nature of the item and its end use in a nuclear facility
    c. assure that the program is sufficiently implemented to be acceptable to the Owner if he conducts audits on sub-tier vendors
    d. working documents as well as program controls

18. What is the primary quality concern of the Owner over other organizations directly contracted for specific consulting or supporting services?
    a. The supporting organizations must be responsive to the Owner's demands to meet scheduled timetables and project milestones.
    b. The supporting organizations must have sufficient manpower and talent to accomplish the task.
    c. The Owner must ensure development and implementation of effective quality assurance programs.
    d. The Owner must make an assessment of the prime contractor's activities.

19. What considerations establish the basis for an organization's audit policy?
    a. Scheduling of end item production
    b. Annual management audit
    c. Number of personnel
    d. Industry requirements and needs of the organization

20. What provisions should management make to assure that the quality program is implemented?
    a. Require the performance of audits to assess the overall adequacy and effectiveness of the quality program.
    b. Require the QA manager to furnish management with audit reports and schedules.
    c. Review audit reports for adequacy of scope, response, corrective action and follow-up.
    d. Review and approve audit checklists.

21. A necessary prerequisite for any successful audit program is:
    a. a written and approved audit procedure that describes the mechanics of the audit program
    b. endorsement by top management of an independent audit program
    c. appropriately trained and qualified auditors and lead auditors
    d. none of the above

22. A company's policy regarding auditing may be influenced by:
    a. investment of time, money, and personnel
    b. degree of commitment of management

    c. company and customer quality requirements

    d. all of the above

23. Implementation of an effective audit program on a controlled and consistent basis requires:

    a. the development of written procedures that describe the mechanics of the audit program

    b. ASQ qualified auditors

    c. development of an annual audit schedule

    d. all of the above

24. The defined responsibilities for carrying out the audit program at the various organizational levels are generally found in:

    a. position job descriptions

    b. personnel manual

    c. company policy statement or department charter

    d. all of the above

25. Although there may be many different organizational structures among NSSS suppliers, A/Es, and utilities, the following may be said of the auditing activity:

    a. There are no "blue prints" for an auditing organization.

    b. It is generally possible to tailor the audit program to the existing management system.

    c. The group with responsibility for the audit program generally reports within the QA function.

    d. all of the above

26. The principle that the auditing organization should have reporting lines of responsibility at the same level as, or at a higher level than the organization, function or group it audits is:

    a. a requirement of ANSI N45.2, Section 19, "Audits"

    b. a requirement of ANSI N45.2. 12 "Requirements of Auditing of Quality Assurance Programs for Nuclear Power Plants"

    c. generally considered the intent of industry standards

    d. required by utility specifications

27. The independence of the audit function is evidenced in:

    a. the lines of the organization chart

    b. the quality and objectiveness of the audit

    c. the number of audit findings reported

    d. all of the above

28. Availability and experience of audit personnel is a consideration in the:

    a. performance of an audit

    b. planning and scheduling of an audit

    c. development of an audit plan

    d. review of a quality program

29. An audit planner generally has much more freedom in planning and scheduling of:

    a. internal audits

    b. external audits

    c. product audits

    d. process audits

30. The first step in establishing an overall audit schedule is to:
    a. determine the basic requirements to which a program or its implementation is going to be evaluated
    b. determine the specific requirements for auditing personnel
    c. establish the required frequencies of the audit and the tentative dates
    d. determine the requirements for preparation of checklists and forms

31. What factors determine whether the frequency of audits should be increased or decreased?
    a. Activities that demonstrate satisfactory understanding of program requirements at the beginning of the project don't need to be audited again.
    b. Change in organization, change in program, reduction in quality, or changes in requirements determine whether the frequency of audits should be increased or decreased.
    c. The frequency of audits cannot be increased or decreased once they are established.
    d. none of the above

32. The number of personnel and the experience and qualifications of personnel assigned to an audit are dependent on:
    a. the scope of the audit
    b. the time available to perform the audit
    c. the subject of the audit
    d. all of the above

33. The minimum number of personnel required to perform an audit is:
    a. one
    b. two
    c. three
    d. four

34. Lead auditors should be trained and certified in accordance with:
    a. ASME Code, Section III, Article NCA-4000
    b. ASME NQA-1-2008/2009 Part III Nonmandatory Appendices 2A-3 "Guidance on the Education and Experience of Lead Auditors"
    c. their company's quality program and individual needs
    d. the ASQ's Nuclear Auditor Handbook

35. If a company does not have personnel qualified as lead auditors, it may:
    a. take credit for audits of its quality program performed by its customers in lieu of performing its own internal audits
    b. hire an outside consulting firm to train their most qualified personnel
    c. use management personnel to perform audits until it qualifies its lead auditors
    d. all of the above

36. The qualification that is least important in the selection of personnel to staff the audit function is:
    a. proficiency in audit techniques
    b. good communication skills
    c. an inquiring mind
    d. education

37. Technical specialists who participate in audits as a member of an audit team should be:
    a. qualified by management as a technical specialist
    b. familiar with the use of checklists and audit procedures
    c. cognizant in areas of their field of expertise
    d. all of the above

38. Examinations of auditors to verify the auditor's comprehension of, and ability to apply, the prescribed body of knowledge and auditing skills may be:
    a. oral
    b. written
    c. practical
    d. all of the above

39. Certification of lead auditors is the responsibility of:
    a. an independent lead auditor
    b. the auditor's employer
    c. ASNT
    d. the Certification Committee of the ASQ Environmental & Energy Division

40. To remain certified, lead auditors should maintain their proficiency by:
    a. performing audits
    b. participating in the training of other auditors
    c. reviewing and studying related information
    d. all of the above

41. The final audit reports presented to the auditees management are considered:
    a. permanent records and must be maintained for six years
    b. nonpermanent records and must be maintained until the completion of the next audit
    c. permanent records and must be maintained for the "life of the plant"
    d. none of the above

42. Nonpermanent supporting audit records should be maintained for about three years or until completion of the next audit and include the:
    a. audit schedule
    b. completed checklists
    c. audit system plan
    d. all of the above

43. Training and qualification records of audit personnel should be maintained current and retained:
    a. as long as the auditor is employed with the company
    b. for the same period of time as required for the audit report with which the auditors are associated
    c. until re-certified
    d. none of the above

44. The key considerations in preparing for an individual audit is:
    a planning
    b defining the audit scope
    c. selecting a lead auditor and competent audit team
    d. all of the above

45. Personnel should be selected for an audit based on:
    a. experience or training that establishes their qualifications as commensurate with the activities to be audited
    b. requirements established by the organization to be audited
    c. geographic proximity of the auditors to the auditees
    d. the desires of the available auditors to further their skills or knowledge

46. An audit team leader should be an individual whose experience and training qualify him to:
    a. organize and direct an audit
    b. report audit findings
    c. evaluate corrective action
    d. all of the above

47. The auditor must prepare an audit schedule that accomplishes his organization's responsibilities and takes into consideration the:
    a. availability of transportation
    b. availability of auditee personnel to support the audit team
    c. time needed to perform the audit
    d. (b) and (c)

48. One of the key points in audit team selection is:
    a. selecting auditors who are independent of the audited activities
    b. selecting all qualified lead auditors
    c. ensuring one of the team auditors is in a management position
    d. having the team leader select the people he likes to work with

49. Audit checklists should be used to:
    a. make it simpler for the auditor to write the audit report
    b. provide a common base for the audit team to expand on
    c. ensure depth and continuity of the audit
    d. eliminate bias on the part of the auditor

50. What is the primary objective of the pre-audit conference?
    a. to discuss schedule with auditee
    b. to set ground rules for conduct of the audit
    c. to introduce audit team to auditee
    d. to establish rapport and set ground rules for conduct of the audit

51. How formal should a pre-audit conference be?
    a. It should be flexible and may be dependent on scope of the audit, size of the audit team, and whether the audit is internal or external.
    b. It depends on whether it is external or internal audit.
    c. Generally, the lead auditor should prepare an agenda for pre-audit conferences.
    d. External audit pre-audit conferences should be more formal than internal audit pre-audit conferences.

52. Who should be present at a pre-audit conference?
    a. President of the company
    b. General Manager of the company
    c. One or more representatives of management, the audit team, and other responsible parties
    d. Audit team, QA Manager and union steward

53. How should an audit be scheduled with the auditee?
    a. It should be written, detailing time and place.
    b. The auditee should not be consulted due to his possible influence on the audit.
    c. A mutual understanding should be reached on the scheduling of the audit.
    d. It should establish starting and stopping times for each day of the audit.

54. Why should an auditor avoid giving advice?
    a. The advice may be wrong.
    b. The auditor's company may be billed for unsolicited advice, which costs the auditee production.
    c. It is not the auditor's job to give advice; his function is to establish criteria and obtain objective evidence.
    d. It is the auditee's responsibility to advise his management.

55. The audit team leader should ensure that sufficient time is scheduled for an audit team critique prior to the post-audit conference and the leader should:
    a. define the audit scope
    b. evaluate the team members' audit performance
    c. direct a discussion of observations and findings
    d. finalize audit report

56. One of the important responsibilities of each auditor when performing an audit is to:
    a. evaluate and analyze his own observations
    b. evaluate performance of other auditors
    c. coordinate the audit progress
    d. none of the above

57. There should be frequent exchange of information between members of the audit team during the audit to:
    a. allow the team to make changes in direction and assignments to better evaluate and achieve objective
    b. allow each member to relay information that may be pertinent to another part of the audit
    c. help keep the audit on schedule and finish on time
    d. all of the above

58. Observations may lead to recommendations that are:
    a. presented at the post-audit conference
    b. included in the audit report
    c. discussed with the auditor's management for possible future audit
    d. all of the above

59. How should an auditor handle diversionary tactics during the audit?
    a. Lead the audit—don't follow the auditee.
    b. Avoid prolonged lunches, lengthy discussions on the part of the auditee, and strive for random sampling rather than asking for information.
    c. (a) and (b).
    d. Make adjustments in the audit for it.

60. The primary objective of the post-audit conference is to:
    a. establish rapport and discuss conduct of the audit
    b. ensure that the audited organization understands all findings and observations

    c. make sure that auditors do not deviate from the checklist

    d. perform a review of procedures against the QA/QC program

61. The post-audit conference with the audited organizations' management should be conducted:
    a. within a specific time frame
    b. immediately following the conclusion of the audit
    c. away from the auditee's offices
    d. not always required

62. Reporting audit findings to the auditee as early as possible, preferably prior to the post-audit conference, will:
    a. allow the audited organization sufficient time to review facts before the post-audit conference to assure there are no surprises
    b. eliminate the post-audit conference
    c. assure that auditors do not deviate from specific questions
    d. put time limits on the audit

63. The audit report must, at a minimum, have the approval of, and be signed by, one of the following prior to transmittal:
    a. a company representative who is conducting the audit
    b. audit team leader
    c. President of the company performing the audit
    d. Personnel Manager of the company performing the audit

64. The audit report should present in an established format:
    a. the audit purpose and findings
    b. the details of the auditee's quality procedures
    c. the education and qualifications of the lead auditor
    d. findings along with the responsible personnel

65. The letter of transmittal of the audit report should include:
    a. a summary of audit results
    b. a response date for replies, if required
    c. distribution to responsible management of both the audited and auditing organization
    d. all of the above

66. The format for reporting audit findings should include:
    a. provisions for recording verification of corrective action and follow-up
    b. provisions for auditors, as appropriate, to offer recommendations for correcting the nonconformance or improving the quality program to prevent recurrence
    c. the audit finding number
    d. all of the above

67. The audit team leader or management of the auditing organization should follow up the audit report to:
    a. maintain his auditor qualification
    b. obtain the written response and evaluate its adequacy
    c. assure the response is written by the Quality Assurance Manager
    d. all of the above

68. Which technique or method should be used to get the supplier's QA Manual for the audit?
    a. Include it with the shipping documents.
    b. Request via telephone.
    c. Specify in the purchase order/contract or specifications that it is a requirement.
    d. Pick it up at sub-supplier's location.

69. The supplier's QA Manual should be reviewed by the:
    a. lead auditor
    b. auditor conducting the audit
    c. auditee
    d. all of the above

70. The QA Manual should be reviewed for:
    a. NDT calibration records
    b. compliance to purchase order/contract requirements
    c. inclusion of purchase ordering data
    d. all of the above

71. An effective method to divert an auditee's attempt at monopolizing the audit team's time with non-relevant material is to:
    a. accept that it cannot be avoided. A good leader will allow for this in planning the audit schedule
    b. caution the QA Manager that the audit will be terminated should his organization continue to attempt to divert the audit team
    c. politely emphasize that there are many areas to cover in a limited amount of time and the schedule needs to be adhered to
    d. insist that the audit schedule must be followed

72. The auditor's real challenge is:
    a. skill at examining records
    b. dealing with people
    c. uncovering every audit finding
    d. getting along with his supervisor

73. To establish a basis for questioning the auditee, the auditor should:
    a. be strictly businesslike and care less about the auditee's feelings or ideas about the quality function
    b. state that he will take notes during discussions with the auditee, whether or not he has the auditee's consent
    c. maintain an appropriate mood and manner, and establish a permissiveness to talk freely in full confidence
    d. none of the above

74. Because the auditor's basic purpose is to objectively evaluate the auditee's quality program activities to contractual requirements, the auditor should:
    a. be concerned with the "who," "where," and "why" the activities satisfy the audit plan
    b. assure that the auditee's QA Manual does not address those requirements in the contract
    c. consider which sampling plan the auditee will prepare
    d. determine when the auditee will be ready for the audit

75. During the quality systems audit it is generally impractical to examine all items; therefore, auditing may involve:
    a. requesting the auditee to perform the required test/inspection, and supply the auditor with the documented results
    b. the use of a documented sampling plan
    c. examining only those items that the auditee supplies
    d. performing inspections or tests only when time permits

76. Which is the most suitable location for an audit interview to be conducted?
    a. At the actual location of the products/manufacturing activities
    b. While on tour of the plant, with the interviewer, his subordinates and any others
    c. A remote, private location or office
    d. QA Manager's office

77. When an auditor identifies a situation or item adversely affecting quality, he should:
    a. make a note, identify the source and gather any other pertinent information for future action, depending on the seriousness of the situation
    b. notify the auditee's management immediately
    c. notify NRC in accordance with 10 CFR 21
    d. notify the audited person's supervisor verbally

78. When the auditee volunteers "bits" of information that are informative to the audit, the auditor should:
    a. disregard entirely, as the auditee may be testing his knowledge of the situation, or trying to divert the auditor from something he is pursuing at the time
    b. notify the auditor's supervisor and terminate the audit
    c. listen carefully and discern by further questioning and more investigation to try to get objective evidence, where possible
    d. notify the auditee's supervisor

79. The use of a tape recorder during the performance of an audit:
    a. can be helpful; however, it should only be used with the knowledge and approval of the auditee
    b. is not considered ethical
    c. may have an adverse effect on feedback, as many people are reluctant to speak as freely
    d. (a) and (c)

80. Which of the following is not considered adequate backup data or objective evidence?
    a. Permanent or nonpermanent documentation, signed by a responsible authority
    b. Observations of activities with a concurring signature by the auditee's representative
    c. Verbal statements made by the auditee
    d. (b) and (c)

81. Audit report findings:
    a. should name the responsible individual
    b. should be presented in an impersonal tense
    c. are deficiencies uncovered during the performance of an audit that cannot be corrected during an audit
    d. (b) and (c)

82. At the post-audit conference, audit findings should be presented by:
    a. the audit team leader
    b. each team member for responsible areas
    c. (a) and (b)
    d. none of the above

83. What information need not be presented with the audit findings?
    a. What the requirement was
    b. Where the deficiency was observed
    c. Proposed corrective action
    d. What the deficiency was

84. Any reference to "observations" by an auditor should be carefully worded in order that all concerned are aware that:
    a. an audit finding does not presently exist
    b. the auditor feels the matter is serious enough to warrant the evaluation by the auditee
    c. the auditor may investigate the matter at some future time
    d. all of the above

85. Which type of individual will normally produce the greatest resistance to change?
    a. non-aggressive manager
    b. introvert
    c. aggressive manager
    d. extrovert

86. An auditor should demonstrate through his actions:
    a. a thorough knowledge of the audit subject
    b. that he is an authority on the subject
    c. confidence in the audit program
    d. all of the above

87. What action by the auditor will put an auditee on the defensive?
    a. Making value judgement statements
    b. Asking loaded questions
    c. Pre-conceived opinions
    d. All of the above

88. What characteristic should the auditor not show during an interview?
    a. Empathy
    b. Sympathy
    c. Humility
    d. Objectivity

89. What is the purpose of an audit interview?
    a. Assure auditee and auditor understand requirements of the quality program
    b. Listen, understand and evaluate the facts of the situation
    c. Attempt to identify the person responsible for a deficiency
    d. All of the above

90. An audit report must reflect:
    a. objectivity
    b. personality

c. sympathy
d. all of the above

91. How is the auditor's organization measured by the audited organization?
    a. Auditor conduct and report
    b. Thoroughness of audit checklists
    c. Number of people conducting audit
    d. All of the above

92. What is the most likely problem that a technical specialist can present to a lead auditor as a member of the audit team?
    a. Over-eagerness
    b. Failure to comply with the ground rules
    c Interference with the audit objective
    d. Wasting audit time solving problems

93. One technique to maintain high auditor morale is:
    a. permit the auditor to present his findings at a post-audit conference
    b. let the auditor complete the checklist
    c. let the auditor resolve the problem
    d. none of the above

94. For an audit to be considered ethical, it must:
    a. be free of surprise
    b. be objective
    c. contain full disclosure
    d. all of the above

ADDITIONAL LEAD AUDITOR EXAM QUESTIONS

Circle Your Answer

1. All those planned and systematic actions necessary to provide adequate confidence that a system, structure, or component in a nuclear power plant will perform satisfactorily in service is the definition of:
   a. Quality
   b. Quality Control
   c. Quality Assurance
   d. Quality Assurance Program

2. **USA Students Only.** Which of the following documents focus on nuclear safety? Circle all that apply.
   a. 10 CFR 50 Appendix B (U.S. Nuclear Regulatory Commission)
   b. 10 CFR 830 Subpart A (U. S. Department of Energy)
   c. ISO 9001 (International Organization for Standardization)
   d. ISO 14001 (International Organization for Standardization)

   Non-USA Students Only. Which of the following documents focus on nuclear safety? Circle all that apply.
   a. IAEA SF-1 (International Atomic Energy Agency)
   b. IAEA GS-R-3
   c. ISO 9001 (International Organization for Standardization)
   d. ISO 14001 (International Organization for Standardization)

3. The eighteen programmatic requirements for quality assurance in ASME NQA-1 is aligned with which US regulatory agency's requirements for quality assurance:
   a. DOD (Department of Defense)
   b. DOE (Department of Energy)
   c. EPA (Environmental Protection Agency)
   d. NRC (Nuclear Regulatory Commission)

4. True or False (circle one): Part II, QA Requirements for Nuclear Facility Applications of the ASME NQA-1-2008 edition is for guidance only.

5. Based on the structure of ASME NQA-1 since 1997 (1997 to current edition), there is/are:
   a. no Nonmandatory Appendices
   b. one Nonmandatory Appendix
   c. two Nonmandatory Appendices
   d. three Nonmandatory Appendices

6. True or False (circle one): Does ASME NQA-1 have guidance to modify an ISO 9001 Quality Program for compliance with NQA-1 requirements?

7. When applying the graded approach, which of the following should be consider?
   a. Complexity of design
   b. Consequences of a malfunction or failure
   c. Importance of safety
   d. Magnitude of the hazard
   e. All of the above

8. Audits are used to determine which of the following about the organization's QA Program? (Circle all that apply.)
   a. Adequacy
   b. Compliance
   c. Effectiveness
   d. All of the above

9. True or False (Circle one): Using the audit schedule as the audit plan for all internal audits meets the requirements of NQA-1 Part 1 Requirement 18.

10. What one thing should management do to assure that the QA program is properly implemented?
    a. Require self-assessment from the quality manager.
    b. Require the performance of independent internal audits.
    c. Evaluate the program by only reviewing nonconformances detected internally.
    d. Evaluate the program based on customer complaints.

11. What is the principal objective for performing audits?
    a. Meeting ASME NQA-1 Requirement 18
    b. Finding nonconformances
    c. Providing information for management
    d. Confirming that quality is the Quality Department's responsibility

12. An audit can be said to be:
    a. a financial review and reconciliation of supplier credit and debits
    b. a review of corrective action replies
    c. an activity to determine blame when something wrong is uncovered
    d. none of the above

13. Which of the following is a valid audit function?
    a. Identify QA program strengths and weaknesses
    b. Verify Quality Department's implementation of the QA program
    c. Provide information on worker performance to supervision for punitive action
    d. Verify the technical adequacy of a design package

14. A performance-based audit is one that:
    a. involves a lot of reviewing of documents
    b. provides feedback that helps improve the process
    c. focuses on regulatory compliance
    d. is just another way of doing a compliance audit
    e. all of the above

15. An audit that crosses multiple functional areas is referred to as a:
    a. compliance audit
    b. performance based audit
    c. vertical audit
    d. horizontal audit

16. When auditing a process, where are problems usually found?
    a. Process boundaries
    b. Process input
    c. Process output
    d. Process activities

17. The major phases of an audit include:
    a. planning, reporting, corrective action, follow-up
    b. plan, do, check, act
    c. preparation, performance, reporting, follow-up
    d. notifying, checklist preparation, performance, formal reporting

18. At a minimum, how many NUCLEAR quality assurance audits must an individual perform to be qualified as a Lead Auditor?
    a. 1
    b. 2
    c. 4
    d. 5

19. True or False (Circle one): A lead auditor that fails to maintain proficiency for a period of two (2) years shall require requalification.

20. Technical specialists who participate in an audit shall be:
    a. licensed professional engineers
    b. unfamiliar with the subject being audited
    c. qualified and meet the requirements of the responsible audit organization
    d. ASME NQA-1 certified auditors

21. Why is the preparation for an audit an important step?
    a. It provides a visual road map to the audit team.
    b. It optimizes the "on the floor" audit time.
    c. It helps the team manage the audit.
    d. All the above
    e. None of the above

22. When an auditing a welding program, the lead auditor should:
    a. not consider the use of a welding engineer
    b. add a welding engineer as a technical specialist who has not worked on the system to be audited
    c. consult with the welding engineer who developed the welding program to be audited
    d. bring in an auditor who is more familiar with welding than the lead auditor

23. The duration of an audit should depend upon the:
    a. scope of the audit
    b. time offered by the auditee
    c. monetary value to the organization
    d. timetable established in the pre-audit conference meeting

24. The "document hierarchy" is important in preparing for an audit because it:
    a. helps identify all the documents associated with the area to be audited
    b. can only be used to perform the document review portion of the audit
    c. is only needed during the audit to document findings
    d. assures completeness of the objective evidence section of the audit checklist

25. Which of the following are REQUIRED to be in an Audit Plan? Circle all that apply.
    a. Audit scope
    b. Audit personnel
    c. Organization to be notified
    d. Lead Auditor Qualification Record

26. Checklist questions should:
    a. be based on valid and current requirements
    b. stay within the scope of the audit
    c. allow effectiveness to be assessed
    d. be adjusted, depending on the status of the QA program
    e. all of the above

27. True or False (Circle one): Assuring proper implementation of the QA program is accomplished during the performance phase of the audit.

28. What interview technique is being used when an auditor allows an auditee to continue to talk after the auditee has answered the auditor's question?
    a. Being courteous
    b. Being a careful listener
    c. Using the silent question
    d. Fully understanding the auditee's response

29. During an audit, the auditee asks whether all activities affecting quality must be documented in instructions, procedures, or drawings. Which of the following should you do?
    a. Tell the auditee that this is consulting, and you are not allowed to do consulting.
    b. Point the auditee to ASME NQA-1 Requirement 5.
    c. Tell the auditee that the answer is yes.
    d. Suggest that the auditee discuss this with one of the other audit team members.

30. During an interview, one auditee indicates that a step in the procedure is very often not performed. What do you do with that information?
    a. Validate the information with other people in the organization.
    b. Initiate a nonconformance, but don't indicate the person who made the statement.
    c. Interviews are not a legitimate form of objective evidence, so there is nothing that can be done.
    d. Ask the auditee how often that really happens.

31. An effective method to divert an auditee's attempt to monopolize the auditor's time with unrelated material is to:
    a. recognize that it cannot be avoided; a good auditor will allow for this in planning the audit schedule
    b. tell the department manager that the audit will be terminated immediately should his organization continue diversionary tactics
    c. politely tell the auditee that there are many areas to cover in a limited amount of time and it is desirable to adhere to the schedule
    d. insist that the individual be removed from their job

32. Open ended questions are best used:
    a. during the opening meeting
    b. in the early stages of the interview
    c. at the end of the interview
    d. in cases where the auditee becomes argumentative

33. When an auditee states that "typically" or "usually" we follow what is in our work instruction, the auditor should:
    a. continue the audit since work instructions are only for guidance
    b. ask the auditee to explain what they do when it is not "typical" or "usual"
    c. recognize that this is a condition adverse to quality and must be documented
    d. tell the auditee that this not usually acceptable, but you will overlook it this time

34. A deficiency or finding is:
    a. based on how much it costs to fix it
    b. OK, as long as the auditee agrees with it
    c. not written if it is corrected before the end of the audit
    d. written when implementation does not match the documented procedure
    e. none of the above

35. An adverse audit finding can be BEST described as a deficiency that is:
    a. supported by objective evidence
    b. identified by the auditee
    c. judged by the auditor to be an adverse audit finding
    d. discovered after the audit

36. When considering whether a condition adverse to quality (CAQ) is a significant condition adverse to quality (SCAQ), the following should be considered:
    a. impact on health and safety of the public or environment
    b. impact on the reliability, availability, or maintainability of the equipment or facility
    c. consequence of recurrence
    d. all of the above
    e. none of the above

37. A deficiency should include which of the following? Circle all that apply.
    a. The nature of the requirement
    b. The nature of the deficiency
    c. Factual evidence obtained
    d. Identification of the person who created the deficiency

38. The auditor's report:
    a. contains findings not presented during the exit meeting
    b. is issued within a reasonable time following the audit
    c. may be used in place of an exit meeting
    d. must be finished before the auditor leaves the auditee's office

39. In the nuclear industry, ASME NQA-1 requires measuring and test equipment being calibrated to ensure that the reference standards contribute no more than one-fourth of the allowable calibration tolerance. This is also referred to as the 4 to 1 test accuracy ratio. Today most calibration service providers are reporting this as a 95% confidence level using a converging factor of $K = 2$. In addition to $K = 2$, which of the following would be a converging factor that would also meet the 4 to 1 test accuracy ratio?
    a. $K < 2$
    b. $K > 2$
    c. $K = 0$
    d. None of the above

40. The authority for conducting audits can be found in which requirement of ASME NQA-1?
    a. Requirement 1 – Organization
    b. Requirement 2 – QA Program
    c. Requirement 16 – Corrective Action
    d. Requirement 18 – Audits

41. If the Quality Department is organizationally reporting only to the Director of Engineering, which of the following requirements might be cited?
    a. Insufficient authority to verify activities affecting quality
    b. Limited access to work areas
    c. Inability to have direct access to responsible managers
    d. Absence of organizational freedom

42. The requirements in ISO 9001 for management review can be used as a guide for regularly assessing the adequacy and effective implementation of the QA program. The condition(s) under which this should be discussed with the auditee is when he or she:
    a. does not regularly assess the adequacy and the effective implementation of its QA program
    b. wants to improve its regularly assessment of its QA program
    c. is looking for areas to cover when it regularly assesses its QA program
    d. all of the above

ADDITIONAL QUESTIONS

Circle Your Answer

43. All those planned and systematic actions necessary to provide adequate confidence that a system, structure, or component in a nuclear power plant will perform satisfactorily in service is the definition of:
    a. Quality
    b. Quality Control
    c. Quality Assurance
    d. Quality Assurance Program

44a. **USA Students Only**. Which of the following documents focuses on nuclear safety? Circle all that apply.
    a. 10 CFR 50 Appendix B (U.S. Nuclear Regulatory Commission)
    b. 10 CFR 830 Subpart A (U. S. Department of Energy)
    c. ISO 9001 (International Organization for Standardization)
    d. ISO 14001 (International Organization for Standardization)

44b. **Non-USA Students Only**. Which of the following documents focuses on nuclear safety? Circle all that apply.
    a. IAEA SF-1 (International Atomic Energy Agency)
    b. IAEA GS-R-3
    c. ISO 9001 (International Organization for Standardization)
    d. ISO 14001 (International Organization for Standardization)

45. A supplier performs heat treatment but does not audit NQA-1 Part I Requirement 9, Special Process annually. The auditor should write a finding based on the following:
    a. Requirement 3, paragraph 100
    b. Requirement 12, paragraph 402
    c. Requirement 18, paragraph 200
    d. None of the above

46. As an audit team member, you have been assigned to audit "acceptance of items and services." You should include the following in your preparation:
    a. The organization's implementing documents of NQA-1 Requirement 7
    b. NQA-1 Requirement 7
    c. Subpart 3.1 7A-1 [editions since 2012: Subpart 3.1-7.1]
    d. Only b and c
    e. a, b, and c

Appendix D
Auditing in a Nuclear Power Plant

INTRODUCTION TO AUDITING AT A NUCLEAR GENERATING SITE

Effective auditing requires an understanding of not just the technical elements of the specific audit, but also the context of the organizational management system to which that audit applies. This in turn enables the auditing organization to insightfully plan for audits and to place audit results, in particular noncompliance, into more meaningful context, thus increasing the value of the audit for the organization.

An example organizational model for an operating nuclear power plant is provided by the Standard Nuclear Performance Model[1] shown below. Note the structure and the content of core processes; those that are fundamental to the operation of the plant, in turn supported by a set of enabling and management processes.[2] The core processes are those which are fundamental to operating the plant in the generation of electricity, while also ensuring the nuclear core is operated safely; that is, within the licensing and design limits of the plant.

In this model, best practice core processes were created by the nuclear industry through the Institute of Nuclear Power Operations (INPO) working groups (for example, the governing document for Work Management is AP-928).

An explanation of specific elements of the model is not needed and is beyond the scope of this Appendix, but the example Design Control audit report in this appendix illustrates this context.

Design Control is fundamental to effectively manage the plant's configuration (Manage Configuration). Design requirements, design calculations and documents, the physical structures, and the way the plan is operated are in harmony. Design Control noncompliance of significance can have immediate implications on whether the plant

---

[1] Fig 1-2 from *The Standard Nuclear Performance Model—A Process Management Approach* Rev 4, published by the Nuclear Energy Institute (NEI). The concept for the SNPM was developed as an objective of the industry Nuclear Power Oversight Committee's Strategic Plan for Improved Economic Performance.

[2] The concept and value of using an organizational model of this type is recognized worldwide as evidenced by organizational performance excellence models, Baldrige and EFQM being predominant. More information on various models is available at the Global Excellence Model Council site.

STANDARD NUCLEAR PERFORMANCE MODEL (SNPM) - AN EXECUTIVE VIEW

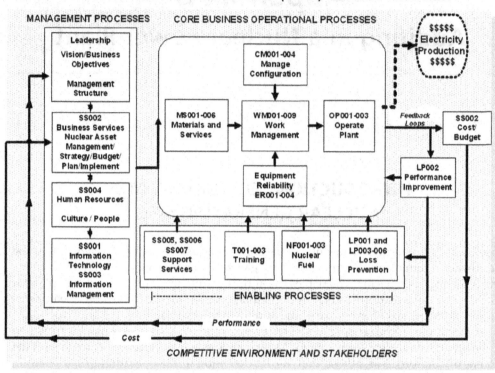

is operating safely or not, or whether safety systems can respond when needed. If the plant is not maintained (Work Management) in accordance with the design or is not operated within design constraints (Operate the Plant), noncompliance of significance may have immediate implications on the safety of continued plant operation. Thus, audits of these core processes will give the most direct information relative to the safe and effective operation of the plant and reactor safety.

This does not mean that support system audits are not important. For example, noncompliance in Training may be of minor consequence; however, if it is determined that Training inadequacies have resulted in operators who are not qualified to operate the Plant, there are immediate safety implications. The support process-to-core process linkage is what makes audit results meaningful relative to safe and effective operation. The auditor must understand this context and should provide such insight to the audited organization that the urgency and priority of any corrective action is understood by all.

The audit should also differentiate between compliance and effectiveness. For example, a plant design may require that physical barriers be designed to protect safety functions in the event of a natural disaster. The organization can comply by producing related calculations and building structures accordingly. These calculations are effective if the design inputs selected and the design methodology are appropriate for the objective of the calculation. Auditor qualifications and expertise are important considerations in determining effectiveness, and technical expertise should be added to the audit team accordingly if needed for a particular audit.

Given the limits of the audit organization resources, it is appropriate when a noncompliance is discovered for the audited organization to determine effectiveness through the Finding process. This requires the organization to:

- Expeditiously determine if the noncompliance resulted in a safety issue if this is the position taken;
- Act, with appropriate urgency, to correct the noncompliance; and
- Provide consideration for further issues that may have resulted from the noncompliance, that is, determine the "extent of condition." This is done by providing the basis for why the noncompliance resulted in an isolated condition, or if not, then assessing the potential for further adverse conditions needing corrective action.

A Design Control audit example of ineffective extent of condition determination follows: A Finding for the Software Quality Assurance (SQA) program at one generating plant did not result in consideration of similar noncompliance at another plant, even though the same program was in use at both plants. While it was determined that no safety issue resulted from the noncompliance due to alternate design methods used, it was still incumbent upon the plant organization to demonstrate this. For Findings of significance, it is appropriate for the audit organization to ensure that extent of condition is considered, thus allowing a noncompliance to be closed with confidence that the corrective action has been effective.

In summary, the audit function is an invaluable service to the organization if it can provide meaningful compliance and effectiveness information to executive management. Understanding the organization's system of interrelated processes and their relationship to nuclear operation and safety is fundamental to the audit organization's capability to produce this information.

	FP-NO-TRN-01	Revision: 8
	Issue Date: 2/12/2018	
Nuclear Department Fleet Procedure		Page 1 of 50
Title: Nuclear Oversight Qualification and Training		
Approval: Darrin Helm NOS Fleet Oversight Manager		

INFORMATION USE

- Procedure should be available, but not necessarily at the work location.
- Procedure may be performed from memory.
- User remains responsible for procedure adherence.

NUCLEAR OVERSIGHT QUALIFICATIONS AND TRAINING
TABLE OF CONTENTS

1.0 PURPOSE

This procedure establishes the training, qualification, and certification requirements for the Nuclear Oversight (NOS) Department. The procedure also establishes requirements for the NOS Discipline Training Committee.

2.0 APPLICABILITY

2.1 This procedure applies to Northern States Power Company, a Minnesota corporation (NSPM), d/b/a Xcel Energy, hereinafter NSPM, Nuclear Oversight (NOS) staff.

2.2 Certification of personnel to perform non-destructive examinations (NDE) should be done in accordance with FP-PE-NDE-03, "Written Practice for Qualification and Certification of NDE Personnel." This procedure does not apply to personnel performing NDE.

3.0 RESPONSIBILITIES

3.1 NOS FLEET OVERSIGHT MANAGER

3.1.1 The NOS Fleet Oversight Manager is responsible for:
1. Maintaining this procedure
2. Certification/Qualification Matrix development
3. Maintaining the NOS Training Plan
4. Performing as the NOS Training Program Owner and is the Chair for the Discipline Training Committee (DTC)
5. Coordinating Audit/Inspection staff training
6. Certifying NOS Supervisor as applicable
7. Certifying NOS staff in the absence of a Supervisor
8. Assuring that the NOS Programs staff meets training commitments and qualification requirements.

3.2 NOS SUPERVISORS

3.2.1 Member of DTC, provides training input to the DTC.
3.2.2 Assure that personnel are assigned functions within their level of qualification and participate in training as assigned. Determine if additional training courses are needed for each individual being certified. (e.g., A supervisor may require additional training such as electrical print reading for QC Inspectors being certified in Electrical or I&C Inspection.)
3.2.3 Assure that the staff meets qualification requirements and training commitments.
3.2.4 Certify Audit Team Leader (ATL) qualifications and Supplier Audit Team Leader (SATL) qualifications.
3.2.5 Certify QC personnel in accordance with this procedure.
3.2.6 Qualify QC personnel in accordance with this procedure.
3.2.7 Evaluate new or additional activities to be performed by QC Inspection personnel to determine the associated certification and/or qualification.
3.2.8 Perform annual reviews of QC Inspection, ATL, and SATL personnel certifications.

3.2.9 Terminate certifications and qualifications of QC Inspection, Project Assessor (PA), ATL, Auditor, and SATL personnel as necessary.

3.2.10 Maintain and transmit required certification and qualification records to Records Management.

3.2.11 Review the certifications and qualifications of contract QC Inspection, SATL and ATL personnel.

3.2.12 Maintain the information in the Certification/Qualification Tracking Matrix and the LMS for their staff including headquarters office staff.

3.2.13 Submit documentation of completed external or professional training for inclusion in LMS or the NOS training qualification/certification Matrix.

3.2.14 Assure that personnel are assigned functions within their level of qualification and participate in training as assigned.

3.2.15 Assure that the staff meets qualification requirements and training commitments.

3.2.16 Provide opportunities for assigned staff to perform functions within their certifications/qualifications to maintain proficiency in those functions.

3.2.17 Suspend personal certifications/qualifications when performance issues warrant and restoring certifications/qualifications when necessary conditions are met.

3.3 NOS STAFF

3.3.1 Auditors
  1. Responsible for maintaining and providing appropriate evidence of qualification.
  2. Participate actively in assigned training to maintain or raise the individual's level of knowledge and skills related to audit activities.
  3. Provide training input through their supervisor to the NOS DTC.
  4. Participate in DTC as requested by their supervisor to provide the appropriate skills/expertise.

3.3.2 Quality Control Inspectors
  1. Provide training input through their Supervisor to the NOS DTC.
  2. Participate in the DTC as requested to provide input on the appropriate skills/expertise required for a specific job function.
  3. Notify the NOS Fleet Nuclear Oversight Supervisor a minimum of 15 days prior to a certification/qualification annual evaluation due date.
  4. Inform the NOS Supervisor of any certification or qualification issues.
  5. Maintain a current eye examination as needed.
  6. Update their resume as needed or prior to the issuance of a new certification.
  7. Participate actively in assigned training to maintain or raise the individual's level of knowledge and skills related to inspection activities.
  8. Perform only those inspections that the individual is certified and/or qualified to perform.
     a. General inspection attributes are common skill sets that can be performed by all Inspectors with an active certification.
     b. Common inspection attributes that share the same criteria can be performed by either discipline certified Inspector. (e.g., Soldering shares the same criteria and thus can be performed by either an Electrical or I&C certified individual.)

3.4   CONTRACT STAFF

3.4.1   Project Field Representatives
1.   Responsible for participating in training as required by the appropriate Project Oversight Plan.

3.4.2   Contract Oversight Auditors
1.   Staff Augmentation Oversight Auditors will complete NOS Mentoring Guides and training as designated by the NOS Fleet Oversight Manager in order for the individual to fulfill their contract responsibilities. For contract staff assigned for less than three months normally no training beyond that required to perform assigned field activities will be required. Those expected to be in place for greater than three months will normally complete the NOS Orientation Mentor Guide (MG-NOS-01).

3.5   TRAINING COMMITTEES

3.5.1   Discipline Training Committee DTC
The DTC is responsible to conduct reviews to evaluate and recommend the initial, continuing, and specific training needs for individuals, groups, teams, and the department.

4.0   DEFINITIONS

4.1   AUDIT PARTICIPATION:

4.1.1   For the purpose of **Audit Team Lead (ATL)** initial qualification and certification, audit participation includes at least one audit within the year preceding the date of qualification. For ATL certification renewal, audit participation includes an audit conducted during the past year. Alternatively, recertification credit may be given in either case for review and study of codes, standards, procedures, regulations, instructions and other documents related to quality assurance programs and program assessment or auditing, or for participation in related training.

4.1.2   For the purpose of **Supplier Audit Team Leader (SATL)** initial qualification and certification, audit participation includes at least one audit as a lead in training within the year preceding the date of qualification. For SATL certification renewal, audit participation includes a supplier audit, survey, or source surveillance conducted in the past year. Alternatively, recertification credit may be given in either case for review and study of codes, standards, procedures, regulations, instructions and other documents related to quality assurance programs and program assessment or auditing, or for participation in related training.

4.2   **Certification:** The act of determining, verifying, and attesting in writing to the qualifications of personnel to perform a required task or function in accordance with specified requirements. The Training Program owner or designee signature on a mentor guide is the Certification that an individual is capable of performing the required task or function. (Specific application of NQA-1-1994 definition.)

4.3   **Confidential Records:** Records that contain personal information such as bank and credit card account numbers; income; Social Security Number; etc.

4.4 **Examination:** An element of inspection consisting of investigation of materials, components, supplies, and services to determine conformance to those specified requirements, which can be determined by such investigation. Examination is usually nondestructive and includes simple physical manipulation, gauging, and measurement.

4.5 **General Examination:** A written examination addressing the basic principles of the applicable discipline.

4.6 **Inspection:** Examination or measurement to verify whether an item or activity conforms to specified requirements.

4.7 **Learning Objective:** A statement that specifies measurable behavior that a trainee should exhibit after instruction. A properly prepared learning objective consists of:
- A statement of behavior (action) the trainee must exhibit
- The conditions under which the action will take place
- The standards of satisfactory performance

4.8 **Lesson Plan:** A primary training tool used by the instructor to guide the learning process. NOS Lesson Plans are not required to comply with Training Department format/content stipulations. Section 5.2, below, provides requirements applicable to NOS Lesson Plans.

4.9 **Limited Certification:** A certification that is restricted to allow inspections only of specified items or activities, not able to perform all inspections associated with the certified discipline (e.g., limiting a Weld Inspector to only inspect welds related to AWS code).

4.10 **Nondestructive Examination (NDE):** Those tests and examinations performed to detect surface or internal discontinuities, or both, in materials, welds, fabricated parts and components. They include radiographic (RT), ultrasonic (UT), liquid penetrant (PT), magnetic particle (MT), eddy current (ET), visual examination (VT-1, 2, 3), and leak testing (LT).

4.11 **Practical Examination:** An examination used to demonstrate an individual's ability in the discipline that will be performed. For Practical examinations, questions, and answers need not necessarily be written, but observations and results must be documented.

4.12 **Qualification:** The characteristics or abilities gained through education, training, or experiences (as measured against established requirements such as standards or tests), and through demonstration of capability, that establish the ability of an individual to perform a required task or function.

4.13 **Quality Control Inspector:** An individual certified in accordance with the Quality Assurance Program to perform QC inspections.

4.14 **Specific Examination:** A written examination to determine an individual's understanding of procedures, standards, specifications, and equipment or instrumentation for a discipline.

4.15 **Testing:** An element of verification for the determination of the capability of an item to meet specified requirements by subjecting the item to a set of physical, chemical, environmental, or operating conditions.

4.16 **Discipline Training Committee DTC:** The DTC is the NOS Fleet level committee that provides strategic oversight of NOS training programs to ensure the initial, continuing, and specific training needs of individuals, groups, teams, and the department are addressed to maintain and improve performance.

4.17 **Verification:** To confirm or substantiate that an item or activity conforms to specified requirements.

5.0 REQUIREMENTS

5.1 DISCIPLINE TRAINING COMMITTEE (DTC)

5.1.1 ATTACHMENT 4, "Nuclear Oversight Discipline Training Committee Charter," details the DTC vision, mission, membership, requirements, and responsibilities.

5.1.2 Individuals and their Supervisors should meet and identify the individual's training needs. Inputs for the identification of the individual's training needs should include, but are not limited to:

1. Initial training/certification requirements
2. Tools as available on Xpressnet for new hires
3. Continuing training requirements
4. Individual performance
5. Individual development needs/plans
6. Core competencies
7. Site-specific/project needs
8. Department needs
9. Succession planning and knowledge transfer
10. Consider industry training opportunities such as identified by the 2017 Nuclear Industry Evaluation Program (NIEP) team which provided a recommendation regarding auditor training: Nuclear Oversight (NOS) evaluated using specialized training for NOS audit personnel such as provided through Nuclear Energy Institute (NEI) and the Electric Power Research Institute (EPRI) (e.g., EP, Security, Cyber Security, Materials and Procurement, etc.).

5.1.3 Individual training needs are compiled and incorporated into a proposed training request.

1. Information should be provided for who needs the training, what training is needed, where the training will be provided (external or internal), when the training is needed, the approximate cost (if applicable), and the potential consequences associated with not providing the training.

5.1.4 Training requests may be submitted to the Discipline Training Committee meeting or presented by the individual's supervisor at the DTC.

NOTE: For emergent training needs, when time is critical and it is not feasible to follow the prescribed procedure, the NOS Fleet Oversight Manager may approve training actions with a notification to the DTC at the next meeting.

5.1.5 The DTC reviews training requests in order to recommend training actions.

5.1.6 Factors to be considered by the DTC include, but are not limited to:

1. Is the need limited to one individual; or does the need encompass multiple individuals (e.g., a team), a particular group (e.g., internal audits, quality control, supplier/projects), or the entire department?
2. Fleet needs
3. Department needs
4. Site needs
5. Core competency
6. Internal versus external training
7. Need for training course/material development
8. Need for refresher training prior to QC recertification

      9. Succession planning

      10. Budget (money and time)

      11. Developmental opportunities

5.1.7 The DTC should review site developed training for incorporation into NOS initial or continuing training. The DTC may also identify other opportunities to use training to improve NOS performance.

5.1.8 Discussion and recommendations should be documented in DTC meeting minutes.

5.1.9 The NOS Fleet Oversight Manager develops a Department Training Plan from the approved training needs.

5.1.10 The DTC reviews the training and qualification status/progress of NOS personnel including auditors, Audit Team Leads, Supplier Assessment Team Leads, and Quality Control Inspectors. The NOS Certification/Qualification Matrix (see Section 5.10) should be used to track the training and qualification status/progress.

5.2 TRAINING PROCESS

5.2.1 The NOS Fleet Oversight Manager SHALL be responsible for the development and overall implementation of the NOS Training Program. Although this program is not an "accredited" training program, training materials should be developed and documented using a logical approach.

5.2.2 NOS Lesson Plans should include:
- The Learning Objective(s) for the training:
- Logical presentation of information to be covered (PowerPoint or other information presentation software maybe used).
- Relevant reference materials, if needed for class use.
- Exercises to reinforce information presented or provide opportunity to practice the activity covered as appropriate.

5.2.3 NOS Lesson Plans should indicate if examinations are required during the training.

5.2.4 A knowledgeable individual should review Lesson Plans prepared by NOS individuals.

5.2.5 Prepared and reviewed Lesson Plans (along with any applicable examinations) should be sent to the NOS Fleet Oversight Manager for approval prior to performing the training.

5.2.6 Approved NOS Lesson Plans should be submitted to headquarter's Records Management by the NOS Fleet Oversight Manager. NOS Training Representative will process the approved lesson into records as needed. LMS personnel will be contacted to link the Lesson Plan in Records to the Training website.

5.2.7 The NOS Fleet Oversight Manager should control NOS Lesson Plans.

5.2.8 Completed NOS training should be recorded in the Learning Management System (LMS) and/or the NOS qualification tracking matrix.

5.3 DOCUMENTATION

5.3.1 Documentation for NOS sponsored/conducted training should include:
- Lesson Plans
- Training Attendance
- Training Date(s)
- Any examinations completed as part of the training

Attendance may be recorded in a format such as ATTACHMENT 2, or equivalent. Documentation for NSPM site Training Department sponsored/ conducted training is provided and maintained according to Training procedures. Completion of training items such as Mentor Guides, JFGs, Lesson Plans, Information Sharing, and External training are entered into the Learning Management System (LMS). Any training items requiring an annual supervisor renewal or QC current eye exam are tracked in the NOS qualification tracking matrix.

5.4   INITIAL TRAINING

5.4.1   Individuals assigned to NOS SHALL complete the job/function specific training applicable to their job assignment as delineated in ATTACHMENT 1, "Nuclear Oversight Training Subject Matrices," except as allowed under 5.4.2 and 5.8.2.

5.4.2   NOS Supervisors should assure that the appropriate LMS curricula are assigned to employees for completion, as identified in ATTACHMENT 1. (For example, a corporate Supply Auditor would be assigned curricula for NOS Orientation (FL-NOS-ORT-001M), Supplier Approval Evaluator (FL-NOS-SAE-001M), Source Surveillances (FL-NOS-SSU-001M), and Supplier Audit Team Leader (FL-NOS-STL-001M).

5.5   CONTINUING TRAINING

5.5.1   NOS staff should receive continuing training in quality programs, auditing, inspection or related topics. Staff augmentation contractors working for NOS at the plant sites should also receive continuing training as determined appropriate by the NOS Fleet Oversight Manager. All NOS staff is required to attend at least one continuing training session per year. It is the Supervisor and Staff members responsibility to track all assigned continuing training and determine make up training as needed. Continuing training is documented in the Learning Management System (LMS).

5.5.2   The following topics should be considered by the DTC on an annual basis for inclusion in continuing training:
- Developing Organizational/leadership/alignment issues
- Effective use of Gap Analysis to develop/define issues
- Safety Culture
- Leadership Skills (for ATLs/SATLs)
- Effective verbal/written/listening communication skills (including skills for interfacing with and presenting concerns/issues to line management)
- Identifying whys, so-whats, insights, and perspectives for NOS issues
- Observation/inspection skills
- QATR, ASME NQA-1, and 10 CFR 50 Appendix B requirements
- NOS procedures
- Writing effective CAPS
- NUPIC Auditor Conference training for Supplier Auditors
- QC inspections (in the specific disciplines) for QC inspectors
- NEI 03-02 audit program training for Internal Supplier Auditors

5.5.3   NOS Supervisors or designees are responsible for submitting continuing training information for entry into LMS. Continuing training is entered into LMS by use of training attendance processes such as Information Sharing, Vendor Training, and continuing training development and implementation.

5.5.4   Feedback from continuing training sessions should be solicited from the trainees and reviewed at DTC.

5.5.5   NOS rotational staff may maintain qualifications in their original position by attending the applicable continuing training provided for the programs of which they were part. (This is in addition to NOS continuing training.)

5.6   QUALIFICATION REQUIREMENTS/PERSONNEL SELECTION

5.6.1   Nuclear Oversight personnel SHALL have a combination of education, experience, and skills commensurate with their functional level of responsibility and which meets the requirements for their assigned positions, as established by applicable position descriptions maintained by Human Resources (HR). However, individuals who do not meet the established formal education requirements need not be automatically excluded from a position where other factors may provide sufficient demonstration of their abilities.

5.6.2   NOS Supervisors SHALL review candidate qualifications and assure requirements are met. Use of alternatives to formal education requirements to fulfill qualification criteria should be documented in the individual's Human Resources file.

5.6.3   The qualifications of contractor/vendor staff (Auditor, PA, SA or QC) acquired to supplement NOS staff should be evaluated. The NOS Supervisors should assure this evaluation is documented and retained, and that qualifications are consistent with the work assigned. Contractor/vendor staff should receive sufficient orientation and training to satisfactorily perform assigned tasks.

5.6.4   Contractor Project Field Representatives or Auditors SHALL participate in training as designated by the appropriate Project Oversight Plan.

5.6.5   IF a vendor not approved on the Qualified Supplier List (QSL) is contracted to provide QC Inspectors to the site, THEN the contract Inspectors SHALL be certified in accordance with this procedure.

5.7   CERTIFICATION/QUALIFICATION

5.7.1   Auditors

1. The NOS Fleet Oversight Manager or designated representative SHALL establish certification/qualification requirements for the following:
   a. Performing Internal Audits
   b. Internal Audit Team Leader (ATL)
   c. Supplier Assessment Certified Lead Auditor (Supplier Audit Team Leader (SATL))
      1) NUPIC—Team Member
      2) NUPIC—Lead Auditor
      3) NUPIC—Commercial Grade Survey Team Leader
      4) NEI—Access Authorization/Background Investigation Lead Auditor
      5) NEI—Fitness for Duty Lead Auditor
      6) NEI—Department of Health and Human Services (HHS) Laboratory Lead Auditor
   d. Source Surveillance
   e. Supplier Approval Evaluator
   f. Other activities based on Mentoring Guide approval

2. Personnel selected for ATL/SATL certification should have education, training, and experience commensurate with the scope, complexity, and special nature of the activities to be assessed. Consideration should be given to a combination of:
   a. College degree in engineering, physical sciences, mathematics
   b. Navy, Department of Energy, or commercial nuclear industry experience in engineering, manufacturing, construction, operation, maintenance, quality assurance, or quality assurance auditing
   c. Certification of competency in engineering science or quality assurance specialties issued and approved by a State Agency or National Professional or Technical Society
   d. For Internal Audit Team Leader certification, demonstration of proficiency and effectiveness as an Auditor is required before assignment to complete the Audit Team Leader (ATL) mentor guide.
3. Certification/qualification for Nuclear Procurement Issues Committee (NUPIC)—Audit positions SHALL be performed in accordance with NUPIC Joint Audit procedures. Certification is documented on QF0131, "Nuclear Oversight Auditor/Assessor NUPIC/NEI Certification of Qualification."
4. Certification/qualification for Nuclear Energy Institute (NEI)—Audit positions SHALL be performed in accordance with NEI 03-02, "Access Authorization and Fitness-for-Duty Audit Program." Certification is documented on QF0131, "Nuclear Oversight Auditor/Assessor NUPIC/ NEI Certification of Qualification."
5. Personnel selected for ATL certification should have two or more years' experience as a Nuclear Oversight Auditor. Consideration of criteria in 5.7.1.2 may allow a person with a minimum of one year experience to be selected for ATL certification with approval of the NOS Fleet Oversight Manager.
6. Personnel selected for ATL or SATL Certification will have demonstrated leadership ability commensurate with leading multi-disciplinary teams to identify, develop and present internal audit or supplier audit issues.

5.7.2 Mentor Guides
1. Mentoring Guides establish job/function specific formal and on-the-job training and knowledge requirements, including prerequisite training, and provide for documenting evaluation of performance capability. NOS Fleet Oversight Manager or designated representative should approve new or revised NOS Mentoring Guides. The NOS Fleet Oversight Manager should control Mentoring Guides separately from this procedure.
2. The NOS Supervisors SHALL complete training necessary to be qualified as mentors. Guidance for students and mentors for using the Mentoring Guides is provided in ATTACHMENT 3.
3. Mentors will be selected and recommended by NOS Supervisors for designation as Mentors. NOS Fleet Oversight Manager, as the NOS Training Program owner or designee, will designate selected personnel to conduct mentoring for selected tasks or activities.
4. Candidates for Mentor Guide related qualification/certification SHALL complete the applicable Mentoring Guide under the direction of a qualified mentor. The mentor should be qualified in the applicable function. Mentors

for functions involving certification should be certified in that function themselves. The timeframe expectations for completing mentoring guides are:

- MG-NOS-01, "Nuclear Oversight Orientation" 1 month from hire start date
- MG-NOS-07, "Performing Internal Audits" 3 months from hire start date
- MG-NOS-08, "Audit Team Leader" 6 months from assignment of mentor guide
- MG-NOS-04, "Supplier Audit and Commercial Grade Survey Team Leader" 15 months from hire start date
- MG-NOS-05, "Source Surveillance" 6 months from hire start date
- MG-NOS-06, "Supplier maintenance" 6 months from hire start date

5. Training associated with qualification to perform a specific function SHALL be completed before the candidate is considered qualified. Such functions may be performed under the direction of a qualified person until the candidate completes necessary training or other qualification requirements. When performing work under the direction of a qualified individual, the qualified person SHALL co-sign with the trainee, whenever the process requires performer signature.

5.7.3 Job Familiarization Guides

Job Familiarization Guides (JFG) provide for reading and/or discussion of subjects relevant to performance of NOS activities, but are in addition to, and not required for, qualification to perform NOS tasks where qualification/ certification is otherwise required. The NOS Fleet Oversight Manager provides JFGs for topics determined as needed by NOS Management. NOS Supervisors/ Manager assign JFGs to NOS staff for completion. After approval NOS JFGs will be added to ATTACHMENT 1 of this procedure.

5.7.4 QC Inspectors

NOTE: For this section the term Qualification stands for QC qualifications that are not included in the Discipline Specific QC certifications listed in section 5.8.2.

1. The QATR establishes certification/qualification requirements for Quality Control Inspectors.
2. Individuals performing visual inspections required by the ASME Boiler and Pressure Vessel Code SHALL be qualified and certified according to Code requirements.
3. Where mentoring is used to complete qualification activities, the mentoring requirements of section 5.7.2 will apply.
4. Individuals should not be qualified without a minimum of one current certification.
5. Qualifications should be considered "Terminated" when the individual no longer maintains any current certifications.
6. The effective period for qualification should be continuing (i.e., no time limit).
7. The NOS Supervisor should document the requirements for each qualification. Examples of the requirements to be considered are:
   a. Additional training is needed
   b. Any additional physical requirements are needed
   c. A competency examination is needed
   d. A performance evaluation is needed

8. Other organizations or individuals may be utilized to provide training for qualifications.

9. Individuals to be evaluated for a qualification should be evaluated to verify that the individual meets the requirements for that qualification.

10. IF the individual meets the requirements for qualification, THEN complete form QF0138, "Quality Control Inspector Qualification." Place the completed form in the individual's certification file.

11. Termination of a qualification

   a. Termination of a qualification should be documented as follows:

      1) When an individual permanently leaves the NOS QC department, write the words "Terminated due to (list reason transfer, retirement, etc.)" on the qualification form.

      2) When an individual no longer has any active certifications, write the words "Terminated no active certifications" on the qualification form.

      3) IF the qualification is terminated for unsatisfactory performance, THEN write the words "Terminated for Cause" on the qualification form. The reason for the termination does not have to be listed.

   b. Submit the QF0138 form for records. Update the NOS Qualification Tracking Matrix for current status.

5.8   CERTIFICATION AND ANNUAL REVIEW

5.8.1   Auditors

1. Persons performing the functions of ATL/SATL SHALL complete the appropriate Mentoring Guide and have their qualifications certified prior to independently serving in those capacities. Personnel being certified as ATL/SATL should act as the lead on an Internal/Supplier Audit under the direction of a qualified ATL/SATL.

2. Personnel being certified as ATL/SATL SHALL pass both written examination and oral interview that evaluate their knowledge of nuclear requirements, QA program requirements, assessment skills, and team leadership skills. The oral interview will be the final performance requirement for certification.

3. The responsible NOS Supervisor or the NOS Fleet Oversight Manager SHALL complete and sign QF0128, "Nuclear Oversight Certification of Qualification," to document the individual has met the specified education, experience and training requirements. Certifications should be effective for not more than one calendar year.

4. The certification attests to the ATL/SATL's ability to properly implement NSPM audit process(es), lead an audit team, present audit results and issues, and effectively organize and report results. ATL/SATL candidates will participate in at least one independent/supplier audit within a year preceding the date of qualification.

5. The completed certification should be retained in the individual's local training file. Certification at one NSPM site/location is valid at all other NSPM sites/locations without further action.

6. Certified individuals SHALL be responsible to maintain audit participation records on QF0130, "NSPM Audit Participation Record," and present them annually to support certification renewal. The responsible NOS Supervisor may renew certification on QF0128, "Nuclear Oversight Certification of

Qualification," if the individual has maintained active participation in the audit process during the past year.

7. Candidates achieving certification (prior to December) in a calendar year will have the "next due date" set to the end of that year to complete the normal annual re-certification for the following year.

8. Certified individuals who do not maintain proficiency to conduct audits, and who wish to restore certification, SHALL be required to re-certify in accordance with this procedure and participate in at least one Nuclear Oversight audit, supplier audit, or supplier commercial grade survey.

9. The NOS Supervisor is responsible for development of questions used for written examinations and oral interviews. Examination questions should be validated by persons already certified. The NOS Fleet Oversight Manager should approve exam questions, and completed examinations should be controlled to minimize the potential for compromise. When an examination is completed separately and not as part of an internal training class, the responsible supervisor should provide for appropriate proctoring. Approved written certification and oral interview questions should be maintained in a controlled library or file for future use.

10. When certification examination is completed as part of externally supplied auditor training, the supplier should provide for examination security and retain appropriate records, and SHALL be required to provide NSPM with the completed examinations, or with the type and general content of the examination, as well as individual results.

5.8.2 QC Inspectors

1. Disciplines requiring certification for Inspectors are:
   a. Civil/Structural Inspections
   b. Electrical Inspections
   c. Instrument and Control (I&C) Inspections
   d. Mechanical Inspections
   e. Nuclear Coatings Inspections (note that while listed under the Civil discipline this is a separate certification)
   f. Receipt Inspections
   g. Welding Inspections
   h. Rad Material Shipping Inspections
      ATTACHMENT 6 contains the Identification codes for each Certification and sub-topic.

2. The completed certification/qualification SHALL be retained in the individual's local training file at the site. Certification at one NSPM nuclear site/location is valid at all other NSPM nuclear sites/locations without further action.

3. Individuals being evaluated for certification SHALL provide a completed QF0136, "Quality Control Inspector Resume," documenting education, work experience, training, and other associated qualifications.

4. The resume should include the following information:
   a. Employer(s), title(s), dates of employment, and job description.
   b. Formal education, name and location of school(s), dates of attendance or class hours, certification, diplomas, degrees, and major topics covered.
      • The resume should include the following information, as applicable:

- Current and previous certifications; including the certifying agency, type and level of certification(s), code or standard used to base the certification(s), and date(s) of the certification.
- The extent of proficiency with inspection and measurement equipment.
- Any additional supporting information.

c. Resume forms should be updated as needed or prior to the issuance of a new certification.

5. Individuals to be certified should as a minimum be a high school graduate or have completed the General Education Development (GED) equivalent.

6. The minimum education requirements should be verified through one or more of the following means:
   a. A copy of a diploma, transcript, or certification, which provides proof of meeting the requirement
   b. Receiving a written confirmation of education completion from the school
   c. Requesting that Human Resources or Security verify education completion and receive written confirmation

7. The verification of education record should be filed with the certification or resume.

8. Qualification and certification as a QC Coatings Inspector will be as follows:
   a. **(Prairie Island Only)** Educational Requirements for designation as QC Coatings Inspector
      - One year of satisfactory performance as a certified Coatings inspector at another facility or organization; or
      - High school graduation plus 3 years of related experience in equivalent inspection, examination, or testing activities; or
      - Completion of college level work leading to an associate degree in a related discipline plus 1 year of related experience in equivalent inspection, examination or testing activities; or
      - Graduation from a 4-year college plus 6 months of related experience in equivalent inspection activities.
   b. **(Prairie Island Only)** Training
      - A person may be qualified and certified as an Xcel Energy QC Coatings inspector with no prior coatings inspection qualification provided the trainee has had at least 3 years of experience in equivalent inspection, examination, or testing activities, has had training documented from an accredited training facility on Coatings, and completes the below requirements for certification.
      - A new "Trainee" SHALL follow the following path to certification:
         - Attend industry coatings training and successfully pass a written exam (80% or better)
         - Perform and pass practical exam (80% or better)
         - Perform under instruction as a "trainee" until 6 months of experience is achieved to satisfy On-The-Job Training (OJT) requirements.
   c. **(Prairie Island Only)** An NOS Supervisor/NOS Fleet Oversight Manager shall determine certification and qualification standards are met and approve certifications and qualifications of QC Coatings inspectors.

d. **(Monticello Only)** Coatings Inspectors are required to be qualified in accordance with ANSI/ASME N45.2.6 - 1978. Only Coatings Inspectors qualified to that standard may perform coatings inspections at Monticello. The Engineering Coatings Program controls and verifies the ANSI/ASME N45.2.6 - 1978 requirements for Coatings Inspectors at Monticello. CD 5.34, "Safety Related Coatings Standard," CD 5.43, "Control of Special Processes," and FL-ESP-PGM-060M, "Safety Related Coatings Program Owner," provide additional guidance on qualifying Coatings Inspectors at Monticello.

9. Evaluation of an individual's competency/capability in a discipline SHALL be validated by the following:

   a. Evaluate the individual's previous work experience in inspection, examination, or testing activities for the discipline to be certified in. The individual being evaluated should be capable of:
      - Planning inspections, examinations and tests.
      - Setting up tests including preparation and set up of related equipment
      - Maintaining surveillance over inspections, examinations and tests
      - Clearly reporting the results of inspection, examination and testing
      - Evaluating the validity and acceptability of inspection, examination and test results

   b. Completing a capability demonstration in the respective discipline (e.g., Completion of documentation of work while under the supervision of a qualified QC Inspector satisfies OJT requirements as a performance evaluation.)

   c. Passing a competency examination to demonstrate proficiency in the respective discipline (optional, as determined by NOS Supervisor)

   d. Documentation showing completion of a Certification Training course for the certification being completed (e.g., Civil Certification training course completion from an external vendor)

10. Active certifications issued in accordance with the parent utility's QA program should be evaluated in accordance with this procedure for continued certification. (e.g., The Inspector is currently certified as a mechanical inspector in accordance with the parent utility's QA program; the Inspector's performance has been satisfactory. The certification should be reissued under this program.)

11. Meet the physical capability requirements for the respective discipline.

   a. Completion of an eye examination and documented on QF0904, "Visual Acuity and Color Vision Test Record for Nondestructive Examination Personnel," which meets the following requirements:
      - Natural or corrected near and far vision to meet the requirements listed on form QF0904
      - Capability to distinguish colors in the Ishihara test, or pass the yarn or wire test

   b. Additional physical capabilities needed in the performance of activities assigned in the respective discipline.

   c. A completed copy of the form(s) used to document meeting the physical requirements may be filed with the certification.

12. IF the individual meets the requirements for certification, THEN complete QF0137, "Quality Control Inspector Certification." Place the completed form in the individual's certification file.
    a. Limitations should be listed on the certification form whether a physical limitation or an inspection limitation. Additionally, limitations should be noted in the NOS Tracking matrix.
13. Annual evaluation/maintaining certification is documented on QF0137, "Quality Control Inspector Certification."
14. Annual evaluation SHALL be performed no later than 15 calendar days past the anniversary date of the certification or previous annual evaluation.
15. Annual evaluations SHALL be done to verify:
    a. The individual had satisfactory performance of inspections in the certified discipline.
        • Performed a minimum of 1 inspection, examination or test.
                                OR
        • Performed Task Monitoring activities associated with the discipline being evaluated.
                                OR
        • Performed training for other inspection personnel; this can also be Peer Inspection personnel.
                                OR
        • Assisted the NOS Supervisor in evaluating, preparing or reviewing competency examination procedures, or procedures for testing individuals to be certified.
    b. The individual meets the physical requirements of the certified discipline.
        • A current eye examination is on file and meets the visual requirements.
        • Other physical requirements for the discipline are met and documentation is on file.
    c. The individual has not had a period of inactivity in the inspection area greater than 1 year for the certified discipline.
        • IF the individual has had a period of inactivity of one year or greater in the certified discipline, THEN the individual SHALL be evaluated in accordance with this procedure.
16. Competency Examinations
    a. Competency examinations may be used to verify knowledge and/or proficiency for certifications or qualifications.
    b. Competency examinations should consist of a minimum of 20 questions.
    c. The NOS QC supervisor is responsible for development and approval of Quality Control Inspector competency examination questions. Questions should be validated by individuals certified in the applicable discipline(s). Approved questions should be sent to the NOS Fleet Oversight Manager for secure retention and future use per 5.8.1.10, above.
17. A grade of 80% or greater for all portions of the examination is considered satisfactory/passing.
    a. Personnel who fail to attain the required passing grade should receive additional documented training. This training should address the

deficiencies, which caused the failure. A candidate should not be reexamined using the examination previously failed.

18. Examinations should be handled as follows:
    a. Examinations and answer keys should be maintained confidential and secure.
    b. Examinations should be maintained in a locked desk, cabinet or secure records area during non-working hours.
    c. Examinations should be proctored at all times by the NOS Supervisor or designee. The proctor should not engage in activities that would divert attention from the examination and possibly cause the examination to be compromised.
    d. IF errors in the test questions are found after the test is taken, THEN change the examination or answer key, as needed. Changes should be explained, initialed and dated.
       • Re-grade and rescore the examinations as needed.
    e. It is permissible for the final number of questions to go below the minimum if questions are deleted due to errors discovered after the test is taken. The NOS Supervisor should evaluate the final test as acceptable to meet the knowledge and capability requirement.

19. Terminating a certification
    a. Certification in a discipline SHALL be terminated for any of the following reasons:
       • The effective period of the certification has lapsed (To restore lapsed certification, the individual who has not performed inspection or testing activities in his/her qualified area for a period of one year SHALL be reevaluated by a redetermination of required capability in accordance with this procedure.)
       • When an individual permanently leaves the NOS QC department (e.g., transfers to another department, retires, etc.)
       • When it has been determined necessary based on unsatisfactory performance of inspection, examination or testing activities

20. Termination of a certification should be documented as follows:
    a. Expiration of the effective period of the certification should be considered sufficient documentation for termination of the certification.
    b. When an individual permanently leaves the NOS QC department, write the words "Terminated due to (list reason transfer, retirement, etc.)" on the certification form.
    c. IF the certification is terminated for unsatisfactory performance, THEN write the words "Terminated for Cause" on the certification form. The reason for the termination does not have to be listed.
    d. Submit the QF0137, "Quality Control Inspector Certification," for entry into records and update the Qualification Tracking Matrix.

5.9   CERTIFICATION SUSPENSION

IF the performance of an ATL, SATL, or QC Inspector does not satisfy the expectations for the position, THEN the NOS Supervisor has the option to suspend the certification. While under suspension, the ATL, SATL, or QC Inspector cannot perform independently in the certified subject, or sign as a certified ATL, SATL, or QC Inspector. The NOS Supervisor should notify the individual of the certification suspension and change the certification status to "Suspended" in the NOS Certification/Qualification Matrix. Upon lifting a certification suspension, the NOS Supervisor should remove the "Suspended" status from the NOS Certification/Qualification Matrix.

5.10 CERTIFICATION/QUALIFICATION MATRIX

5.10.1 The NOS Fleet Oversight Manager should ensure the NOS Certifications/ Qualifications are in the NOS Qualification Tracking Matrix. The NOS Qualification Tracking Matrix should establish, by position, the job/function specific requirements needed for each Certification/Qualification. The NOS Fleet Oversight Manager should control the NOS Qualification Tracking Matrix structure separately from this procedure. The NOS Fleet Oversight Manager should provide a means for tracking individual completion of required training. Individual training items such as Mentor Guides, JFGs, Lesson Plans and external training will be tracked in the Learning Management System (LMS). The NOS Qualification Tracking Matrix will track the learning items and their current qualification status related to the reoccurring annual renewals and eye exams as applicable.

5.10.2 The NOS Supervisor should maintain current certification/qualification information within the LMS and/or NOS Qualification Tracking Matrix.

5.11 CONTRACT QC INSPECTORS

5.11.1 Disciplines requiring certification for Quality Control Inspectors are:
1. Civil/Structural Inspections
2. Electrical Inspections
3. Instrument and Control (I&C) Inspections
4. Mechanical Inspections
5. Nuclear Coatings Inspections
6. Receipt Inspections
7. Welding Inspections
8. Rad Material Shipping Inspections

5.11.2 Contract QC Inspectors are to be indoctrinated using FP-NO-QC-05, "Quality Control Indoctrination Procedure." Completion of the Indoctrination process for contract QC Inspectors is tracked using a QC Contractor Qualification Matrix. This matrix is maintained current by the NOS QC Supervisor or designee.

6.0 RECORDS

6.1 The following SHALL be considered quality records, to be retained as records with retention periods as indicated. Documentation used for changes to LMS SHALL be sent for LMS entry and the documents placed in training files as lifetime record.
1. Mentoring Guides (when revised and approved) (Lifetime)
2. Completed Mentoring Guides (Lifetime)
3. Personnel certification and qualification records including annual renewals and related exemptions (Lifetime)
4. Vision examination records (Lifetime)
5. Audit participation records (Lifetime)
6. Attendance lists for internally presented training (Lifetime)

7. Evidence of completion for outside training (Lifetime)
8. Approved Lesson Plans (3 years)
9. Completed written examinations (internally generated) (Lifetime)
10. Completed Job Familiarization Guides (JFG) (Lifetime)

7.0 REFERENCES

7.1 SOURCE DOCUMENTS
7.1.1 NSPM-1, "Quality Assurance Topical Report"
7.1.2 ASME NQA-1-1994 Edition

7.2 REFERENCE DOCUMENTS
7.2.1 QF0128, "Nuclear Oversight Certification of Qualification"
7.2.2 QF0130, "NSPM Audit Participation Record"
7.2.3 QF0131, "Nuclear Oversight Auditor/Assessor NUPIC/NEI Certification of Qualification"
7.2.4 QF0136, "Quality Control Inspector Resume"
7.2.5 QF0137, "Quality Control Inspector Certification"
7.2.6 QF0138, "Quality Control Inspector Qualification"
7.2.7 QF0904, "Visual Acuity and Color Vision Test Record for Nondestructive Examination Personnel"
7.2.8 QF104003, "Exemption and Equivalent Qualification Process Form"
7.2.9 FP-PE-NDE-03, "Written Practice for Qualification and Certification of NDE Personnel"
7.2.10 MG-NOS-01, "Nuclear Oversight Orientation"
7.2.11 MG-NOS-07, "Performing Internal Audits"
7.2.12 MG-NOS-08, "Audit Team Leader"
7.2.13 MG-NOS-04, "Supplier Audit and Commercial Grade Survey Team Leader"
7.2.14 MG-NOS-05, "Source Surveillance"
7.2.15 MG-NOS-06, "Supplier maintenance"
7.2.16 FP-T-SAT-40, "Implementation Phase"
7.2.17 FP-NO-QC-05, "Quality Control Indoctrination Procedure"
7.2.18 CAP 501000003110, "NIEP Recommendation: Auditor Training"
7.2.19 CAP 501000003113, "NIEP Recommendation: Continuing Training"

7.3 COMMITMENTS
7.3.1 None

8.0 REVISION SUMMARY

8.1 Added paragraph 5.1.2.10 to provide guidance to Supervisor and Employees to consider attending Industry training per NIEP CAP 501000003110.
8.2 Revised section 5.5.1 to include responsibilities for tracking Continuing training and make up training per NIEP CAP 501000003113.
8.3 Revised section 5.8.1 and ATTACHMENT 5 to change Oral Exam requirements to an oral interview. Revised the Oral Examination guidance to identify the supervisor responsibilities for developing and implementing the Oral Interview for ATL and SATL qualification.

9.0 ATTACHMENTS

9.1 ATTACHMENT 1, "Nuclear Oversight Training Subject Matrices"
9.2 ATTACHMENT 2, "NOS Training Attendance Record"
9.3 ATTACHMENT 3, "Guidance for Students and Mentors for Mentoring Guide Completion"
9.4 ATTACHMENT 4, "Nuclear Oversight Training Advisory Committee Charter"
9.5 ATTACHMENT 5, "Oral Interview Process"
9.6 ATTACHMENT 6, "LMS Codes for NOS Topic Certifications"

ATTACHMENT 1
NUCLEAR OVERSIGHT TRAINING SUBJECT MATRICES

MENTORING GUIDE OR LESSON NUMBER/ (IDENTIFICATION NUMBER)	ANNUAL CERTIFICATION	COURSE/TOPIC	POSITION				
			NOS FLEET OVERSIGHT MANAGER	AUDIT/SUPPLIER/QC NOS SUPERVISORS	AUDITORS	SUPPLIER AUDITOR / PROJECT ASSESSOR
JOB/FUNCTION SPECIFIC TRAINING /NUCLEAR OVERSIGHT SPECIFIC MENTORING GUIDES						
MG-NOS-01 / (FL-NOS-ORT-001M)	N/A	Nuclear Oversight Orientation	R	R	R	R
MG-NOS-07 / (FL-NOS-AUD-001M)	N/A	Performing Audits	O	O/N/N	R	N
MG-NOS-08 / (FL-NOS-ATL-002M)	(Documented on QF0128)	Audit Team Leader	O	O/N/N	R	N
MG-NOS-04 / (FL-NOS-STL-001M)	(Documented on QF0128)	Supplier Audit Team Leader	O	N/O/N	N	R/O
FL-NOS-STL-002U	(Initial Cert Documented on QF0131)	NUPIC – Team Member	O	N/O/N	N	R/O
FL-NOS-STL-003U	(Initial Cert Documented on QF0131)	NUPIC – Lead Auditor	O	N/O/N	N	R/O
FL-NOS-STL-004U	(Initial Cert Documented on QF0131)	NUPIC –Commercial Grade Survey Team Lead	O	N/O/N	N	R/O

ATTACHMENT 1 CONT'D
NUCLEAR OVERSIGHT TRAINING SUBJECT MATRICES

MENTORING GUIDE OR LESSON NUMBER/ (IDENTIFICATION NUMBER)	ANNUAL CERTIFICATION	COURSE/TOPIC	POSITION				
			NOS FLEET OVERSIGHT MANAGER	AUDIT/SUPPLIER/QC NOS SUPERVISORS	AUDITORS	SUPPLIER AUDITOR / PROJECT ASSESSOR
FL-NOS-STL-005U	(Initial Cert Documented on QF0131)	NEI – Access Authorization/ Background Investigation Lead Auditor	O	N/O/N	N	O
FL-NOS-STL-006U	(Initial Certification Documented on QF0131)	NEI – Fitness for Duty Lead Auditor	O	N/O/N	N	O
FL-NOS-STL-007U	(Initial Cert Documented on QF0131)	NEI – HHS Laboratory Lead Auditor	O	N/O/N	N	O
MG-NOS-05 / (FL-NOS-SSU-001M)	N/A	Source Surveillances	O	N/R/N	N	R
MG-NOS-06 / (FL-NOS-SAE-001M)	N/A	Supplier Approval Evaluator	O	N/R/N	N	R
CONTINUING TRAINING						
	N/A	Nuclear Oversight Continuing Training	R	R	R	R

LEGEND: R = Required
            O = Recommended, not required
            N = Not required

* Required only for those personnel designated to be mentors

ATTACHMENT 1 CONT'D
NUCLEAR OVERSIGHT TRAINING SUBJECT MATRICES

TOPIC TITLE / IDENTIFICATION CODE	ANNUAL CERTIFICATION	DISCIPLINE							
QC Safety-Related/Nuclear Coatings Discipline (ID# FL-NOS-QC-CVL)	(Documented on QF0137)	N	N	N	N	R	N	N	N
NOS QC Radioactive Material (RAM) Shipment Inspection (ID# FL-NOS-QC-RAM) (Classroom Trng. required every 3 years.)	(Documented on QF0137)	N	N	N	N	N	R	N	N
QC Receipt Inspection Discipline (ID# FL-NOS-QC-REI)	(Documented on QF0137)	N	N	N	N	N	N	R	N
QC Weld Inspection (ID# FL-NOS-QC-WLD)	(Documented on QF0137)	N	N	N	N	N	N	N	R

Legend:

R = Required
N = Not Required

POSITION	QC INSPECTORS
Continuing Training	
Nuclear Oversight Continuing Training (As identified by Supervisor or DTC)	Required

ATTACHMENT 2
NOS TRAINING ATTENDANCE RECORD

NOS Training Attendance Record

Class Title/Subject: _____

Class Number:_____Date(s): _____

Type: Initial Continuing Hours: _____

Instructor(s): _____

NAME (Print)	ID NUMBER (Emp #)	SIGNATURE	SITE

ATTACHMENT 3
GUIDANCE FOR STUDENTS AND MENTORS
FOR MENTORING GUIDE COMPLETION

Student Instructions:

Knowledge Requirements

Review the knowledge objectives to become familiar with the knowledge to be obtained by completing the mentoring guide. Using the listed standards and references, acquire the knowledge needed to satisfy the stated objectives through self-study, discussions with other incumbents or subject matter experts, or practical experience. Arrange an interview with the mentor to evaluate the learning achieved and discuss the listed familiarization topics. Bring the guide to the mentor interview.

Performance Requirements

Complete performance requirements by actually performing the major steps of the process. In some cases, it may be necessary to simulate or discuss a particular step, as allowed by the Mentor. The preference should be to Perform whenever possible, or to Simulate the activity where it is not feasible to Perform it. Use of the "Discuss" option should be minimized. Review each step with the Mentor before starting, and as often as needed during performance. Where the governing procedure requires the performer's identity be recorded or requires a signature on a record, be sure to get the mentor or another qualified person to concur the work is correct and provide a co-signature.

Mentor Instructions:

Knowledge Requirements

Review the knowledge objectives and discuss with the trainee. Evaluation of the trainee's mastery of the knowledge objectives is expected. However, qualitative evaluations may be used. For example, trainee mastery could be assessed using the following techniques:

- Asking hypothetical or situation questions and having the trainee provide an answer
- Asking the trainee to state, describe, paraphrase, or discuss the requirement
- Asking the trainee what referenced documents provide guidance about the requirement
- Asking the trainee to explain how applicable forms are completed

Some knowledge objectives may require use of the applicable referenced documents because of the infrequent need to use the knowledge, the extent and complexity of presentation, or the level of detail and amount of material to be covered. Except when noted by an asterisk (*) behind the objective number, the trainee may use the listed standards or reference materials during the interview. When using listed standards or reference materials, the trainee should be able to quickly choose the applicable document and reference the required information.

Performance Requirements

Evaluate trainee ability to meet performance requirements through discussion, observation, and review of product. In some cases, it may be necessary for the trainee to simulate or discuss a particular step because of the exact situation. The preference should be to Perform whenever possible, or to Simulate the activity where it is not feasible to Perform it. Use of the "Discuss" option should be minimized. Where the governing procedure requires the performer's identity be recorded or requires a signature on a record, the mentor or another qualified person must concur the work is correct and provide a co-signature. The Mentor, may, depending on trainee performance, request that any step(s) be satisfactorily demonstrated multiple times until satisfied the trainee has demonstrated adequate proficiency. Only one signature is required for each step in the Mentoring Guide, to be placed when the Mentor is satisfied that trainee performance meets expectations, regardless of how many times a step is performed.

ATTACHMENT 4
NUCLEAR OVERSIGHT DISCIPLINE
TRAINING COMMITTEE CHARTER

VISION

Achieve excellence in the performance of Nuclear Oversight (NOS) activities through effective use of training.

MISSION

Discipline Training Committee (DTC) mission is to ensure that training is effectively used to maintain and continuously improve performance of NOS audit and inspection activities.

Continuing improvement in performance supports continuing improvement in station and fleet performance.

MEMBERSHIP

NOS DTC membership includes the NOS Fleet Oversight Manager and NOS supervisors. Committee membership consists of:
- NOS Fleet Oversight Manager—Chair
- All NOS Supervisors

REQUIREMENTS
- The NOS DTC meets at least once per year with the goal of completing two meetings per year.
- The NOS DTC chair is responsible to ensure appropriate skills and talents are available for individual DTC meetings based on the topics to be addressed.
- The NOS DTC chair is responsible for ensuring meeting agendas are developed and issued in advance of meetings to support preparation by DTC members.
- Meeting minutes are issued for each meeting and include clearly defined action items that are tracked to completion with identification of Who, What, and by When.
- Minimum quorum requirements are:
  - NOS DTC Chair
  - Fleet Oversight Manager, Two NOS Supervisors, and one Incumbent

ATTACHMENT 4 CONT'D
NUCLEAR OVERSIGHT DISCIPLINE
TRAINING COMMITTEE CHARTER

RESPONSIBILITIES

NOS DTC Members
- Solicit input from department personnel to support an effective DTC.
- Provide input to the DTC agenda.
- Prepare for each DTC meeting.
- Actively participate in each DTC meeting and provide feedback.
- Take responsibility for completing assigned action items on time.
- Support NOS training through active involvement and assignment of appropriate resources.

NOS Fleet Oversight Manager
- Ensure DTC meetings are conducted at the frequency specified in the requirements section.
- Chair the DTC meetings.
- Ensure meeting quorum requirements are met.
- Update department training plan after approval.
- Ensure DTC meeting agendas are developed and distributed in accordance with the requirements section.
- Ensure meeting minutes are developed and maintained in accordance with the requirements section.
- Assign clearly defined action items with due dates to appropriate individuals, and track to completion.

DTC AGENDA ITEMS

The standing agenda for Fleet DTC meetings considers the following for inclusion as appropriate:
- Ensure quorum requirements are met.
- Ensure expertise is available to address items on the agenda.
- Review and approve previous NOS DTC meeting minutes.
- Review status of open action items.
- Review NOS auditor/assessor/inspector performance as a consideration for training needs.
- Review status/progress of NOS personnel qualifications/certifications.
- Review training feedback from personnel and make adjustments as needed.
- Review Site/Fleet generated training subjects for applicability to NOS Staff.
- Create and assign new action items.
- Review training recommendations from Missed Opportunity Reviews since the last DTC.
- Review Self-Assessment results since the last DTC.
- Review NOS Procedure Revisions since the last DTC.

ATTACHMENT 4 CONT'D
NUCLEAR OVERSIGHT DISCIPLINE
TRAINING COMMITTEE CHARTER

- Review NOS benchmarking since the last DTC.
- Review Qualification Matrices for all personnel and update as necessary.
- Review NOS line experience and other experience and update as necessary.
- Review the following areas that could impact the training program:
  - Cross-cutting issues (new performance indicators, process/procedure changes, future station projects, etc.)
  - Current NOS (NQML) KPIs
  - Industry regulations or standards (OSHA, ACADs, NUREGs, etc.)
  - Management expectations
  - Anticipated staffing or succession plan issues
  - Personnel Development
  - External program evaluations
- Review other topics of discussion.
- Schedule the next meeting.
- Critique the meeting.

MINUTES

The NOS Fleet Oversight Manager ensures that DTC meeting minutes are distributed for use. DTC minutes are not retained as records.

ATTACHMENT 5
ORAL INTERVIEW PROCESS

The final performance requirement for Audit Team Leader/Supplier Audit Team Leader certification is satisfactory completion of an oral interview that evaluates the student's capability to:

- Demonstrate leadership of team.
- Demonstrate effective communication of difficult issues.
- Demonstrate ability to deal with conflict within team/line/supplier organization.
- Demonstrate adaptability to changing conditions, such as adjusting scope.

The assigned Mentor(s) should work with the responsible NOS Supervisor to set up and conduct an oral interview composed of questions developed to assess the student's leadership abilities as an ATL/SATL. The Oral interview participants will be determined by the responsible NOS Supervisor.

The following guidance should be used to prepare and implement an oral interview.

Preparation

Responsible NOS Supervisor will:

- Establish date for the oral interview and notify the Oral Interview Participants and student. NOTE: It is recommended to schedule the interview in a room that is less susceptible to distractions.
- Develop interview questions with input from NOS Management.

Pre-Job Brief

Conduct an Oral Interview Preparation Meeting prior to the interview:

- Discuss format/agenda/logistics of the oral interview.
- Review status of preparations and questions; obtain consensus that it will satisfy demonstration of performance requirements.
- Review lessons learned from previous Interview.

ATTACHMENT 5 CONT'D
ORAL INTERVIEW PROCESS

AGENDA

Opening

1. Introduce the Oral Interview Participants to the student (if not acquainted).
2. Discuss the Purpose of the Oral Interview. The purpose of the oral interview is to evaluate the student's performance capability to:
   - Demonstrate leadership of team.
   - Demonstrate effective communication of difficult issues.
   - Demonstrate ability to deal with conflict within team/line/suppler organization.
   - Demonstrate adaptability to changing conditions, such as adjusting scope.
3. Discuss the Oral Interview Format, Process, and Logistics:
   - The interview will be conducted as a closed reference oral examination.
   - The Oral Interview members will take turns asking questions and will take notes.
   - Upon completion of the review, the student will be asked to leave the room and remain nearby.
   - Following the review, the Oral Interview members will confer.
   - The student will be asked to return to the room.
   - The Oral Interview members will provide the student the interview conclusions.
   - Potential conclusions include:
     - The student passed the oral interview with no additional actions.
     - The student will be required to perform specific follow-up actions as identified by the interviewers. Upon completion of the follow-up actions, the NOS Supervisor will provide the conclusions as to whether the student passed the review.
     - If needed, the student will be rescheduled for another oral interview after more time to gain knowledge and experience has passed.
   - In each of the potential conclusions listed above, the NOS Supervisor is likely to provide insights to the student of areas where the student's knowledge or understanding met requirements but demonstrated a gap to excellence.
   - The student may ask for clarification on a question.
   - If unsure of the intent of the question, the student should answer the question to the best of their ability; the Oral Interview members will ask follow-up questions if necessary.

Conduct the Oral Interview
The Oral Interview participants administer interview.

ATTACHMENT 6
LMS CODES FOR NOS TOPIC CERTIFICATIONS

Item Title	Item ID	Prerequisite Curricula	Curricula
MG-NOS-01 Nuclear Oversight Orientation (Mentor Guide)	FL-NOS-ORT-001M		FL-NOS-QA-ASSESSMENT
NOS QA Auditor (Curricula)	FL-NOS-QA-AUDITOR		FL-NOS-QA-AUDITOR
MG-NOS-01 Nuclear Oversight Orientation (Mentor Guide)	FL-NOS-ORT-001M		FL-NOS-QA-AUDITOR
MG-NOS-07 Performing Internal Audits (Mentor Guide)	FL-NOS-AUD-001M		FL-NOS-QA-AUDITOR
NOS QA Audit Team Lead (ATL) (Curricula)	FL-NOS-QA-ATL		FL-NOS-QA-ATL
MG-NOS-08 Audit Team Leader (Mentor Guide)	FL-NOS-ATL—002M	FL-NOS-QA-AUDITOR	FL-NOS-QA-ATL
NOS QA Supplier (Curricula)	FL-NOS-QA SUPPLIER		FL-NOS-QA SUPPLIER
MG-NOS-01 Nuclear Oversight Orientation (Mentor Guide)	FL-NOS-ORT-001M		FL-NOS-QA SUPPLIER
MG-NOS-04 Supplier Audit Team Leader (Mentor Guide)	FL-NOS-STL-001M		FL-NOS-QA SUPPLIER
MG-NOS-05 Source Surveillances	FL-NOS-SSU-001M		FL-NOS-QA SUPPLIER
MG-NOS-06 Supplier Approval Evaluator	FL-NOS-SAE-001M		FL-NOS-QA SUPPLIER
NOS Supplier NUPIC Certification			FL-NOS-QA-NPC

ATTACHMENT 6 CONT'D
LMS CODES FOR NOS TOPIC CERTIFICATIONS

Item Title	Item ID	Prerequisite Curricula		Curricula
NUPIC - Team Member	FL-NOS-QA-STL-002U	FL-NOS-QA SUPPLIER		FL-NOS-QA-STL-002
NUPIC - Lead Auditor	FL-NOS-QA-STL-003U	FL-NOS-QA SUPPLIER	FL-NOS-QA-STL-002	FL-NOS-QA-STL-003
NUPIC - Commercial Grade Survey Team Leader	FL-NOS-QA-STL-004U	FL-NOS-QA SUPPLIER	FL-NOS-QA-STL-003	FL-NOS-QA-STL-004
NOS Supplier NEI Certification				FL-NOS-QA-NEI
NEI - Access Authorization/Background Investigation Lead Auditor	FL-NOS-QA-STL-005U	FL-NOS-QA SUPPLIER		FL-NOS-QA-NEI
NEI - Fitness for Duty Lead Auditor	FL-NOS-QA-STL-006U	FL-NOS-QA SUPPLIER		FL-NOS-QA-NEI
NEI - HHS Laboratory Lead Auditor	FL-NOS-QA-STL-007U	FL-NOS-QA SUPPLIER		FL-NOS-QA-NEI
Nuclear Oversight Supply JFGs JFG-NOS-04, NOS Supply Oversight Orientation	FL-NOS-SOO-001G	FL-NOS-SOO		
Nuclear Oversight Supply JFGs JFG-NOS-05 NOS Supply Oversight Project Assessor	FL-NOS-SPA-001G	FL-NOS-SPA		

ATTACHMENT 6 CONT'D
LMS CODES FOR NOS TOPIC CERTIFICATIONS

Item Title	Item ID	Prereqs	Curricula
NOS QC Civil/Structural Inspection Certification	FL-NOS-QC-CVL		FL-NOS-QC-CVL
C1 Parts Verification	FL-NOS-CVL-010U		FL-NOS-CVL-010
C3 Measuring & Testing Equipment (M&TE)	FL-NOS-CVL-030U		FL-NOS-CVL-030
C5 Testing	FL-NOS-CVL-050U		FL-NOS-CVL-050
C12 Excavations and Soils	FL-NOS-CVL-120U		FL-NOS-CVL-120
C13 Concrete Inspection	FL-NOS-CVL-130U		FL-NOS-CVL-130
C13.5 General requirements for safety-related block wall installation	FL-NOS-CVL-135U		FL-NOS-CVL-135
C13.6 General Requirements for Concrete Core Drilling	FL-NOS-CVL-136U		FL-NOS-CVL-136
C13.7 General Requirements for Grouting of Abandoned Bolt Holes, Base Plates (Both Structural Steel)	FL-NOS-CVL-137U		FL-NOS-CVL-137
C14 Structural Steel	FL-NOS-CVL-140U		FL-NOS-CVL-140
C14.1 General Requirements for Structural Steel Erection Inspection	FL-NOS-CVL-141U		FL-NOS-CVL-141
C14.2 General Requirements for Fireproofing of Structural Steel	FL-NOS-CVL-142U		FL-NOS-CVL-142
C15 Roofing	FL-NOS-CVL-150U		FL-NOS-CVL-150
C17 Caulking	FL-NOS-CVL-170U		FL-NOS-CVL-170
NOS QC Nuclear Coatings Inspection Certification	FL-NOS-QC-CVL		FL-NOS-QC-CVL

ATTACHMENT 6 CONT'D
LMS CODES FOR NOS TOPIC CERTIFICATIONS

Item Title	Item ID	Prereqs	Curricula
C16 Coatings	FL-NOS-CVL-160U		FL-NOS-CVL-160
NOS QC Electrical Inspection Certification			FL-NOS-QC-ELE
E0 Requested Inspections	FL-NOS-ELE-000U		FL-NOS-ELE-000
E1 Parts Verification	FL-NOS-ELE-010U		FL-NOS-ELE-010
E3 Measuring & Test Equipment (M&TE)	FL-NOS-ELE-030U		FL-NOS-ELE-030
E4 Physical Condition, Assembly, Installation and Removal	FL-NOS-ELE-040U		FL-NOS-ELE-040
E4.1 Material Condition	FL-NOS-ELE-041U		FL-NOS-ELE-041
E4.4 Cable Installation	FL-NOS-ELE-044U		FL-NOS-ELE-044
E18 EQ Equipment	FL-NOS-ELE-180U		FL-NOS-ELE-180
E19 Terminations, Splices, and Jacket Repair	FL-NOS-ELE-190U		FL-NOS-ELE-190
E20 Soldering	FL-NOS-ELE-200U		FL-NOS-ELE-200
NOS QC I&C Inspection Certification			FL-NOS-QC-ICI
I1 Parts Verification	FL-NOS-ICI-010U		FL-NOS-ICI-010
I3 Measuring & Test Equipment (M&TE)	FL-NOS-ICI-030U		FL-NOS-ICI-030
I4 Physical Condition, Assembly, Installation and Removal	FL-NOS-ICI-040U		FL-NOS-ICI-040
I18 Environmental Qualification (EQ)	FL-NOS-ICI-180U		FL-NOS-ICI-180
I19 Terminations, Splices, and Jacket Repair	FL-NOS-ICI-190U		FL-NOS-ICI-190
I20 Soldering	FL-NOS-ICI-200U		FL-NOS-ICI-200

ATTACHMENT 6 CONT'D
LMS CODES FOR NOS TOPIC CERTIFICATIONS

Item Title	Item ID	Prereqs	Curricula
I22 Instrument Repair/Replacement/Calibration	FL–NOS–ICI–220U		FL–NOS–ICI–220
NOS QC Mechanical Inspection Certification			FL–NOS–QC–MEC
M1 Parts Verification and Material Control	FL–NOS–MEC–010U		FL–NOS–MEC–010
M3 Measuring and Testing Equipment	FL–NOS–MEC–030U		FL–NOS–MEC–030
M4 Physical Condition, Assembly, Installation	FL–NOS–MEC–040U		FL–NOS–MEC–040
NOS QC Radioactive Material (RAM) Shipment Inspection Certification (Training good for 3 yrs)	FL–NOS–RAM–000U		FL–NOS–QC–RAM
NOS QC General Inspection Certification			FL–NOS–QC–GEN
G0 Requested Inspections	FL–NOS–GEN–000U		FL–NOS–QC–GEN
G1 Parts Verification	FL–NOS–GEN–010U		FL–NOS–QC–GEN
G2 Foreign Material Exclusion	FL–NOS–GEN–020U		FL–NOS–QC–GEN
G6 Dimensions/Measurements	FL–NOS–GEN–060U		FL–NOS–QC–GEN
G7 Torque	FL–NOS–GEN–070U		FL–NOS–QC–GEN
G8 Lubrication	FL–NOS–GEN–080U		FL–NOS–QC–GEN
G9 Tubing Installation and Removal	FL–NOS–GEN–090U		FL–NOS–QC–GEN
G10 Anchor Bolts	FL–NOS–GEN–100U		FL–NOS–QC–GEN
G11 Fire Barriers	FL–NOS–GEN–110U		FL–NOS–QC–GEN
NOS QC Welding Inspection Certification	FL–NOS–WLD–000U		FL–NOS–QC–WLD

NUCLEAR OVERSIGHT
AUDIT PLAN

NOTE: STANDARD AUDIT PLAN APPLIES TO THIS AUDIT

AUDIT TITLE	AUDIT NUMBER
DES	A-DES-Plant X

SCOPE	REQUIREMENTS
This audit verifies design control measures are established and implemented to assure compliance with applicable regulatory requirements, the design basis and as specified in the license to ensure that structures, systems, and components can fulfill their specified safety functions to prevent undue risk to the health and safety of the public.	10 CFR 50.59 10 CFR 50, Appendix B, Criteria I, II, III, V, VI, XVI, XVII NSPM-1 (QATR) NQA-1-1994 IT Quality Services Interface Agreement CD 1.1, 1.2, 14.1 PINGP Tech Specs PINGP USAR

AUDIT SCHEDULE	
AUDIT START	AUDIT FINISH

ACTIVITIES TO BE AUDITED	

	➢ Design Control to include:
	  • Design Inputs (incl. design bases)
	  • Design Description and Analysis (incl. calculations)
	  • Design Output
	  • Design Interface
	  • Design Verification
	  • Design Approval
	  • Design Changes (incl. ECs, 50.59)
	  • Post-MOD/Design Testing
	  • Temporary Modifications
	➢ Vendor Interface Program
	➢ PINGP TS 5.5.12 Technical Specifications Bases Control Program
	➢ PINGP TS 5.6.5 Core Operating Limits Report (COLR)
	➢ Software Quality Assurance
	➢ IT Quality Services Interface Agreement
	➢ Plant Operating Review Committee
	➢ Organization/Responsibilities
	➢ Training and Qualifications
	➢ Procedures and Document Control
	➢ Corrective Action
	➢ Records

NUCLEAR OVERSIGHT
AUDIT PLAN

ORGANIZATIONS TO BE NOTIFIED	Engineering, Projects, IT, Regulatory Affairs, Nuclear Fuels Analysis and Design

AUDIT PERSONNEL	XXX – Audit Team Leader XXX – NOS Auditor XXX – NOS Auditor XXXX – NOS Auditor XXXX – Technical Specialist – [on loan from Plant Z] XXXX – Internal Technical Specialist

APPLICABLE DOCUMENTS	10 CFR 50.59 10 CFR 50.71(e) 10 CFR 50, Appendix B 10 CFR 50, Appendix A, General Design Criterion 1 NSPM-1, QATR NQA-1, 1994 MNGP Tech Specs MNGP USAR Generic Letters 83-28, 90-03 NRC Reg Guide 1.187, Guidance for Implementation of 10 CFR 50.59, Changes, Tests, and Experiments, November 2000 NEI 96-07, Guidelines for 10 CFR 05.59 Implementation, November 2000 Industry Inspection Reports/NCVs/Findings; OEE Corporate Directives 14.1, 1.1 Fleet Procedures PINGP Site Procedures FL-ESP-TPD IT Quality Services Interface Agreement

Prepared by: (ATL) (print/sign/date)	XXX
Approved by: (Audit Supervisor) (print/sign/date)	XXX

NUCLEAR OVERSIGHT
AUDIT CHECKLIST

AUDIT # <u>A-DES-[Plant Y]</u> CHECKLIST

PREPARATION	
Prepared by:	<u>XXXXXXXX</u> Date <u>XXXXXX</u>
SAP <u>DES</u> Rev <u>1</u>	Audit Dates:

COMPLETION	
Completed by:	<u>Enter Auditor Name</u> Date: xx/x/2018
Approved by (ATL):	<u>XXXXXXX</u>_____Date: xx/x/2018 <u>(print/sign)</u>

Checklist Contents		
Element/Sub-Element	**Audit Requirement**	**Page Number**
10 CFR 50 Appendix B Criteria	**Appendix B criteria that are included in every standard audit plan**	
QA-I	Organization	
QA-II	Quality Assurance Program (training elements)	
QA-V	Instructions, Procedures and Drawings	
QA-VI	Document Control	
QA-XVI	Corrective Action	
QA-XVII	Quality Assurance Records	
10 CFR 50 Appendix B Criteria	**Appendix B criteria that are included in DES standard audit plan**	
QA-III	Design Control (Design Inputs, Design Process/Design Analyses – including calculations, Change Control, Interface Control, Documentation and Records, Design Verification, Modification Testing, Temporary Modification)	
QATR Element	**QATR sections applicable to this audit and not included in other elements**	
B.17	Computer Software Control	
C.1	Methodology – Plant Operating Review Committee	
Licensing Basis Criteria (R-xx, T-xx)	**Regulatory, Tech Spec, and other licensing bases criteria that apply to EP Audit Scope**	

NUCLEAR OVERSIGHT
AUDIT CHECKLIST

Checklist Contents		
Element/Sub-Element	**Audit Requirement**	**Page Number**
R-01	10 CFR 50.59 Changes, tests and experiments.	
R-02	10 CFR 50.71(e) Maintenance of records, making of reports. [USAR Updates]	
R-03	10 CFR 50.72/73 Reportability	
R-04	Vendor Interface Program	
T-01	TS 5.5.9 Technical Specifications (TS) Bases Control Program	
T-02	TS 5.6.3 Core Operating Limits Report	
Other Requirements (Element/Sub-element) (OR-xx)	**USAR, Procedures**	
OR-01	IT Quality Services Interface Agreement	
Optional Scope (Element/Sub-element) (O-xx)	**(Management Direction)**	
O-02	Operating Experience	

Form retained in accordance with retention schedule identified in Procedure XX
Retention: 10 years

NUCLEAR OVERSIGHT
AUDIT CHECKLIST

QA-I	10 CFR 50 Appendix B Requirement Included in All Audits

QA-I - Organization
The authority and duties of persons and organizations performing activities affecting the safety-related functions of structures, systems, and components shall be clearly established and delineated in writing.

A.2 Organization
See Quality Assurance Topical Report, current revision, for requirements.

A.3 Responsibility
See Quality Assurance Topical Report, current revision, for requirements.

A.4 Authority
See Quality Assurance Topical Report, current revision, for requirements.

NQA-1, 1994
See above QATR sections, which specify applicable NQA-1, 1994 requirements.

Auditor Instructions

1. Verify that the organizational structure, responsibilities, and authorities are clearly defined for each organizational position *at headquarters and at the site* within:

   a. Design Engineering
   b. Nuclear Projects
   c. IT for Software Quality Assurance

2. Verify that the actual organization in use by the site aligns with the structure defined; this includes verification that personnel in these organizations understand the structure, responsibilities, and authorities.

Documents Reviewed

Document Number	Title	Rev

NUCLEAR OVERSIGHT
AUDIT CHECKLIST

Documents Reviewed		
Document Number	**Title**	**Rev**

Persons Contacted	
Name (Last Name, First Name)	**Position**

Results		
SAT ☐	**UNSAT** ☐	**CAP #(s)**

Document reviews determined that [Plant Y] Design Control is effectively meeting 10 CFR 50 Appendix B; criterion I – Organization.

- Review of the Corporate and Site Organizational charts, corporate directives (CD 5.10., CD 5.20, CD 5.31), and fleet procedures (see references in documents section) found that roles and responsibilities are clearing defined for site and contract employees to conduct design control activities for groups involved such as site engineering, nuclear projects, and IT for software quality assurance.

- The audit activities conducted as part of the remaining Checklist elements did not reveal any concerns for this area.

No issues identified.

QA-II	10 CFR 50 Appendix B Requirement Included in All Audits

QA-II - Quality Assurance Program (training elements)

The program shall provide for indoctrination and training of personnel performing activities affecting quality as necessary to assure that suitable proficiency is achieved and maintained.

A.1 Methodology
See Quality Assurance Topical Report, current revision, for requirements.

A.5 Personnel Training and Qualification
See Quality Assurance Topical Report, current revision, for requirements.

B.1 Methodology
See Quality Assurance Topical Report, current revision, for requirements.

NQA-1, 1994
See above QATR sections, which specify applicable NQA-1, 1994 requirements.

Auditor Instructions

NUCLEAR OVERSIGHT
AUDIT CHECKLIST

Verify that personnel performing quality-related tasks are qualified and proficient. Where individual performance is observed, a sample of the tasks and/or functions observed are evaluated to ensure task performance is indicative of training.

Verify that supplemental personnel who perform work at the station are trained and qualified to perform the assigned tasks.

Documents Reviewed		
Document Number	**Title**	**Rev**

Persons Contacted	
Name (Last Name, First Name)	**Position**

Results

SAT ☐	UNSAT ☐	CAP #(s)

Verified through document reviews and interviews that [Plant Y] is meeting the requirements of 10 CFR 50 Appendix B criterion II, QATR section A.5, and NQA-1-1994 Basic Requirement 2 with Supplements 2S-1 and 2S-4.

- Auditors verified that, for the sample of modifications and the 50.59 screenings reviewed for checklist elements QA-III and R-01, personnel were confirmed using qualifications reports to be qualified to perform the activities.

- For SQA, auditors confirmed that cited Software Product Managers had the applicable qualification.

- Lesson plans and program descriptions received a qualitative review to determine adequacy of the training. Auditors confirmed that the applicable training went through the SAT process, including a task analysis using the fleet procedure series FP-T-SAT-XX series.

No issues identified.

QA-V	10 CFR 50 Appendix B Requirement Included in All Audits (from SAP)

QA-V - Instructions, Procedures and Drawings

Activities affecting quality shall be prescribed by documented instructions, procedures, or drawings, of a type appropriate to the circumstances and shall be accomplished in accordance with these instructions, procedures, or drawings.

NUCLEAR OVERSIGHT
AUDIT CHECKLIST

Instructions, procedures, or drawings shall include appropriate quantitative or qualitative acceptance criteria for determining that important activities have been satisfactorily accomplished.

A.1 Methodology
See Quality Assurance Topical Report, current revision, for requirements.

B.1 Methodology
See Quality Assurance Topical Report, current revision, for requirements.

NQA-1, 1994
See above QATR sections, which specify applicable NQA-1, 1994 requirements.

Auditor Instructions

1. Verify that work documents are implemented as written.

    a. Procedure/Work Instruction Use and Adherence is maintained in accordance with IAW the Fleet and site procedures:

    b. Supervisor or equivalent review and approval are required prior to workers marking steps as not applicable. (FP-G-DOC-03 Rev 12) 5.4.11

    c. Documents are the latest approved revision. (FP-G-DOC-03 Rev 12) 5.1.2

    d. Place keeping is maintained as required. (FP-G-DOC-03 Rev 12) 5.3.2

2. Verify that Fleet, site, and department directives, procedures, and instructions are aligned with the applicable regulations and codes for the program and/or process.

Documents Reviewed		
Document Number	**Title**	**Rev**

Persons Contacted	
Name (Last Name, First Name)	**Position**

Results		
SAT ☐	UNSAT ☐	CAP #(s)

Based on interviews, observations, and document reviews, [Plant Y] Design Control is effective and meeting the requirements of 10 CFR 50 Appendix B, Criterion V.

- Fleet procedures (primarily the FP-E-MOD-XX series) govern activities for the design control process (see QA-III for comprehensive listing) and align with applicable regulatory requirements.

NUCLEAR OVERSIGHT
AUDIT CHECKLIST

- Verification activities for the Design Control process are delineated in the fleet procedures (primarily the FP-E-MOD-XX series and FP-E-SE-03). A sample review of ECs found that overall the reviews, approvals, and verification activities are effectively implemented.

Two issues were identified associated with procedure use and adherence.

NOS Finding: SQA Program Requirements Not Met As discussed in the checklist element OR-01, Software quality control, a contributor to the NOS Finding in NOS SQA (CAP01525686) was that the site overall had a misunderstanding as to when SQA Plans were required as part of the design process. Adherence to the requirement was not met in several instances leading to the NOS Finding. (CAP01525686, See OR-01 for additional details)

NOS ID: Active T-Mod File not meeting FP-E-MOD-03 requirements (see QA-IIIh). The Active Temporary Modification (TMod) file located in the Work Execution Center (WEC) has several issues that are not compliant with the requirements of FP-E-MOD-03, "Temporary Modifications." Consequence: Failure to maintain an accurate and up-to-date active T-Mod file may result in questions regarding current plant configuration. (CAP01525638)

QA-VI	10 CFR 50 Appendix B Requirement Included in All Audits (from SAP)

QA-VI - Document Control

Measures shall be established to control the issuance of documents, such as instructions, procedures and drawings, including changes thereto, which prescribe all activities affecting quality. These measures shall assure that documents, including changes, are reviewed for adequacy and approved for release by authorized personnel and are distributed to and used at the location where the prescribed activity is performed. Changes to documents shall be reviewed and approved by the same organizations that performed the original review and approval unless the applicant designates another responsible organization.

B.14 Document Control
See Quality Assurance Topical Report, current revision, for requirements.

NQA-1, 1994
See above QATR sections, which specify applicable NQA-1, 1994 requirements.

Auditor Instructions

1. Verify that procedures and controlled documents covering quality-related aspects of design control activities are developed in accordance with procedures:

   a. Controlled copies are maintained by the organization (latest revision).

   b. Methods have been established to assure that documents, including changes, are evaluated under the provisions of 10 CFR 50.59 for unreviewed safety questions.

NUCLEAR OVERSIGHT
AUDIT CHECKLIST

c. Critical steps are identified and appropriate levels of confirmation or verification are used.

d. Level of use is appropriate.

e. Qualified Review is conducted when appropriate for changes.

f. Only controlled drawings reflecting as-build conditions are used to perform or plan quality-related work.

g. Drawings are appropriately stamped or marked to indicate control.

h. Required cross-organizational, cross-discipline, and technical reviews are completed.

i. Temporary Changes being used appropriately.

Documents Reviewed		
Document Number	**Title**	**Rev**

Persons Contacted	
Name (Last Name, First Name)	**Position**

Results		
SAT ☐	UNSAT ☐	CAP #(s)

Based on interviews, observations, and document reviews, [Plant Y] Design Control Program is meeting the requirements of 10 CFR 50, Appendix B, Criterion VI, and Document Control. A program is established and implemented to control development, review, approval, issue, use, and revision of Design Control Documents and Corporate, Fleet, and Site procedures.

- Fleet procedure series FP-G-DOC-XX provides governance on changes to fleet and site procedures, while FP-G-CD-01 provides governance for controlling documents.

- Design basis documents are maintained and controlled through the design control process via the fleet procedure series FP-E-MOD-XX, with special considerations for Setpoints (FP-E-SPT-01), specifications (FP-E-SPEC-01), Document Only changes (FP-E-DOC-01), Drawings (FP-E-DWG-XX series), Vendor manuals (FP-E-VEN-01), and software (FP-IT-SQA-XX series).

- Work management planning, FP-WM-PLA-01, requires use of controlled documents to plan or reference in use during conduct of maintenance work activities. Controlled Construction drawings (FP-E-DWG-03) provide a means through the EC process to provide control over information during the construction phase of projects

NUCLEAR OVERSIGHT
AUDIT CHECKLIST

that still use the work management process to implement the work activities through the QA program.

- The sample of ECs, as discussed in checklist element QA-III, reviewed determined that overall the process and procedures are effective and adequate controls are in place to meet regulatory requirements.

- Level of use is sufficient of procedures, typically "Information use" for design control activities. Review process provides means to verify accuracy and validation within the process.

No issues were identified.

QA-XVI	10 CFR 50 Appendix B Requirement Included in All Audits (from SAP)

QA-XVI - Corrective Action

Measures shall be established to assure that conditions adverse to quality, such as failures, malfunctions, deficiencies, deviations, defective material and equipment, and nonconformances are promptly identified and corrected. In the case of significant conditions adverse to quality, the measures shall assure that the cause of the condition is determined and corrective action taken to preclude repetition. The identification of the significant condition adverse to quality, the cause of the condition, and the corrective action taken shall be documented and reported to appropriate levels of management.

A.6 Corrective Action
See *Quality Assurance Topical Report, current revision, for requirements.*

B.13 Corrective Action
See *Quality Assurance Topical Report, current revision, for requirements.*

NQA-1, 1994
See above QATR sections, which specify applicable NQA-1, 1994 requirements.

Auditor Instructions

1. Verify that personnel are identifying and correcting conditions adverse to quality in a timely and effective manner.

   a. Sample and review related identified conditions adverse to quality in the past 2 years (minimum).

   b. Sample and review related identified significant conditions adverse to quality in the past 2 years (minimum). If feasible, all related SCAQs (in past 2 years) should be reviewed.

   c. Review last NOS audit identified CAPs.

NUCLEAR OVERSIGHT
AUDIT CHECKLIST

2.	Verify that CAP issues are appropriately defined in extent and clearly document action taken. Validate effectiveness.

Documents Reviewed

Document Number	Title	Rev

Persons Contacted

Name (Last Name, First Name)	Position

Results

SAT ☐	UNSAT ☐	CAP #(s)

Based on interviews and document review, [Plant Y] design control is meeting the requirements of 10 CFR 50 App B Criteria XVI for Corrective Action Program. No Corrective Action Program issues were identified.

- Review of CAPs (CAQ) since January 2015 indicate that individuals in organizations involved with the Design Control processes are submitting ARs for problems identified.

- No SCAQ CAPs identified in the last two years with the owed to group designated as Eng Design Group.

- Interviews indicate that individuals in organizations involved with the Design Control processes do not demonstrate a reluctance to submit CAPs nor were issues found that were previously known yet did not get into the CAP process and subsequently addressed in a timely manner.

- Site response to CAPs for applicable NOS assessments (2016-01-001 and 2015-01-030) were reasonable and no repeat issues.

- Sample of CAP responses (CAQ) for Eng Design Groups were defined in extent and clearly document action taken.

QA-XVII	10 CFR 50 Appendix B Requirement Included in All Audits (from SAP)

QA-XVII Quality Assurance Records

Sufficient records shall be maintained to furnish evidence of activities affecting quality. . . . Records shall be identifiable and retrievable. Consistent with applicable regulatory requirements, the applicant shall establish requirements concerning record retention, such as duration, location, and assigned responsibility.

Form retained in accordance with retention schedule identified in Procedure XX
Retention: 10 years

NUCLEAR OVERSIGHT
AUDIT CHECKLIST

B.15 Records
See Quality Assurance Topical Report, current revision, for requirements.

NQA-1, 1994
See above QATR sections, which specify applicable NQA-1, 1994 requirements.

Auditor Instructions

Verify that design documentation and records, which provide evidence that the design and verification process meet requirements are collected, stored, and maintained in accordance with QATR B.15 and associated implementing procedures.

Documents Reviewed		
Document Number	**Title**	**Rev**

Persons Contacted	
Name (Last Name, First Name)	**Position**

Results

SAT ☐	UNSAT ☐	CAP #(s)

Based on interviews and document reviews, [Plant Y]'s implementation of the Design Control processes are meeting requirements of 10 CFR 50 Appendix B Requirement criterion XVII, Quality Assurance Records.

- Design control records are identified in the respective engineering procedures (see listing in Checklist element QA-III), particularly in the FP-E-MOD-xx Series, FP-E-SE-XX series, and FP-E-DBD-01 as well as on the Xcel Energy Records Retention Schedule.

- Auditors reviewing completed ECs and CWOs reviewed records "index entry" through passport SharePoint. During those reviews, no record discrepancies were identified for the sample of closed ECs. This review provides evidence that EC and CWO electronic records are being generated as outlined in FP-G-RM-02.

No issues identified.

QA-III	10 CFR 50 Appendix B Criteria Included in DES Standard Audit Plan
QA-III - Design Control	

NUCLEAR OVERSIGHT
AUDIT CHECKLIST

Measures shall be established to assure that applicable regulatory requirements and the design basis, as defined in § 50.2 and as specified in the license application, for those structures, systems, and components to which this appendix applies are correctly translated into specifications, drawings, procedures, and instructions. These measures shall include provisions to assure that appropriate quality standards are specified and included in design documents and that deviations from such standards are controlled. Measures shall also be established for the selection and review for suitability of application of materials, parts, equipment, and processes that are essential to the safety-related functions of the structures, systems and components.

Measures shall be established for the identification and control of design interfaces and for coordination among participating design organizations. These measures shall include the establishment of procedures among participating design organizations for the review, approval, release, distribution, and revision of documents involving design interfaces.

The design control measures shall provide for verifying or checking the adequacy of design, such as by the performance of design reviews, by the use of alternate or simplified calculational methods, or by the performance of a suitable testing program. The verifying or checking process shall be performed by individuals or groups other than those who performed the original design, but who may be from the same organization. Where a test program is used to verify the adequacy of a specific design feature in lieu of other verifying or checking processes, it shall include suitable qualifications testing of a prototype unit under the most adverse design conditions. Design control measures shall be applied to items such as the following: reactor physics, stress, thermal, hydraulic, and accident analyses; compatibility of materials; accessibility for inservice inspection, maintenance, and repair; and delineation of acceptance criteria for inspections and tests.

Design changes, including field changes, shall be subject to design control measures commensurate with those applied to the original design and be approved by the organization that performed the original design unless the applicant designates another responsible organization.

B.2 Design Control
See Quality Assurance Topical Report, current revision, for requirements.

B.3 Design Verification
See Quality Assurance Topical Report, current revision, for requirements.

NQA-1, 1994
See above QATR sections, which specify applicable NQA-1, 1994 requirements.

Auditor Instructions

Documents Reviewed		
Document Number	**Title**	**Rev**

NUCLEAR OVERSIGHT
AUDIT CHECKLIST

Documents Reviewed		
Document Number	**Title**	**Rev**

Persons Contacted	
Name (Last Name, First Name)	**Position**

Results
SAT ☐   UNSAT ☐   CAP #(s)

Modification Number	Design Inputs	Design Process	Design Analyses	Design Verification	Change Control	Interface Control	Documentation and Records	Modification Testing

Audit Sample Size Discussion

To obtain the sample for audit review, SQL report EC-0274 obtained all Engineering Changes (ECs) with a status change since 5/1/2014 of "Approved" to "Closed." From the listing, a smart sample was determined using criteria such as safety-related, plant or regulatory impact, or SQA related to provide a well-rounded selection. A review of selected items against the list of recent ECs reviewed as part of the CDBI inspection eliminated some ECs to maximize the breadth of the audit.

Mod Type / Sub Type	Sample Reviewed	Population
DOC	3	387
EQV	3	176
EVAL	1	208
MOD	16	474
Full Design Change	4	54
ECN	1	287
GMOD	0	1

NUCLEAR OVERSIGHT
AUDIT CHECKLIST

MMOD	0	55
TMOD	7	45
WMOD	0	32
SPT	4	28
Total	**35**	**1273**

Note: Additional ECs were reviewed during the course of the Audit as a result of issues found or a reference tie.

Note: For this Audit, modifications related to core design and governed by procedures series DP-NF-XXX-YY were not reviewed.

B.17	**QATR Requirement** **(Specific to this audit and not included in other elements)**

B.17 Computer Software Control
See Quality Assurance Topical Report, current revision, for requirements.

NQA-1, 1994
See above QATR section, which specifies applicable NQA-1, 1994 requirements.

CD 14.1 "Software Quality Assurance"
See CD 14.1, current revision, for requirements.

Auditor Instructions

A. Verify administrative policies and procedures for digital software quality assurance exist and contain guidance on the following:
- The software products to which it applies
- The organizations responsible for performing the work, achieving software quality and their tasks and responsibilities
- Required documentation
- Procedures that guide software development and methods to assure compliance These procedures provide guidance for the following:
  - o Developing requirements for the digital technology including specifying functionality, performance, design constraints, attributes and external interfaces (requirements phase)
  - o Ensuring the digital asset is designed according to specified requirements (design phase)
  - o Ensuring the digital asset is built according to specified requirements (implementation phase)
  - o Ensuring the as-built digital asset meets requirements through testing (test phase)
  - o Ensuring the installed digital asset functions according to requirements (installation and checkout phase)
  - o Provides for the implementation of user guides or procedures (operations / maintenance phase)
- The required software reviews (verification and validation)
- The dispositioning of verification review comments

NUCLEAR OVERSIGHT
AUDIT CHECKLIST

- The methods for error reporting and corrective action
- Requirements for software to be identified
- A formal system to ensure any changes are approved and well documented
- Periodic checks are performed to ensure software integrity
- Modifications to both computer and plant hardware should be evaluated for their effect on computer software and software modified where appropriate
- A process is defined for retiring the digital technology
- Record copies of required documentation

B. Perform a sampling of software utilized in the design control process to validate SQA requirements are met.

Documents Reviewed		
Document Number	**Title**	**Rev**

Persons Contacted	
Name (Last Name, First Name)	**Position**

Results		
SAT ☐	UNSAT ☐	CAP #(s)

C.1	QATR Requirement (Specific to this audit and not included in other elements)

C.1 Methodology – Plant Operating Review Committee
Maintain plant operating review committees to review overall plant performance, and advise site Management on matters related to nuclear safety. Appendix A establishes the minimum requirements for these committees.

Appendix A   Plant Operating Review Committee
See QATR Appendix A, current revision, for requirements

Auditor Instructions

Validate PORC involvement as required for design control and 10 CFR 50.59 issues. Review PORC meeting minutes and sampled MOD packages for evidence of appropriate PORC review.

Evaluate a sample of USAR and TS changes for evidence of PORC review.

Documents Reviewed

NUCLEAR OVERSIGHT
AUDIT CHECKLIST

Document Number	Title		Rev

Persons Contacted	
Name (Last Name, First Name)	Position

Results		
SAT ☐	UNSAT ☐	CAP #(s)

QA-Additional 02. Verified through document reviews and interviews that [Plant Y] Engineering Design Control is meeting the requirements for the Plant Operating Review Committee (QATR Appendix A) for reviewing changes or modifications to plant systems or equipment that affect nuclear safety.

- PORC meetings minutes were reviewed to verify that the committee was reviewing ECs and related 50.59/72.48 evaluations (see list above). FP-OP-PRC-01 provides governance of the PORC and outlines the PORC reviews in Attachment 1.

- PORC meeting minutes show that PORC reviews are approval/disapproval "in writing" as outline in FP-OP-PRC-01, attachment 1.

See checklist element R-01 for more details on 10 CFR 50.59.

No issues identified.

R-01	Regulatory Requirements Source/Requirements to Verify

R-01 10 CFR 50.59 – Changes, Tests and Experiments

(a) Definitions for the purposes of this section:

(1) Change means a modification or addition to, or removal from, the facility or procedures that affects a design function, method of performing or controlling the function, or an evaluation that demonstrates that intended functions will be accomplished.

(2) Departure from a method of evaluation described in the FSAR (as updated) used in establishing the design bases or in the safety analyses means:

(i) Changing any of the elements of the method described in the FSAR (as updated) unless the results of the analysis are conservative or essentially the same; or

(ii) Changing from a method described in the FSAR to another method unless that method has been approved by NRC for the intended application.

NUCLEAR OVERSIGHT
AUDIT CHECKLIST

(3) Facility as described in the final safety analysis report (as updated) means:

(i) The structures, systems, and components (SSC) that are described in the final safety analysis report (FSAR) (as updated),

(ii) The design and performance requirements for such SSCs described in the FSAR (as updated), and

(iii) The evaluations or methods of evaluation included in the FSAR (as updated) for such SSCs that demonstrate that their intended function(s) will be accomplished.

(4) Final Safety Analysis Report (as updated) means the Final Safety Analysis Report (or Final Hazards Summary Report) submitted in accordance with Sec. 50.34, as amended and supplemented, and as updated per the requirements of Sec. 50.71(e) or Sec. 50.71(f), as applicable.

(5) Procedures as described in the final safety analysis report (as updated) means those procedures that contain information described in the FSAR (as updated) such as how structures, systems, and components are operated and controlled (including assumed operator actions and response times).

(6) Tests or experiments not described in the final safety analysis report (as updated) means any activity where any structure, system, or component is utilized or controlled in a manner that is either:

(i) Outside the reference bounds of the design bases as described in the final safety analysis report (as updated) or

(ii) Inconsistent with the analyses or descriptions in the final safety analysis report (as updated).

(b) This section applies to each holder of an operating license issued under this part or a combined license issued under part 52 of this chapter, including the holder of a license authorizing operation of a nuclear power reactor that has submitted the certification of permanent cessation of operations required under § 50.82(a)(1) or § 50.110 or a reactor licensee whose license has been amended to allow possession of nuclear fuel but not operation of the facility.

(c)(1) A licensee may make changes in the facility as described in the final safety analysis report (as updated), make changes in the procedures as described in the final safety analysis report (as updated), and conduct tests or experiments not described in the final safety analysis report (as updated) without obtaining a license amendment pursuant to Sec. 50.90 only if:

(i) A change to the technical specifications incorporated in the license is not required, and

(ii) The change, test, or experiment does not meet any of the criteria in paragraph (c)(2) of this section.

NUCLEAR OVERSIGHT
AUDIT CHECKLIST

(2) A licensee shall obtain a license amendment pursuant to Sec. 50.90 prior to implementing a proposed change, test, or experiment if the change, test, or experiment would:

(i) Result in more than a minimal increase in the frequency of occurrence of an accident previously evaluated in the final safety analysis report (as updated);

(ii) Result in more than a minimal increase in the likelihood of occurrence of a malfunction of a structure, system, or component (SSC) important to safety previously evaluated in the final safety analysis report (as updated);

(iii) Result in more than a minimal increase in the consequences of an accident previously evaluated in the final safety analysis report (as updated);

(iv) Result in more than a minimal increase in the consequences of a malfunction of an SSC important to safety previously evaluated in the final safety analysis report (as updated);

(v) Create a possibility for an accident of a different type than any previously evaluated in the final safety analysis report (as updated);

(vi) Create a possibility for a malfunction of an SSC important to safety with a different result than any previously evaluated in the final safety analysis report (as updated);

(vii) Result in a design basis limit for a fission product barrier as described in the FSAR (as updated) being exceeded or altered; or

(viii) Result in a departure from a method of evaluation described in the FSAR (as updated) used in establishing the design bases or in the safety analyses.

(3) In implementing this paragraph, the FSAR (as updated) is considered to include FSAR changes resulting from evaluations performed pursuant to this section and analyses performed pursuant to Sec. 50.90 since submittal of the last update of the final safety analysis report pursuant to Sec. 50.71 of this part.

(4) The provisions in this section do not apply to changes to the facility or procedures when the applicable regulations establish more specific criteria for accomplishing such changes.

(d)(1) The licensee shall maintain records of changes in the facility, of changes in procedures, and of tests and experiments made pursuant to paragraph (c) of this section. These records must include a written evaluation that provides the bases for the determination that the change, test, or experiment does not require a license amendment pursuant to paragraph (c)(2) of this section.

(2) The licensee shall submit, as specified in § 50.4 or § 52.3 of this chapter, as applicable, a report containing a brief description of any changes, tests, and experiments, including a summary of the evaluation of each. A report must be submitted at intervals not to exceed 24 months. For combined licenses, the report must be submitted at intervals not to exceed 6 months during the period from the date of application for a combined license to the date the Commission makes its findings under 10 CFR 52.103(g).

NUCLEAR OVERSIGHT
AUDIT CHECKLIST

(3) The records of changes in the facility must be maintained until the termination of an operating license issued under this part, a combined license issued under part 52 of this chapter, or the termination of a license issued under 10 CFR part 54, whichever is later. Records of changes in procedures and records of tests and experiments must be maintained for a period of 5 years.

Auditor Instructions

1. Review administrative guidance related to 10 CFR 50.59 Applicability Reviews.

   a. Verify guidance conforms to regulatory requirements.
   b. Verify exclusion criteria for specific programs or procedures are clearly identified and specified.
   c. Verify guidance clearly directs the next steps in the evaluation process (i.e., exit the process, proceed to a screening or evaluation, or initiate a license amendment request).

2. Perform a detailed review of a representative sample of recent 10 CFR 50.59 Applicability Reviews (Design Engineering related) that have been approved for use to verify that the correct process was chosen for the change under consideration. If any portion of an activity is not controlled by one of the alternate processes identified in 10 CFR 50.59, then verify that a 10 CFR 50.59 Screening was completed for that portion not covered by the alternate processes.

3. Verify approved procedures are in place for the governance of 10 CFR 50.59 Screening Reviews.

4. Perform a detailed review of a representative sample of recent 10 CFR 50.59 Screening Reviews (Design Engineering related) to verify that each answer includes a complete response, with justification, to each 10 CFR 50.59 Screening question. Answers to 10 CFR 50.59 Screening questions shall not consist solely of a negative restatement of the question.

5. For the sample of screening reviews selected for review, verify that it appropriately concludes that the change, test, or experiment or permanent modification can be accomplished without obtaining a license amendment. (Reference: IP 71111.17T, Evaluations of Changes, Tests, or Experiments and Permanent Plant Modifications)

6. Verify approved procedures are in place for the governance of 10 CFR 50.59 Evaluations and verify these procedures meet the regulatory requirements for evaluating the effects of proposed activities in accordance with 10 CFR 50.59(c)(2).

7. Perform a detailed review of a representative sample of recent 10 CFR 50.59 Evaluations (Design Engineering related) and verify that each answer includes a complete response, with justification, to each 10 CFR 50.59 Evaluation question. Answers to 10 CFR 50.59 Evaluation questions shall not consist solely of a negative restatement of the question.

8. For the sample of 10 CFR 50.59 evaluations selected for review, verify that it appropriately concludes that the change, test, or experiment or permanent modification

NUCLEAR OVERSIGHT
AUDIT CHECKLIST

can be accomplished without obtaining a license amendment. (Reference: IP 71111.17T, Evaluations of Changes, Tests, and Experiments and Permanent Plant Modifications)

9. Verify approved procedures are in place for the governance of 10 CFR 50.59 reports and submittals and verify these procedures meet the regulatory requirements of 10 CFR 50.59(d)(2).

10. Verify 50.59 screenings and evaluations are properly maintained:

   a. Screenings and evaluations related to plant changes are maintained for the term of the operating license.
   b. Screenings and evaluations associated with procedure changes or test records are maintained for 5 years.

Documents Reviewed		
Document Number	**Title**	**Rev**

Persons Contacted	
Name (Last Name, First Name)	**Position**

Results		
SAT ☐	**UNSAT** ☐	**CAP #(s)**

Based on interviews, observations, and/or document reviews, [Plant Y] is meeting the requirements of §50.59, "Changes, tests, and experiments" with no issues identified.

1. CD 5.1, FP-E-SE-03, and FG-E-SE-03 provide governance of §50.59 applicability reviews, screenings and evaluations that meet regulatory requirements.

2. A review of a representative sample of applicability determinations, screenings and evaluations verified compliance with §50.59 requirements.

3. Screenings and Evaluations reviewed were retained as a record with the controlling modification engineering change documentation.

R-02	**Regulatory Requirements** **Source/Requirements to Verify**

10 CFR 50.71(e) Maintenance of records, making of reports (USAR)

(e) Each person licensed to operate a nuclear power reactor under the provisions of § 50.21 or § 50.22, and each applicant for a combined license under part 52 of this chapter, shall update periodically, as provided in paragraphs (e) (3) and (4) of this section, the final

NUCLEAR OVERSIGHT
AUDIT CHECKLIST

safety analysis report (FSAR) originally submitted as part of the application for the license, to assure that the information included in the report contains the latest information developed. This submittal shall contain all the changes necessary to reflect information and analyses submitted to the Commission by the applicant or licensee or prepared by the applicant or licensee pursuant to Commission requirement since the submittal of the original FSAR, or as appropriate, the last update to the FSAR under this section. The submittal shall include the effects of all changes made in the facility or procedures as described in the FSAR; all safety analyses and evaluations performed by the applicant or licensee either in support of approved license amendments or in support of conclusions that changes did not require a license amendment in accordance with § 50.59(c)(2) or, in the case of a license that references a certified design, in accordance with § 52.98(c) of this chapter; and all analyses of new safety issues performed by or on behalf of the applicant or licensee at Commission request. The updated information shall be appropriately located within the update to the FSAR.

(1) The licensee shall submit revisions containing updated information to the Commission, as specified in § 50.4, on a replacement-page basis that is accompanied by a list that identifies the current pages of the FSAR following page replacement.

(2) The submittal shall include (i) a certification by a duly authorized officer of the licensee that either the information accurately presents changes made since the previous submittal, necessary to reflect information and analyses submitted to the Commission or prepared pursuant to Commission requirement, or that no such changes were made; and (ii) an identification of changes made under the provisions of § 50.59 but not previously submitted to the Commission.

(3)(i) A revision of the original FSAR containing those original pages that are still applicable plus new replacement pages shall be filed within 24 months of either July 22, 1980, or the date of issuance of the operating license, whichever is later, and shall bring the FSAR up to date as of a maximum of 6 months prior to the date of filing the revision.

(ii) Not less than 15 days before § 50.71(e) becomes effective, the Director of the Office of Nuclear Reactor Regulation shall notify by letter the licensees of those nuclear power plants initially subject to the NRC's systematic evaluation program that they need not comply with the provisions of this section while the program is being conducted at their plant. The Director of the Office of Nuclear Reactor Regulation will notify by letter the licensee of each nuclear power plant being evaluated when the systematic evaluation program has been completed. Within 24 months after receipt of this notification, the licensee shall file a complete FSAR that is up to date as of a maximum of 6 months prior to the date of filing the revision.

(iii) During the period from the docketing of an application for a combined license under subpart C of part 52 of this chapter until the Commission makes the finding under § 52.103(g) of this chapter, the update to the FSAR must be submitted annually.

(4) Subsequent revisions must be filed annually or 6 months after each refueling outage provided the interval between successive updates does not exceed 24 months. The revisions must reflect all changes up to a maximum of 6 months prior to the date of filling. For nuclear power reactor facilities that have submitted the certifications required by § 50.82(a)(1), subsequent revisions must be filed every 24 months.

NUCLEAR OVERSIGHT
AUDIT CHECKLIST

(5) Each replacement page shall include both a change indicator for the area changed, e.g., a bold line vertically drawn in the margin adjacent to the portion actually changed, and a page change identification (date of change or change number or both).

(6) The updated FSAR shall be retained by the licensee until the Commission terminates their license.

Auditor Instructions

Note: Be alert through the course of the audit for instances where there should have been a USAR change but one did not occur.

1. Verify approved procedures are in place for the control of revisions and changes to the USAR and verify these procedures meet the following requirements:

   a. Periodic updating of the USAR originally submitted as part of the application for the operating license, to assure that the information included in the report contains the latest information developed. This submittal shall contain all the changes necessary to reflect information and analyses submitted to the Commission by the licensee or prepared by the licensee pursuant to Commission requirement since the submission of the original USAR or, as appropriate, the last updated USAR.

   b. The updated USAR shall be revised to include the effects of: all changes made in the facility or procedures as described in the USAR; all safety analyses and evaluations performed by the licensee either in support of approved license amendments or in support of conclusions that changes did not require a license amendment; and all analyses of new safety issues performed by or on behalf of the licensee at Commission request.

   c. These procedures shall contain the requirements for USAR changes submitted through the design change process as well as the licensing processes.

2. Perform a detailed review of a representative sample of recently implemented design changes and verify that a sample of required USAR changes have been made as required by approved procedures. The updated information shall be appropriately located within the update to the USAR.

3. Verify the recent USAR update was properly submitted to the NRC and contained the following attributes:

   a. Replacement pages for changed sections were provided as part of the submittal.

   b. The submittal is certified by an authorized officer of the corporation.

   c. Changes are clearly indicated (i.e., revision bars, dated pagination, etc.).

Documents Reviewed		
Document Number	**Title**	**Rev**

NUCLEAR OVERSIGHT
AUDIT CHECKLIST

Persons Contacted	
Name (Last Name, First Name)	**Position**

Results		
SAT ☐	UNSAT ☐	CAP #(s)

Verified through document review and interviews that [Plant Y] Engineering Design Control is meeting the requirements 10 CFR 50.71(e) Maintenance of records, making of reports

- The recent USAR update was properly submitted to the NRC (Ref: AR01461561).

- FP-E-SAR-01 provides governance and direction for USAR Changes and includes provisions for Periodic updating and describes the types of the changes required that meet requirements of 10 CFR 50.71(e).

- Confirmed that a sample of recent changes and the evaluations are incorporated into the USAR.

- A sample of recent LARs were reviewed and found to meet the requirements of FP-R-LIC-07.

No issues identified.

R-03	Regulatory Requirements Source/Requirements to Verify

R-03 10 CFR 50.72/73 - Reportability

Would any degraded or unanalyzed equipment condition, or other condition, identified during the audit have required reporting to the NRC under 10 CFR 50.72 or 10 CFR 50.73, and was such report made in the required time frame?

Auditor Instructions

Verify all issues identified during the course of this audit against the reporting requirements of 10 CFR 50.72/73.

Sample and review any 50.72 or 50.73 reports submitted by the site related to plant design issues for compliance and accuracy.

Documents Reviewed		
Document Number	**Title**	**Rev**

NUCLEAR OVERSIGHT
AUDIT CHECKLIST

Persons Contacted	
Name (Last Name, First Name)	**Position**

Results		
SAT ☐	UNSAT ☐	CAP #(s)

Document reviews determined that [Plant Y] is meeting 10 CFR 50.72/73 for Reportability. No degraded or unanalyzed equipment condition, or other condition, identified during the audit that required reporting to the NRC under 10 CFR 50.72 or 10 CFR 50.73.

No issues were identified.

R-04	Regulatory Requirements Source/Requirements to Verify

R-04 Vendor Interface Program

Generic Letter 90-03, Relaxation of Staff Position in Generic Letter 83-28, Item 2.2 part 2 "Vendor Interface for Safety-Related Components"

...an adequate vendor interface program should include:
(a) A program with the NSSS vendor as described in the VETIP, which covers all the safety-related components within the NSSS scope of supply. This program should include provisions for assuring receipt by the licensee/applicant of all technical information provided by the NSSS vendor; and
(b) A program of periodic contact with the vendors of other key safety-related components not included in (a) above.

For vendor interface, licensees and applicants shall establish, implement and maintain a continuing program to ensure that vendor information for safety-related components is complete, current and controlled throughout the life of their plants, and is appropriately referenced or incorporated in plant instructions and procedures. Vendors of safety-related equipment should be contacted and an interface established. Where vendors cannot be identified, have gone out of business, or will not supply information, the licensee or applicant shall assure that sufficient attention is paid to equipment maintenance, replacement, and repair, to compensate for the lack of vendor backup, to assure reliability commensurate with its safety function (GDC-1). The program shall be closely coupled with action 2.2.1 (equipment classification). The program shall include periodic communication with vendors to assure that all applicable information has been received. The program should use a system of positive feedback with vendors for mailings containing technical information. This could be accomplished by licensee acknowledgement for receipt of technical mailings. It shall also define the interface and division of responsibilities among the licensee and the nuclear and non-nuclear divisions of their vendors that provide service

NUCLEAR OVERSIGHT
AUDIT CHECKLIST

on safety-related equipment to assure that requisite control of and applicable instructions for maintenance work on safety-related equipment are provided.

The programs in (a) above should provide for the licensee or applicant to receive all updates to instruction and maintenance manuals, technical information bulletins, revised test procedures, and updated replacement parts information. The programs should include provisions that ensure the licensee receives all such vendor issued information pertinent to its safety-related equipment.

The program described in (b) above is not intended to be as extensive as the program in (a), but is intended to be a good faith, documented effort to periodically contact the vendors of key, safety-related components (such as auxiliary feedwater pumps, batteries, inverters, battery chargers, cooling water pumps, valve operators, diesel generators, and safety-related electrical switchgear), not already included in the interface program of (a) above, to obtain any technical information applicable to this equipment.

Documented periodic contact via telephone is sufficient. It is expected that a reasonable and prudent review of operating experience, availability of vendor information, and component safety significance using insights obtained from generic or plant specific probabilistic risk analyses will yield a set of component vendors that will make up each licensee's program. In the event that vendors have gone out of business, cannot be identified, or will not supply information, the licensee or applicant should implement or continue to maintain a program that will assure that sufficient attention is paid to equipment maintenance, replacement, and repair to compensate for the lack of vendor backup such that equipment reliability commensurate with its safety function is assured.

Generic Letter 90-03, Relaxation of Staff Position in Generic Letter 83-28, Item 2.2 Part 2 "Vendor Interface for Safety-Related Components" (Supplement 1)

The purpose of this supplement is to clarify the examples of key safety-related equipment listed on page 2 of Generic Letter 90-03. Subsequent to issuing the generic letter, we discovered that due to an administrative error diesel generators and safety-related electrical switchgear were inadvertently deleted from the list of examples of key, safety-related components on page 2 of the generic letter. Therefore, the last paragraph on page 2 of the generic letter should be modified to include these two items.

Auditor Instructions

1. Measures are established to periodically contact vendors of key safety-related components to obtain current technical information.

2. Measures are established to review and incorporate relevant VETIP information into station procedures.

3. Measures are established to control and maintain VETIP records.

4. Through interview or document review, verify the following:
   a. The existence of a vendor or vendor document database or list that requires periodic vendor re-contact to ensure vendor changes are maintained current for safety-related components under the NSSS scope of supply and key safety-related

NUCLEAR OVERSIGHT
AUDIT CHECKLIST

components. Key safety-related components include, but are not limited to, applicable components of the diesel generators, electrical switchgear, auxiliary feed water pumps, batteries, inverters, battery chargers, cooling water pumps, and valve operators.

b. Vendors are solicited on a periodic basis to ensure vendor changes are maintained current for key safety-related equipment and issues identified during these solicitations are appropriately resolved.

c. When vendors have gone out of business, cannot be identified, or will not supply information, verify that the licensee implemented or maintains a program to ensure that sufficient attention is paid to equipment maintenance, replacement, and repair to compensate for the lack of vendor backup such that equipment reliability commensurate with its safety function is assured.

d. Re-contact vendor results are documented and maintained in controlled files.

e. For engineering design changes verify that new vendors or new vendor information is incorporated into the VETIP.

5. Through document review, select a sample of recently updated vendor documents (vendor technical information or manuals) and verify that for each:

a. The updated information was reviewed by appropriate personnel.
b. The review appropriately identified relevant impacts to station documents.
c. Station documents were appropriately revised or tracked for revision.

6. Through document review, select a sample of engineering changes (modifications) and verify:

a. Changes to vendor documents are reviewed to determine if a corresponding change is needed to station procedures.
b. Procedure revisions required as a result of changes to vendor documents are properly implemented or tracked for implementation.
c. Through document review, verify relevant vendor advisories are incorporated into the vendor document.

7. Through document review verify the following:

a. Vendor documents are controlled and updated at required locations.
b. Vendor documents do not contain conflicting or superseded records.
c. Vendor documents are complete with no missing sections.

Documents Reviewed		
Document Number	**Title**	**Rev**
Results		
SAT ☐	UNSAT ☐	CAP #(s)

NUCLEAR OVERSIGHT
AUDIT CHECKLIST

Document reviews and interviews determined that [Plant Y] is meeting requirement associated with maintaining vendor manuals up-to-date to meet requirements of Generic Letter 90-03.

- Fleet procedure FP-E-VEN-01 provides overall governance while site procedure 1382 discusses the specific approach that [Plant Y] will actively solicit vendors for new information associated with Safety-Related Technical manuals and use of the EC doc-only change process for updating Vendor Tech manuals.

- The last two Work Orders (0516620, 0496558) were reviewed to determined adequacy and timeliness of site efforts. GAR actions track engineering reviews and doc only ECs are used to revise VTMs. WOs are scheduled for 1Q of each year (PMID 10080-06) to meet the annual requirement to solicit vendors for changes to safety-related technical manuals.

No issues identified.

T-01	Regulatory Requirements Source/Requirements to Verify

T-01 TS 5.5.9 Technical Specifications (TS) Bases Control Program

See TECH-SPECS, current revision, for requirements.

Auditor Instructions

Validate that the site Technical Bases Control Program is adhering to the Tech Spec requirements.

Documents Reviewed		
Document Number	**Title**	**Rev**

Persons Contacted	
Name (Last Name, First Name)	**Position**

Results

SAT ☐	UNSAT ☐	CAP #(s)

Interviews and Document reviews indicated that TS 5.5.9 Technical Specifications (TS) Bases Control Program is being maintained as required as verified through document reviews and interviews.

NUCLEAR OVERSIGHT
AUDIT CHECKLIST

- Corporate directive CD 5.10 provides established high level direction for the program requirements while fleet procedures FP-E-CLB-01 and FP-R-LIC-07 provide adequate guidance to maintaining technical bases and the process for changes.
- Procedures also contain provisions to ensure that the bases are maintained consistent with the USAR.
- A sample of recent license amendment requests found the site is following process requirements.

See checklist element R-01 for related 10 CFR 50.59 screenings for audit results in reviewing site's process to ensure that changes to bases without prior NRC approval is adequately screened and evaluated.

T-02	Regulatory Requirements Source/Requirements to Verify

T-02 TS 5.6.3 CORE OPERATING LIMITS REPORT (COLR)

See TECH-SPECS, current revision, for requirements.

Auditor Instructions

1. Validate that the site Technical Bases Control Program is adhering to the Tech Spec requirements.
2. Verify the core reload design change meets requirements of QA-III.
3. Verify applicable calculations supporting the COLR.
4. Verify the applicable USAR updates are made for core reloads.
5. Confirm COLR and any mid-cycle revisions or supplements, are provided upon issuance for each reload cycle to the NRC.

Documents Reviewed		
Document Number	**Title**	**Rev**

Persons Contacted	
Name (Last Name, First Name)	**Position**

Results		
SAT ☐	UNSAT ☐	CAP #(s)

OR-01	Other Requirements (USAR, Procedures) Source/Requirements to Verify

OR-01 - IT Quality Services Interface Agreement

(CD 1.1 Section 4.9)

NUCLEAR OVERSIGHT
AUDIT CHECKLIST

Written agreement between NSPM/Xcel Energy Nuclear Department and the NSPM non-nuclear organization providing the service to establish an approved Quality Assurance Program. The agreement creates an extension of the NSPM Quality Assurance Topical Report to address the services provided by the outside organizations.

(CD 1.1 Section 5.1.5)
The NSPM Quality Assurance Program consists of: QATR, Corporate Directives, Headquarter Department Procedures, Fleet Program/Process Descriptions, Fleet Procedures, Interface Agreements, and each generating site's implementing documents. The relationship between these documents and responsible organizations is displayed in Attachment 3.

(CD 1.1 Section 5.3.4)
Delegation involving Xcel Energy organizations outside of NSPM/Xcel Energy Nuclear Department supplied safety or quality related services should be accomplished through:
1. Quality Services Interface Agreements, signed by representatives of both organizations and Nuclear Oversight. The Interface Agreements should establish appropriate quality assurance expectations and controls for supplied services from outside the NSPM/Xcel Energy Nuclear Department, equivalent to the actions that would be taken to dedicate the same service from a commercial grade supplier. Attachment 5 is an example Agreement that illustrates typically expected content. Some agreements may require different content or approval signatures.

(CD 1.1 Section 5.3.5)
Nuclear Department organizations requiring supplied services that require the use of an approved Quality Assurance Program SHALL work with the interfacing organization to develop an agreement on the interface scope. The agreement SHALL identify which Quality Assurance Program elements are in the scope of the agreement and which parties are responsible for implementing those elements.

(CD 1.1 Section 5.3.6)
A written interface agreement SHALL be generated and follow the Interface Agreement maintenance and review process. A sample agreement can be found in Attachment 5. (See FP-BS-IFA-01, "Interface Agreement Maintenance and Review")

(CD 1.1 Section 5.3.10)
Quality Service Interface Agreements are an extension of the Quality Assurance Topical Report, and NSPM Nuclear Department organizations using interface agreements should review each revision of the Quality Assurance Topical Report to determine if the changes affect the agreement parameters. (See FP-BS-IFA-01, "Interface Agreement Maintenance and Review")

See the Current revision of the IT Quality Services Interface Agreement

Auditor Instructions

Documents Reviewed		
Document Number	**Title**	**Rev**

NUCLEAR OVERSIGHT
AUDIT CHECKLIST

Documents Reviewed		
Document Number	**Title**	**Rev**

Persons Contacted	
Name (Last Name, First Name)	**Position**

Results		
SAT ☐	UNSAT ☐	CAP #(s)

O-01	Optional Scope Source/Requirements to Verify

O-01 FP-NO-AUD-01 Requirement – Picture of Excellence

Evaluate if there were any challenged tenets of the Xcel Energy Nuclear Performance Model (the picture of Excellence Nuclear Leaders Handbook).

Auditor Instructions

Evaluate if there were any challenged tenets of the Xcel Energy Nuclear Performance Model (the picture of Excellence Nuclear Leaders Handbook).

Documents Reviewed		
Doc #	**Title**	**Rev**
INPO 12-012	Traits of a Healthy Nuclear Safety Culture	1
INPO 15-005	Leadership and Team Effectiveness Attributes	0
NA	The Xcel Energy Nuclear Performance Model (Picture of Excellence Nuclear Leaders Handbook)	NA

Persons Contacted	
Name (Last Name, First Name)	**Position**

Results		
SAT ☐	UNSAT ☐	CAP #(s)

Auditors collectively reviewed identified issues and engagement with site staff and management to determine any weaknesses with traits or behaviors associated with a healthy Nuclear Safety Culture (INPO 12-012). One improvement opportunity and one positive observation was discussed at the audit exit.

Two traits impacted by the same behaviors are discussed below:

NUCLEAR OVERSIGHT
AUDIT CHECKLIST

Leadership Safety Values and Actions Personal (Area for Attention)

LA.6 – Roles Responsibilities and Authorities: Leaders clearly define roles, responsibilities, and authorities to ensure nuclear safety. (Traits of a Healthy Nuclear Safety Culture)

Behavior: Leaders ensure roles, responsibilities, and authorities are clearly defined, understood, and documented.

Personal Accountability (Area for Attention)

PA.2 – Job Ownership: Individuals understand and demonstrate personal responsibility for the behaviors and work practices that support nuclear safety. (Traits of a Healthy Nuclear Safety Culture)

Behavior: Individuals take ownership for the preparation and execution of assigned work activities.

Audit Example (–):The behaviors associated with the Engineering department understanding and implementation of the Software Quality Assurance program, the site's behaviors in managing plant modification approval without completed SQA Plans, and enforcement of SQA program standards by the program owners have challenged design bases regulatory requirements with installed and turned-over equipment. While no other technical consequence has been identified from this audit, the continuation of these behaviors invite future risk to configuration control and challenges to safety. From the Picture of Xcellence the behaviors identified run counter to the Work Practices and Supervisory Oversight enablers of an Engaged, Thinking Organization.

Continuous Learning (Positive Observation)

CL.2 - Self-Assessment: (Traits of a Healthy Nuclear Safety Culture)

Behavior: The organization values the insights and perspectives assessments provide.

Audit Example (+): Engineering and Business System management and staff engagement demonstrated support for the learning opportunities that the NOS audit provided. The audit team experienced strong willingness by management and staff to understand the NOS concerns and provide constructive responses to aid in issue development.

NUCLEAR OVERSIGHT
AUDIT CHECKLIST

O-02	Optional Scope Source/Requirements to Verify

O-02 FP-NO-AUD-01 Requirement - Operating Experience

Review internal and external Operating Experience per the guidance of FP-NO-AUD-01.

Auditor Instructions

Verify through document review, interviews, and/or direct observations that internal and external Operating Experience is being evaluated.

Documents Reviewed		
Document Number	**Title**	**Rev**
FP-NO-AUD-01	Internal Audits	9
FP-PA-OE-01	Operating Experience Program	25
Results		
SAT ☐ UNSAT ☐	CAP #(s)	

Form retained in accordance with retention schedule identified in Procedure XX
Retention: 10 years

2016 NUCLEAR OVERSIGHT FLEET DESIGN CONTROL (A-DES-[PLANT X]) TABLE OF CONTENTS

Audit Title: Design Control
Location(s): Nuclear Plant sites
Entrance Date: Exit Date: 7/15

Audit Scope:

This audit verifies [Plant X] compliance and effectiveness in implementing design control requirements established by 10 CFR 50 to ensure safety-related and important to safety structures, systems, and components will perform their designed functions to protect the health and safety of the public during normal and accident conditions. Requirements include 10 CFR 50, Appendix B; NSPM-1, Quality Assurance Topical Report (QATR); NQA-1, 1994; 10 CFR 50.59; Business Systems Quality Services Interface Agreement; Operating License Specifications and Limitations; and the Updated Safety Analysis Report (USAR).

The following program elements were audited:

- Design Control
  - Design Inputs (incl. Bases)
  - Design Analysis (incl. calculations)
  - Design Verification
  - Design Changes (incl. ECs, 50.59)
  - Design Interface
  - Inspections
  - Post-MOD/Design Testing
- Temporary Modifications
- Software Quality Assurance
- Organization/Responsibilities
- Training and Qualifications
- Procedures and Document Control
- Corrective Action
- Records

Summary of Results:

Nuclear Oversight (NOS) concludes that Plant X is effectively implementing the Design Control program elements to regulatory requirements as stated above with two exceptions; one in the area of Software Quality Assurance (SQA) and another with Vendor Manual Control.

The audit identified two findings, one deficiency, with a total of 25 total NOS identified Action Requests issued.

I) (Finding) Software Quality Assurance (SQA) program requirements have not been adequately implemented during the engineering change process to assure that software/firmware controls are properly implemented to assure configuration control is maintained for computer software potentially impacting safety. Changes to computer software affecting Systems, Structures and Components (SSCs) are required to comply with Quality Assurance Topical Report (QATR) section B.17 "Computer Software Control" and Company Directive (CD) 14.1, "Software Quality Assurance." Specifically, NOS identified issues such as missed SQA requirements in approved and installed modifications; installing equipment without evaluating SQA requirements; and not approving an SQA plan prior to Engineering Change (EC) approval. In addition, the site identified similar issues during review of ECs from the NOS Stop Work Order (Corrective Action (CAP) 01527964).

II) (Finding) The station's control of safety-related Vendor Technical Manuals (VTM) has not been effective in ensuring they remain current to preclude the potential for use of incorrect information as required by 10 CFR 50 Appendix B Criteria VI, "Document Control"; QATR B.14 "Document Control"; and the [Plant X] commitment to NRC Generic Letter 90-03, Relaxation of Staff Position in Generic Letter 83-28, Item 2.2 Part 2 "Vendor Interface for Safety-Related Components" (CAP 01528261).

III) (Deficiency) Fleet Engineering has not provided adequate oversight of the IT function/services provided to the Nuclear organization, and implementation of Engineering Change processes fleet-wide, to ensure Software Quality Assurance (SQA) requirements of the Quality Assurance Program are being met. Fleet Engineering is responsible both for nuclear department oversight of Information Technology (IT) services provided by Xcel Energy Business Systems through the Business Systems Quality Services Interface Agreement, and for oversight of performance of design activities at the Xcel Energy nuclear sites (CAP 01528970).

Findings/Deficiencies:

I)   **(Finding) SQA Program Requirements Not Met (CAP 01527964)**

Software Quality Assurance (SQA) program requirements have not been adequately implemented during the engineering change process to assure that software/firmware controls are properly implemented to assure configuration control is maintained for computer software potentially impacting safety. Changes to computer software affecting Systems, Structures and Components (SSCs) are required to comply with Quality Assurance Topical Report (QATR) section B.17 "Computer Software Control" and CD 14.1, "Software Quality Assurance." Specifically, NOS identified issues such as missed SQA requirements in approved and installed modifications; installing equipment without evaluating SQA requirements; and not approving an SQA plan prior to EC approval. In addition, the site identified similar issues during review of ECs from the NOS Stop Work Order (CAP01526022).

Quality Assurance, procedure, and other requirements include:

- QATR, B.17, "Computer Software Control," states that "NSPM establishes and implements provisions to assure that computer software used in applications affecting safety is prepared, documented, verified and tested, and used such that the expected output is obtained and configuration control is maintained." To meet these provisions, the Company commits to compliance with the requirements of NQA-1-1994, Supplement 11S-2 "Supplementary Requirements for Computer Program Testing" and Subpart 2.7 "Quality Assurance Requirements of Computer Software for Nuclear Facility Applications."
- NQA-1-1994, Subpart 2.7, Section 6.1, "Plan(s) for Software Quality Assurance," requires that a plan for assuring software quality assurance shall be in existence for each new software project at the start of the software life cycle, or for procured software when it enters the purchaser's organization.
- Quality Services Interface Agreement Between Nuclear Business unit and Business Systems (IT), which states that Business Systems (IT) is responsible for assuring that the site's Software Quality Assurance Program requirements are implemented and enforced successfully within their respective units.
- FP-E-MOD-02 "Engineering Change Control," section 5.13.4 requires that if the design change adds a software product, then the requirements of

the SQA Program found in FP-IT-SQA-01 "Software Quality Assurance (SQA) Program" should be applied. FP-IT-SQA-01, section 5.5.8 requires a SQAP for SQA Level 1 and 2 software. However, for plant installed equipment the site Software Review Board has generally allowed use of the Engineering Change and Work Management processes as the SQA controlling procedures in lieu of the SQA process.

The following issues were identified:

1) SQA requirements are not defined for EC024306 (CAP01527537).
   Some Software Quality Assurance (SQA) requirements for Level 2 digital equipment installed under EC24306 "Replace U1 & U2 Train A Service Building UPS System" are not defined in engineering change design documents (QF0525) or through a SQA plan (QF1508) as required by NQA-1-1994, Subpart 2.7, section 6.1 "Plan(s) for Software Quality Assurance" and FP-IT-SQA-01, "Software Quality Assurance Program."

2) EC installed digital component without evaluating SQA requirements (CAP01527417).
   Engineering Equivalency (EC 24422) "OBSOLETE TIMER RELAY FOR AFW PUMPS—LUBE OIL" authorized an equivalent replacement of the AFW PMP AUX L-O PMP TIME DELAY RELAYs (62/121E-19, 62/211E-6, 62/221E-7, 62/111E-2), which are digital components containing programmable software/firmware, without determining the SQA classification level and associated SQA requirements as required by FP-IT-SQA-01 "Software Quality Assurance (SQA) Program."

3) Site NOS identified that R10 SQA requirements were not met (CAP01526022).
   Redundant R-10 Particulate Monitoring Channel modification did not implement Software Quality Assurance requirement during the engineering design process for EC 25498. As a result, NOS issued a Stop Work Order for [Plant X] Design Engineering.

4) EC22499 lacks SQA Review and Approval (CAP01527398).
   The Engineering Change for the Instrument Air Compressor Replacement (EC022499) lacks the documented reviews and approval of the Software Quality Assurance (SQA) Plan as required by NQA-1, Subpart 2.7, "Quality Assurance Requirements of Computer Software for Nuclear Facility Applications," and Corporate Directive (CD) 14.1, "Software Quality Assurance." The EC lacks documented reviews of the Software Product Manager and the department supervisor or manager as required by FP-IT-SQA-06, "The Software Planning Phase." Contributing to the shortfall is that the EC addresses SQA requirements within the EC (MOD) process yet bypasses using the forms/process associated with the fleet SQA procedures (e.g., QF1508, Software Quality Assurance Plan).

5) EC 11780-Approved before SQAP Completion (CAP01527540).
   The engineering change for "Unit 1 Heater Drain Tank Pump Drive Replacement" (EC011780) was approved without an approved (QF1508) "Software Quality Assurance Plan." The SQAPs are required prior to MOD approval per FP-IT-SQA-06, "The Software Planning Phase." The EC package in SharePoint contained a QF1508 for the Rosemount 5300 Transmitter and a QF1508 for the Siemens GEN IV VFD; however, neither was signed by the Software Product Manager or the SQA Lead.

6) SQA requirements potentially not met (CAP01492962, NOS identified, issued 09/11/2015).

Software Quality Assurance (SQA) requirements for the 121 and 122 SPENT FUEL POOL WIDE RANGE LEVEL INDICATOR (2852502 and 2852402) may have not been fully met. This SQA Level 2 software was certified using the vendor's SQA activities in EC 23555 (Fukushima Response Spent Fuel Pool Instrumentation); however, a comparison to validate that the vendors' Software Quality Assurance Plan (SQAP) meets the intent of the NSPM site's SQA Program documentation and control requirements for the approved classification level was not performed.

As a result of response to the SQA Stop Work Order (CAP01526022), the site identified the following issues:
- DAR01526838, EC23796 Design Description does not include results of QF1501
- DAR01526839, SQA not properly addressed in EC 23092, GEN AVR
- DAR01526703, EC 20576 and Level 3 Software Configuration Control
- DAR01526967, HDTP Project SQA Classification
- DAR01527098, SQA Status in EC23914 QF0525 is open ended
- DAR01527103, SQA, EC21498, Radio Fleet Software, No QF1508 found

Consequence: The Software Quality Assurance Program provides assurance that the software product meets requirements such as Specifications, Testing, Cyber Security, Impact Analysis, Configuration Management, and Disaster Recovery. Not clearly establishing SQA requirements through the SQA program creates a risk that computer software used in applications affecting safety will not be adequately prepared, documented, verified and tested, and used such that the expected output is obtained and configuration control is maintained as required by QATR B.17.

Insight: The SQA Program Owner (IT) has not consistently established and reinforced high standards for the effective implementation of the SQA program when important software is impacted by Engineering Changes. Use of the EC process in lieu of the established SQA plan document (QF1508) requires individuals to assure SQA requirements are met without the benefit of tools developed and available to assure all requirements are included, creating a vulnerability to meeting requirements. This vulnerability was exacerbated by a lack of understanding in the Engineering organization of the requirements of the SQA program and how those requirements were different from the EC process, a misunderstanding that was not previously identified and addressed. NOS previously identified shortfalls in SQA implementation for the SFP level instrumentation project at both sites (CAP01492962 at [Plant X], CAP01492694 at [Plant Y]), which were not evaluated sufficiently to identify the broader performance issue. Interviews indicated that business systems and engineering invoked procedural provisions that permitted use of alternate processes (EC and WO processes) in lieu of SQA controlling procedures to establish and control SQA requirements for plant installed digital equipment in the engineering change and work order processes. As a result, responsible engineers relied on the SQA leads and Software Product Managers (SPMs) to provide the needed input on the requirements and to informally ensure the requirements are properly documented into design documents. Individuals also indicated a lack of alignment on responsibilities associated with ensuring software quality assurance requirements are identified, implemented, and verified as required by the SQA program and the EC process.

Note: [Plant Y] received a similar NOS Finding on 6/20/2016 (CAP01525686).

II **(Finding) Safety-Related Vendor Technical Manual Control Deficiencies (CAP01528261)**

The station's control of safety-related Vendor Technical Manuals (VTM) has not been effective in ensuring they remain current to preclude the potential for use of incorrect information as required by 10 CFR 50 Appendix B, Criteria VI, "Document Control"; QATR B.14 "Document Control"; and [Plant X]'s commitment to NRC Generic Letter 90-03, Relaxation of Staff Position in Generic Letter 83-28, Item 2.2 Part 2 "Vendor Interface for Safety-Related Components." Specifically, some changes to safety-related VTM's are not being evaluated or implemented and VTM changes identified by the Periodic Vendor Contact Program have not been screened for evaluation for nearly two years.

Quality Assurance, procedure, and other requirements include:

- 10 CFR 50 Appendix B, Criteria VI. Document Control: Measures shall be established to control the issuance of documents, such as instructions, procedures, and drawings, including changes thereto, which prescribe all activities affecting quality. These measures shall assure that documents, including changes, are reviewed for adequacy and approved for release by authorized personnel and are distributed to and used at the location where the prescribed activity is performed. Changes to documents shall be reviewed and approved by the same organizations that performed and approved the original review unless the applicant designates another responsible organization.
- QATR B.14, Document Control: NSPM establishes and implements provisions to specify the format and content (see Appendix B for procedures), and control the development, review, approval, issue, use, and revision of documents that specify quality requirements or prescribe activities affecting quality or safe operation to assure the correct documents are being employed.
- Generic Letter 90-03, Relaxation of Staff Position in Generic Letter 83-28, Item 2.2 Part 2 "Vendor Interface for Safety-Related Components": An adequate vendor interface program should include a program of periodic contact with the vendors of key safety-related components.

[Plant X] has committed to implement a periodic vendor contact program to meet the requirements of Generic Letter 90-03 (Passport COMM 01194155-01). FP-E-VEN-01 "Vendor Manual Control" implements requirements for compliance with the Vendor Re-Contact Program.

Vendor Manual Control Deficiencies identified:

1) The site has not performed VTM initial screening for approximately 30 Safety-Related VTM changes received since August 2014 and identified by the Periodic Vendor Re-Contact Program as required by FP-E-VEN-01 "Vendor Manual Control," section 5.3. FP-E-VEN-01, "Vendor Manual Control," step 5.3.3, states "The initial Screening should be completed within 14 days of receipt." Failure to perform initial screening results in the organization not knowing the potential risk present by the VTM changes.

2) The site has not performed VTM revision reviews for 25 of 38 Safety-Related VTM changes identified by the Periodic Vendor Re-Contact Program as required by FP-E-VEN-01 "Vendor Manual Control," section 5.4. The revision

reviews not performed are during the period of August 2012 to August 2014. FP-E-VEN-01, "Vendor Manual Control," step 5.4.1, states the responsible engineer assigned to conduct the review of VTM should complete the review within 60 days. Failure to perform revision reviews results in the organization not knowing the potential risk present by the VTM changes.

3) A sampling of 2014–2015 Engineering Change's (EC) affecting Safety-Related Vendor Manuals revealed that in 5 of 8 instances the Safety-Related Vendor Manuals have not had the changes implemented. The proposed document changes have been prepared, reviewed, and approved; however the GAR that implements the change through typing, final review, and distribution has not been completed. Examples include:

- EC 21390, Steam Line Radiation Monitoring System VTM (GAR01473207)
- EC 21838, Sequential Events Recorder/Annunciation System VTM (GAR01477703)
- EC 25227, Okonite and Rockbestos Cables VTM (GAR01497155)
- EC 25598, AFW Pump Turbine VTM (GAR01475972)
- EC 21916, Aux Bldg Supply Steam Exclusion Supply Dampers VTM) (GAR01388428-01)

Consequence Not maintaining current safety-related VTMs increases the risk of using incorrect information when performing activities such as maintenance and technical evaluations on safety-related Structures, Systems, or Components (SSCs), which could impact their ability to perform a specified safety function(s).

Insight: Based on discussion with the design engineering manager and the VDC/VRC, the organization did not recognize the potential risk presented to safety-related SSCs as a result of not performing initial screening and reviews of changes made to safety-related VTMs. Review of the Non-CAP Action Request actions associated with this issue revealed that approximately 40 actions are past their due date and some are in INPROG status. This indicates a lack of adherence to FP-E-VEN-01 "Vendor Manual Control" and FP-PA-ARP-03 "Non-CAP Action Request Process" requirements for establishing and completing assigned actions by the due date.

In addition, NOS identified one other related issue in the Vendor Re-Contact Program that supports the NOS Finding:

Vendor Re-Contact Program Docs Not Placed Into Records: The Periodic Vendor Contact program documents, such as vendor contact reports, status-transmittal reports, and monthly vendor document comparison report publication transmittals have not been placed into records since August 2015 as required by section 7.0 of SWI ENG-20 (CAP01528253).

> **Consequence:** Not having documents placed into records risks the ability to retrieve these records when required.

> **Insight:** The design engineering manager and the VDC/VRC indicated that recent personnel transitions challenged the program performance and oversight.

III. **(Deficiency) Corporate Oversight of SQA Program Is Inadequate (CAP01528970)**

Fleet Engineering has not provided adequate oversight of the IT function/services provided to the Nuclear organization, and implementation of

Engineering Change processes fleet-wide, to ensure Software Quality Assurance (SQA) requirements of the Quality Assurance Program are being met. Fleet Engineering is responsible both for nuclear department oversight of Information Technology (IT) services provided by Xcel Energy Business Systems through the Business Systems Quality Services Interface Agreement, and for oversight of performance of design activities at the Xcel Energy nuclear sites.

Nuclear Oversight identified shortfalls in SQA implementation (SQA Plans) at both sites during the Spent Fuel Pool (SFP) Instrumentation modification special audits performed in September 2015 (CAP01492694, CAP01492962).

An extent of condition performed by [Plant Y] in response to CAP01492694 identified an additional seven Computer Work Orders (CWOs) not being completed as required for implemented software (CAP01492685); however, the underlying organization performance was not identified and there was not an extent of condition at [Plant X].

As part of the SFP Instrumentation Audit exit in September 2015 and distribution of the audit report in October 2015, and through periodic leadership updates, corporate leadership was briefed that the identification of shortfalls in both sites' SQA implementation for the SFP instrument modification was an indication of a potential broader vulnerability.

Despite the indications of potential vulnerabilities in implementing SQA program requirements during the EC process, corporate oversight in IT and Engineering was insufficient to self-identify the broader issue and ensure the sites addressed the underlying causes to assure ongoing effective implementation of the SQA program.

A Software Quality Assurance Plan (sometimes referred to as the SQAP) provides assurance that the software product meets requirements such as Cyber Security, Impact Analysis, Configuration Management, and Disaster Recovery. Not having an established SQAP prior to engineering change approval and turnover creates a risk that computer software used in applications affecting safety will not be adequately prepared, documented, verified and tested, and used such that the expected output is obtained and configuration control is maintained as required by QATR B.17.

As part of the Design Control Audit, NOS subsequently identified the following:

- Three (3) additional instances of missing SQA Plans for approved MODs (CAP01525102, DAR01525106, and CAP01525452). An NOS Finding was issued to MNGP in June 2016 (CAP01525686), highlighting SQA requirement concerns.
- Following inadequate site response to the NOS Finding on SQA at [Plant Y], NOS identified shortfalls in the application of SQA requirements to the R-10 modification, which was approaching turnover. NOS subsequently issued a Stop Work order (CAP01526022) in June 2016. The site performed an extent of condition for in-process ECs and found six site-identified instances of SQA requirements shortfalls within the past year (DAR01526838, DAR01526839, DAR01526703, DAR01526967, DAR01527098, and DAR01527103).

- An NOS Finding was issued in July 2016 (CAP01527964). The audit identified five additional instances of missing SQA documentation for approved, active, modified, or closed MODs since May 2014 (DAR01527537, DAR01527417, DAR01526022, DAR01527398, and DAR01527540).

Consequence: The failure to identify and resolve the performance gap in SQA performance is contrary to INPO Performance Criteria CO.3-9, which states that: "The corporate staff ensures performance gaps are resolved and increases monitoring in response to declining performance or when performance assessments from diverse inputs conflict."

Insight: Corporate leadership did not follow up on warning signs of gaps in SQA implementation in the Engineering Change process. Issues were addressed on an individual basis without adequate consideration for potential organizational performance gaps and consequences. Those performance gaps identified by NOS included lack of alignment on roles and responsibilities for SQA program implementation, and use of less rigorous means for assuring SQA program requirements were met.

IV. (Other CAPS) The NOS Design Control Audit Team identified the following less significant issues.

Drawing not updated as required by FP-DE-DSG-01: A physical change was made to the safety-related plant without updating plant drawings as required by FP-DE-DSG-0, "Conduct of Design Engineering." A work order only modification (WMOD25938) removed Floor Grating Baffles for the D2 ZG System under work order WO00525131. In July 2015, the site removed a Tuttle and Bailey Style T-60 louver or Ventilation Grille from a Supply Ventilation Duct on the Unit 1 Diesel Rooms Ventilation System (D2 Room) without updating plant drawing NF-39609-10 (CAP01527644).

> **Consequence:** Not adequately and timely updating and maintaining the system design consistent with design and licensing basis documentation negatively impacts configuration control.

> **Insight:** The Design Engineer indicated a controlled document showing the louvers could not be located at the time of the EC design input phase. However, site planners were able to locate drawing NF-39609-10, which reflected the louvers and subsequently included the drawing in work order task WO00525131.

Doc quality issues with Design Input forms: Review of two MOD Type Engineering Changes (ECs) identified several errors and omissions in the application of procedures for Design Input Consultations, Form QF0515A "Design Input Checklist" and Form QF0516 "Design Input Consultation" contrary to FP-E-MOD-04, "Design Inputs." The ECs were EC18840, SI Test Line Valve for LLRT Unit 1 and EC23207, Replace Unit 2 Automatic Voltage Regulator (CAP01527645).

> **Consequences:** Lack of procedural adherence with design control process requirements could result in missing design inputs necessary to assure applicable regulatory requirements and licensing design basis are correctly translated into design outputs.

> **Insights:** Design Eng Supervisor indicated that individuals are not always exhibiting good attention to detail and is an on-going problem. He further indicated the need to do more thorough quality reviews.

Recommended PMs for U2 AVR not established or tracked: A tracking action has not been established to implement a Preventive Maintenance (PM) strategy for the recently installed Automatic Voltage Regulator (AVR) on PI Unit 2 (EC23207) contrary to the Design Description and the "Design Input consultation" (QF0516) for Preventive Maintenance. The Automatic Voltage Regulator (AVR) Instruction Manual states that both the 24VDC power supplies and 48VDC power supplies should be replaced on a 6–7-year cycle. Similarly, ventilation filters inside the cabinet should be replaced on a 2–3-year cycle. (CAP01527621)

> **Consequence:** Not establishing a PM strategy for installed plant equipment increases the risk of failure of power supplies, resulting in a loss of the AVR and Generator/Turbine Trip.

> **Insight:** Responsible Engineer indicated that the project focused on immediate need to install and commission AVR to support operation.

50.59 Screening did not specify if UFSAR change is required: The 50.59 screening (#5013) for EC 24172, "Revise AOV Calculation 01110-C-021 to reduce the maximum allowed supply air pressure," did not indicate if a UFSAR change is required or not required by checking the applicable boxes on form QF-0501. This is contrary to FG-E-SE-03, "50.59 Resource Manual," section 5.3.4, which states that whether a 10 CFR 50.59 evaluation is required or not, state whether any UFSAR changes are required (CAP01527297).

> **Consequence:** The proposed activity being screened may require UFSAR information to be updated to maintain the most current information. This updated information is required to be provided to the NRC in accordance with 10 CFR 50.71(e).

Review of ECN impact on 50.59 not documented: Engineering Change Notice (ECN) 24617 did not adequately document the impact review of 10 CFR 50.59 screening and evaluation that were prepared and approved for the original EC17584 as required by FP-E-MOD-08 "Engineering Change Notices" (DAR01527528).

> **Consequence:** Not thoroughly documenting the 50.59 impact reviews risks not having sufficient information for subsequent approvers to verify the results do not change the conclusion of the 50.59 screening and evaluation.

> **Insights:** Responsible engineer indicated that he had performed a review and concluded the 50.59 screening and 50.59 evaluation were not impacted but believed citing the 50.59 screening was sufficient. Responsible engineer indicated that the ECN would have benefited by the inclusion of Evaluation in the Passport attribute.

A Document-Only Change (EC 530) to a SR Vendor Manual had a Technical Review performed versus a Design Verification: A Document-Only Change (EC 530) to Safety-Related Vendor Manual, "REACTOR COOLANT GAS VENT SYSTEM" (NX- 21384-1) had a Technical Review performed versus a Design Verification. This is contrary to FP-E-MOD-07, "Design Verification and Technical Review," which requires design verification be performed when 10 CFR 50, Appendix B, Criteria III, Design Controls apply. Criteria III requires that measures shall be provided for verifying design adequacy such as performance of design reviews (DAR01527497).

> **Consequence:** Not meeting design verification requirements poses the risk that a change implemented to a Vendor Technical Manual (VTM) would not receive expected rigor required by 10 CFR 50 Appendix B, Criteria III, Design Control.

Insights: The program engineer indicated he was not aware VTMs contain a safety classification and thus thought that a technical review of the change would be adequate.

Qualification Question for ECN 50.59 Impacts Reviews: FP-E-MOD-08 "Engineering Change Notices" steps 5.3.1.5 through 5.3.1.7 assign responsibility to the Responsible Engineer (RE) to review 50.59 documents, determine if ECN changes impact these documents, and document results of this review under the ECN Passport attribute. As the qualifications for an RE do not necessarily include 50.59 Screening and 50.59 Evaluation, there can be no assurance that RE will be knowledgeable and qualified to the extent needed to perform this responsibility. NOS found one example where the RE for ECN document impact reviews for EC17584, RHR MOV Logic Change, had 50.59 screening qualifications yet lacked the 50.59 evaluation qualifications commensurate for reviewing the 50.59 evaluation (Evaluation 1112) (CAP01527588).

Consequences: An individual performing a 50.59 impact review without the requisite 50.59 process knowledge may not recognize potential 50.59 changes.

Insights: Qualification requirements for ECN driven 50.59 document reviews are not clearly defined in FP-E-MOD-08. Engineering Supervisors indicated that Responsible Engineers are managed such that they are qualified to perform ECNs and 50.59 screenings. The Fleet Design Engineering CFAM and the Design Engineering Supervisor indicated that to effectively perform the ECN impact review on a 50.59 evaluation, the review would require the qualification for the 50.59 evaluation.

MMods do not meet criteria to be called minor: Four minor modifications (MMODs) do not meet the criteria for "Minor" as outlined by the Fleet procedure FP-E-ECR-01, "Engineering Change Request," The four MMODs each exceeded the number of engineering programs, disciplines, or departments permitted by the criteria and two of the modifications exceeded the total cost stipulation (CAP01527062).

Consequence: Processing a large or complex modification as a MMOD may diminish the project controls and oversight, potentially affecting the quality or increasing the risk of errors.

Insights: The Design Engineering Manager indicated that when the MMOD criteria was first established not as many separate programs needed to be considered, adding the procedure FP-E-ECR-01 may need to be updated to reflect current standards.

EC11780-Approved before SQAP Completion Detailed Description: The engineering change for "Unit 1 Heater Drain Tank Pump Drive Replacement" (EC011780) was approved without an approved fleet form QF1508, "Software Quality Assurance Plan." An approved Software Quality Assurance Plan (SQAP) is required for software products classified as Level 1 or 2 prior to MOD approval per FP-IT-SQA-06, "The Software Planning Phase." The EC SharePoint folders contained two QF1508 forms for two different modification related software products but neither were signed by the Software Product Manager or the SQA Lead (DAR01527540).

Consequence: The Software Quality Assurance Plan (sometimes referred to as the SQAP) provides assurance that the software product meets requirements such as Cyber Security, Impact Analysis, Configuration Management, and Disaster

Recovery. Not having an established SQAP prior to engineering change approval and turnover creates a risk that computer software used in applications affecting safety will not be adequately prepared, documented, verified and tested, and used such that the expected output is obtained and configuration control is maintained as required by QATR B.17.

Insights: Responsible Engineer stated that he missed the SQAP requirements in the EC process. Engineering Supervisor stated that there appears to be an organizational problem with Level 2 SQA implementation as documented in ARs cross referenced to CAP01526022.

MMods do not meet criteria to be called minor: Four minor modifications (MMODs) do not meet the criteria for "Minor" as outline by the Fleet procedure FP-E-ECR-01, "Engineering Change Request." The four MMODs each exceeded the number of engineering programs, disciplines or departments permitted by the criteria and two of the modifications exceeded the total cost stipulation (CAP01527062).

Consequence: Processing a large or complex modification as a MMOD may diminish the project controls and oversight potentially affect the quality or increasing the risk of errors.

Insights: The Design Engineering Manager indicated that when the MMOD criteria was first established not as many separate programs needed to be considered, adding the procedure FP-E-ECR-01 may need to be updated to reflect current standards.

SQA requirements are not defined for EC024306: Some Software Quality Assurance (SQA) requirements for Level 2 digital equipment installed under EC24306 "Replace U1 & U2 Train A Service Building UPS System" are not defined in engineering change design documents (QF0525) or through a SQA plan (QF1508) as required by NQA-1-1994, Subpart 2.7, section 6.1 "Plan(s) for Software Quality Assurance" and FP-IT-SQA-01, "Software Quality Assurance Program." Minimum SQA Elements as defined in FP-IT-SQA-0, step 5.5.8 that were missing in the EC design documents include an Impact Analysis, a Contingency Plan, a Disaster Recovery Plan, and Media Control requirements (DAR01527537).

Consequence: The Software Quality Assurance Plan (sometimes referred to as the SQAP) provides assurance that the software product meets requirements such as Cyber Security, Impact Analysis, Configuration Management, and Disaster Recovery. Not having a complete and approved SQAP that documents all the required elements risks that software used in applications affecting safety will not be adequately prepared, documented, verified and tested, and used such that the expected output is obtained and configuration control is maintained as required by QATR B.17, Software Quality Assurance.

Insights: Responsible Engineer indicated that he relied on the assigned Software Product Manager/Systems Engineer to determine what Software Quality Assurance documentation was needed. The Software Product Manager/Systems was not available for interview.

EC22499 lacks SQA Review and Approval: The Instrument Air Compressor Replacement modification (EC022499) lacks the documented reviews and approval of the Software Quality Assurance (SQA) Plan as required by NQA-1, Subpart 2.7, "Quality

Assurance Requirements of Computer Software for Nuclear Facility Applications," and Corporate Directive (CD) 14.1, "Software Quality Assurance." The digital controller for the new instrument air compressors is classified as SQA Level 2 and is Critical Digital Asset-related, requiring a SQA Plan with the associated documented reviews and approvals. In lieu of a SQA Plan, the EC addresses SQA requirements within the EC-MOD process bypassing the use of forms and associated process governance provided by fleet SQA procedures. However, the EC process lacks specific guidance to ensure the plan meet all the required elements while obtaining the necessary reviews and approvals (DAR01527398).

Consequence: Increased risk that the engineering change (MOD) does not address all required SQA elements, which ensures high quality software; the qualified Software Product Manager and supervisor/manager reviews and Software Product Manager Approval provide additional assurance that quality requirements are met before proceeding with plant modification.

Insights: The Site IT Manager indicated that reviews of the program and procedures, with the current allowance of using the MOD and WO processes, has recognized that there are missing responsibilities defining how the SPM remains engaged in EC design development (which would otherwise be part of process using the SQA program procedures and the QF1508, "Software Quality Assurance Plan").

EC installed digital component without evaluating SQA requirements: Engineering Equivalency (EC24422) "Obsolete Timer Relay for AFW Pumps—Lube Oil" installed equivalent digital replacement AFW PMP AUX L-O PMP TIME DELAY Relays (62/121E-19, 62/211E-6, 62/221E-7, 62/111E-2), without determining the SQA classification level and associated SQA requirements as required by FP-IT-SQA-01 "Software Quality Assurance (SQA) Program" (DAR01527417).

Consequence: Not meeting Software Quality Assurance (SQA) Program requirements risks the software used in applications affecting safety will not be prepared, documented, verified and tested, and used such that the expected output is obtained and configuration control maintained as required by QATR B.17 Computer Software Control.

Insights: The design engineer who prepared the EC indicated that he was not aware of the Software Quality Assurance (SQA) requirements of FP-IT-SQA-01 and thus did not request a consultation from the SQA/IT Department.

2015 SQA Program Self-Assessment Not Completed: In 2015, the site did not complete a self-assessment of the Software Quality Assurance Program (SQAP) as directed by the Software Review Board (SRB) to meet requirements of CD 14.1, "Software Quality Assurance" and FP-IT-SQA-02, "Software Review Board." Business Systems closed the action (SAR01392707) by crediting an NOS SQA concern (CAP01492962) discovered during the 2016 NOS Fukushima Audit. The SRB was not informed of closing the SA action using this basis in lieu of performing a snapshot evaluation. Self-assessment and NOS audit are to be independent functions and defined separately in the QATR (DAR01527111).

Consequence: Not performing self-assessments misses opportunities to detect compliance or programmatic deficiencies such as issues related to procedure use and adherence or the quality of the SQA deliverables. The last SQA self-assessment was completed in 2013 (SAR01275560).

Insights: IT Manager indicated the Assignee and "Owed To" made an inappropriate decision in crediting the NOS audit and NOS discovery of SQA issues to satisfy as the SRB self-assessment. The action owed to indicated that the action may have been closed due to the belief that the extent of condition evaluation of the NOS CAP reviewed a sufficient sampling of the SQA documents to constitute a process review. NOS identified a similar issue during the recent [Plant Y] NOS Design Control Audit (CAP01525174).

1R-10/2R-10 Modification turned over inappropriately for TS compliance: Modification EC25498 had been turned over (partially) and accepted by Operations and credited for Technical Specification compliance when 1R-10/2R-10 lacks the same control room alarms capabilities as R11/R12. Specifically the 1R-10/2R-10 Sample Pump Low Flow Alarm control room alarm required for operability is not available in the control room. Site issued DAR01525558 on June 18, 2016, for a concern that not all R10 alarms are indicated in the Control Room and paperwork identifies that four Alarms that are present in the Control room for 1R11/2R11 that are not present in the Control room for 1R-10/2R-10 (Paper not in motion, Low Flow, Torn Paper, Low Paper). The evaluation for the AR indicated that the alarms would be installed prior to final turnover. (DAR01527412)

> **Consequence:** Potential for non-compliance with Plant License for Tech Spec 3.4.16 Condition "B," required containment radionuclide monitor inoperable, if 1R10/2R10 is credited for Tech Spec Compliance when 1R11/2R11 is removed from service.
>
> **Insight:** Discussion with the Engineering, Projects, and Operations personnel who were present during the EC Modification partial turnover indicated that they considered the lack of Alarm Function and eventually that was the basis for partial turnover. Discussion with a senior member of OPS Management indicated the reason why Operations accepted the modification without the low flow alarm feature was because Tech Spec 3.4.16 Condition B is a 30-day LCO. Operators perform rounds once every 12 hours; as such any low flow condition on 1R10 / 2R10 would be detected by Operations on their normal rounds in the Control rod Drive room.

1R10/2R-10 channels check pot not meet TS Definition: The surveillance procedures that perform 1R-10, 1R-11 2R-10, and 2R11 channel checks do not perform an alternate instrument comparison as defined by the technical specialization of Channel Check. With the recent addition of 1R10/2R10 (EC025498), an independent instrument channel measuring the same parameter could potentially be performed comparing 1R-10 to 1-R11 (2R-10 to 2R-11). However, recently revised operations log procedures (SP1001B, SP1001C, SP1001D and SP2001B, SP2001C, SP2001D) that perform the channel checks only direct separate operational checks for each. EC25498, "U1 & U2 - R-10 Particulate Radiation Monitoring Channel Project (Redundant to R-11 for Modes 1–4) To Prevent TS LCO Entries," installed R-10 as a redundant rad monitor measuring the same parameter as R-11. (DAR01527474)

> **Consequence:** Not performing a channel check comparison misses the opportunity to potentially identify a failing radiation monitor as well as not meeting the technical specification SR 3.4.16.1 to Perform CHANNEL CHECK every 12 hours.

Insights: The Radiation Monitoring System Engineer indicated he believed a comparison between R-10 and R-11 channel indication because the Radiation Monitors are different models, have different flow rates, the detectors have different sensitivities. As a result, the System Engineer determined that a deviation acceptance criterion between channels R-10 and R-11 was not possible.

Portable lead shielding potentially impacting HELB Function: Lead shielding on 735′ AUX Building GRID Location N.9/7.7 potentially could impact HELB Function and lacks formal documentation. (DAR01527022)

Issues include:

- No formal 50.59 screening required for temporary lead shielding left in the plant for greater than 90 days per H41.
- The Access Control shielding log (1078) does not contain the shielding package (769) as required by RPIP 1716.
- The Lead Shielding Cart exceeds aspect ratio 2-1 and not seismically restrained as required by H41 and 5AWI 8.5.0, "Housekeeping and Material Condition." Potential concern is that the cart exceeds the aspect ratio of 2-1 and is not seismically restrained in accordance with H41 which may allow the cart to tip and impede the safety-related High Energy Line Break pressure relief function of DOOR 184.

Consequence: Failure to maintain an accurate and up-to-date Shielding Log may result in questions regarding current plant configuration.

Insights: Longstanding unidentified issue, interview with RP Supervisor indicated the Temporary Lead Shielding had been in place for > 29 years.

CAP01527022: OPS Status notes do not consider Operability: Operations SRO review of CAP01527022, "Lead shielding potentially impacting HELB Function," did not address all effects on operability as required by FP-OP-OL-01, "Operability/ Functionality Determination." The NOS identified issue found Lead Shielding Package located on the 735′ elevation of the AUX Building lacks documentation and an evaluation of potential impacts to nearby HELB door 184. The basis for the Operability determination is lacking information relative to the non-conforming condition (DAR01527274)

Consequence: a degraded or nonconforming condition and its effect on safety-related SSCs has not been evaluated as required, with a potential to result in a loss of safety function.

Potential for loose material, Safeguards Cooling Water Pump Area: NOS audit team field walk-down identified a potential for loose material in the Safeguards Cooling Water Pump Area, which is a Critical Drainage area as specified by Site Internal Flooding AWI (5AWI 8.9.0). The Engineering Change to install plastic magnetically attached bump covers over two safety-related 121 MD Cooling Water Pump Temperature controllers in 2014 did not consider flooding concerns and the impact on flooding calculation ENG-ME-458 (DAR01526806).

Consequence: Failure to maintain Plant equipment in accordance with seismic and loose material control requirements has the potential to affect nuclear safety.

Insight: Document review of the QF0506 Modification Classification form indicated only the 1st question was answered prior to the Design Manager downgrading from safety-related to a WO only–DOC-type EC. Document review indicated the rest of the form's questions (2–10) on potential program or system interactions were not answered, specifically seismic or internal flooding.

TMOD TAG Log not completed as required when Tags installed: The tag log section of QF0540, "TMOD Control Form" for three of the five active TMODs in the ACTIVE T-MOD (file kept in main control room) had not been completed for installed TMOD tags contrary to FP-E-MOD-03, "Temporary Modifications." FP-E-MOD-03, section 5.4.2 states that after tags are installed, "Update the T-MOD tag log on the QF0540." The information to be logged on QF0540 includes the tag number, location installed by, and installed date. The three ACTIVE TMODS that had incomplete QF0540 tag logs are EC026946, Cooling Tower Vibration Switch Bypass; EC027092, D5/D6 High Outlet GAS Temperature Alarm disable; and EC025991, Drain Sump B to Sump A (CAP01527102).

> **Consequence:** Failure to maintain an accurate and up-to-date active TMOD file may result in questions regarding current plant configuration.

> **Insights:** The duty STA in the work control center was not aware of a reason why the tag log section had not been completed. Work order tasks that installed the TMOD tags do not have steps to update the QF0540 tag log. NOS identified a similar issue during the recent [Plant Y] NOS Design Control (CAP01525638).

NOS ID: Recurring TMOD not closed as required by FP-E-MOD-03: The Engineering Change for Recurring TMOD for 11/12/21/22 Battery Room temporary cooling (EC19801) is currently in "APPROVED" versus "CLOSED" status contrary to FP-E-MOD-03, "Temporary Modifications," FP-E-MOD-03, step 5.8.3 states that "After the procedure is issued, the EC should be advanced to 'CLOSED' status and the EC and supporting documents should be forwarded to the group responsible for records retention following final approval of the associated procedure." Site procedures C37.15, TP1636, and TP1637 provide guidance for installing and removing the TMOD for 11/12/21/22 Battery Room temporary cooling (DAR01527075).

> **Consequence:** EC for TMOD not at status as specified may lead to loss of the record of the EC, as the EC is not turned into records until the EC is taken to CLOSED status.

> **Insights:** Document review did not identify any action or trigger to advance the EC19801 to Closed Status when the installation and removal steps for the reoccurring TMOD 19801 were incorporated into site procedures for summer and winter Checklists (TP-1636 and TP-1637).

NOS Design Audit—Tech Specialist Insights: An external Software Quality Control (SQA) technical specialist that participated in the 2016 [Plant X] NOS Design Control audit identified several insights contrasting the SQA programs at [Plant X] with Tennessee Valley Authority (TVA) practices. The technical specialist briefed the Business Systems Director of Application and Development, Site IT Manager, the Design Engineering Manager, Site NOS Supervisor, and design engineering supervisors on July 1. The NOS audit staff reviewed the insights and determined that they do not constitute concerns with Design Control regulatory compliance or performance effectiveness. The insights are captured in the AR SharePoint folder (DAR01527437).

INPO Traits of a Healthy Nuclear Safety Culture

Observations related to INPO traits were noted that both met expectations (+) and did not meet expectations (-). The observations are identified with a brief statement below.

One trait impacted by the same behaviors discussed below:

Work Processes *(Area for Attention)*

>**WP.3 Documentation:** The organization creates and maintains complete, accurate, and up-to-date documentation.

>Behavior: Design documentation, procedures, and work packages are complete, thorough, accurate, and current.

>Audit Example (–): Implementation of design control processes resulted in missed recognition of shortfalls in meeting SQA regulatory requirements. NOS observed the site using procedurally allowed deviation from adherence to detailed SQA fleet processes, as has been discussed; that practice brought added risk of missed requirements as executed. Mechanisms that should have ensured SQA requirements were addressed were not effective at detecting shortfalls. As a result, Design control processes have not consistently ensured complete, thorough, and accurate design documentation for plant changes (CAP01527964). In addition, deficiencies in maintaining safety-related vendor technical manuals do not support this nuclear safety culture trait (CAP01528261).

Leadership and Team Effectiveness Attributes:

Observations related to INPO attributes were noted that did not meet expectations (-). The observations are identified with a brief statement below. Two attributes were challenged by the behaviors discussed below:

>**Leadership Effectiveness**

>**LE.9 Achieving Sustainable Results:** Leaders achieve sustainable results by shaping organizational behaviors and by relentlessly reinforcing high standards to achieve ownership and accountability for performance.

>**Team Effectiveness**

>**TE.5 Leadership Team Decision-Making:** Teams effectively leverage the collective talent of diverse team members to make sound decisions.

>Audit Example (–): By going outside of SQA fleet process as approved by the Software Review Board, a reduction in involvement of software quality assurance expertise occurred in the design control process. For example, SQA program requires the assigned, qualified Software Product Manager document review and approval of SQA plans, and in some cases, the SQA program requires additional dedicated SQA plan reviews, including documented independent reviews, prior to EC approval. These reviews have not been occurring or have not been documented in all cases. While no other technical consequence has been identified from this audit, the continuation of these behaviors invites future risk to configuration control and further challenges to compliance and potentially safety.

Picture of Xcellence

From the Picture of Xcellence, the behaviors identified above run counter to enablers Work Practices, Verification and Validation, and Supervisory Oversight. In addition, identified weaknesses with SQA do not support Right Picture: Knowing what "Xcellence" looks like.

Prepared by: _____   **Date:**
              Lead Auditor

Approved by:_____   **Date:**
              NOS Program Manager

NUCLEAR OVERSIGHT
AUDIT REPORT

QA Program Elements:

Criterion	Title	Results
I	Organization	Effective
II	Quality Assurance Program	Effective
III	Design Control	Effective w/Concerns
V	Instructions, Procedures and Drawings	Effective w/Concerns
VI	Document Control	Effective w/Concerns
XVI	Corrective Action	Effective
XVII	Quality Assurance Records	Effective w/Concerns
QATR C.1/C.2	Self-Assessment	Effective w/Concerns
QATR B.17 / NQA-1 Subpart 2.7 / CD 14.1	Computer Software Control	Ineffective

Regulatory Elements:

Source	Requirement	Results
10 CFR 50.59	Changes, Tests, and Experiments	Effective w/Concerns
10 CFR 50.71(e)	Maintenance of records, making of reports [USAR updates]	Effective w/Concerns
10 CFR 50.72/73	Reportability	Effective
GL 83-28	Vendor Equipment Technical Information Program	Ineffective
NQA-1, 1994	Quality Assurance Requirements for Nuclear Facilities Applications	Effective
Tech Spec	5.5.12 TS Bases Control Program	Effective
Tech Spec	5.6.5 Core Operating Limits Report	Not Evaluated this Audit

Audit Personnel:
[AAA], Audit Team Lead
[BBB], Auditor
[CCC], Auditor
[EEE], Auditor
[FFF], Site Assessor
[GGG], Technical Specialist, I & C Design Engineer, [loaned alternate utility]
[HHH], Technical Specialist Peer, Principle Design Engineer, [Plant Y]

NUCLEAR OVERSIGHT
AUDIT REPORT

Supporting Information

Corrective Action Documents:

	Description	Level
01527964	NOS Finding: SQA Program Requirements Not Met	B
01528261	NOS Finding: Vendor Manual Control Deficiencies	B
01527062	MMods do not meet criteria to be called minor	C
01527102	TMOD TAG Log not completed as required when Tags inst	C
01527297	50.59 Screening UFSAR change	C
01527588	Qual question for ECN 50.59 Impact Review	C
01527621	Recommended PMs for U2 AVR not Established	C
01527644	Drawing not updated as required by FP-DE-DSG-01	C
01527645	Doc quality issues with Design Input forms	C
01528253	Vendor Re-Contact Program Docs Not Placed Into Records	C
01528970	Corp Oversight of SQA Program Inadequate (Fleet)	C
01526806	Potential for loose material, Safeguards Clg Water Pmp Rm	DAR
01527022	Lead shielding potentially impacting HELB Function	DAR
01527075	Recurring TMOD not closed as required by FP-E-MOD-03	DAR
01527111	2015 SQA Program Self-Assessment Not Completed	DAR
01527274	CAP01527022 OPS notes do not consider Operability	DAR
01527398	EC22499 lacks SQA Plan Review and Approval	DAR
01527412	1R-10/2R-10 inappropriately accepted Turnover for TS	DAR
01527417	EC installed digital comp without evaluating SQA requirements	DAR
01527437	NOS Design Audit - Tech Specialist Insights	DAR
01527474	1R10/2R-10 channels check pot not meet TS Definition	DAR
01527497	Doc-Only Change to a SR VTM did not have a Design Verify	DAR
01527528	Review of ECN Impact on 50.59 not documented	DAR
01527537	SQA requirements are not defined for EC024306	DAR
01527540	EC 11780 Approved before SQAP Completion	DAR

NUCLEAR OVERSIGHT
AUDIT REPORT

Personnel Contacted: (attended entrance; contacted; attended exit)

Name	Entrance	Audit Contact	Exit	Department
	x	NA	x	Site NOS Manager
	x	NA	x	Site NOS Supervisor
	x	NA		[Plant Y] Principal Design Engineer
	x	NA		Tech Specialist, Design I&C, TVA
	x	NA	x	NOS Auditor
	x	NA	x	NOS Auditor
	x	NA	x	NOS Auditor
	x	NA	x	NOS assessor
	x	NA		NOS Audit Supervisor
	x	x	x	Acting Site Design Eng Manager
	x	x	x	Design Engineering CFAM
	x	x		Director, Business Applications
		x		Acting Site Nuclear Projects Manager
		x	x	Site IT manager
		x		Regulatory Affairs
		x		Design Engineering
		x		Design Engineering
			x	Plant Manager
			x	Bus Support Director
		x	x	EFIN Engineering
		x		IT Analyst
		x		IT Analyst
		x		Design engineering
		x		IT Supervisor
		x		Design Engineering
		x		IT Analyst
		x		Project Manager
		x		NOS Assessor
		x		Planner
		x		IT Manager
		x		NOS Assessor
		x		Ops Procedure Writer
		x		PRA engineer
		x		Design Engineer
		x		Engineering Supervisor
		x		Engineering Supervisor
		x		Technical Training Supervisor

NUCLEAR OVERSIGHT
AUDIT REPORT

Name	Entrance	Audit Contact	Exit	Department
		x		Engineering Supervisor
		x		Shift Manager
		x		Design Engineering Analyst
	x	NA	x	NOS Programs Manager
		NA	x	NOS Audit Supervisor
		x		General Manager Fleet Engineering
		x		System Engineer

NUCLEAR OVERSIGHT
AUDIT REPORT

Documents Reviewed:

Document Number	Title	Rev#
71111.18	Plant Modifications	NA
Calc 01110-C-021	AOV COMP LVL CALC FOR VLVS CV-31423 & CV-31457	1
10 CFR 73.58	Safety/Security Interface Requirements for Nuclear Power Reactors	NA
1ES-1.2	Transfer to Recirculation	22
2016-01-001	NOS Observation Report	NA
2C15	Residual Heat Removal System Unit 2	49
5AWI 3.1.1	Return to Power After Reactor Trip	19
5AWI 3.19.3	Software Quality Assurance Requirements	14
5AWI 3.3.1	Tech Spec Change 5awi 3.3.1 Review Committee	17
5AWI 4.10.0	Technical Specification Bases And Technical Requirements Manual Control Programs	14
5AWI 4.9.0	Safety Analysis Reports	20
C.2	QATR Self Assessments	9
CALC	ENG-CS-285 (Evaluation of 130 Ton Turbine Crane)	0
CALC	ENG-CS-105 (Seismic Evaluation of Turbine Building Overhead)	0
Calc ENG-EE-145	UPS Inverter Panel Load Study	3C
Calc ENG-ME-094	FHA Combustible Loading Calculation	5B
Calc PI-216-06P5	PIPESTRESS ANALYSIS, RH SYSTEM, U2, PART 5	0
Calc PI-216-06P7	PIPESTRESS ANALYSIS, RH SYSTEM, U2, PART 7	0
Calc PI-996-125-M01	Instrument Air Flow and Pressure Drop Analysis	0
Calc S-11164-041-01	Design of Foundation for 121 TSC Recall Cabinet	0
CAP01182488	12 Circ. Water Pump lock out and RX Trip	NA
CAP01335068	EC19784/19786 Control Room Recorder Replacement	NA
CAP01355310	SCT turned Maintenance Rule a(2) yellow (at risk)	NA
CAP01463399	Digital Upgrade not evaluated in 50.59 for EC 22499	NA
CAP01463411	EC 22499 – Lack of rigor in performing Digital Upgrade	NA
CAP01473259	Deficiency in 50.59 Eval. for Inst Air Comp mod.	NA
CAP01477432	Add the equipment installed under EC23419 (SFPI)	NA
CAP01492962	SQA requirements potentially not met	NA
CAP01526022	SQA Stop Work Order	NA
CD 1.1	Quality Assurance Program Structure	12
CD 14.1	Software Quality Assurance	10
CD 14.3	Cyber Security Program Directive	2
CD 3.3	Performance Assessment Program	8
CD 5.1	10 CFR 50.59 Implementation	4
CD 5.10	Design Basis Document Standard	2

NUCLEAR OVERSIGHT
AUDIT REPORT

Document Number	Title	Rev#
CD 5.20	Fleet Modification Program	5
CD 5.24	Reactor Vessel Integrity Program Standard	4
CD 5.29	Conduct of Engineering-Fix It Now Team (E-FIN)	3
CD 5.31	Configuration Management	1
Contract 36205	Master Nuclear Services Agreement	NA
Contract 55104	Engineer of Choice Contract: [AAA], Inc.	0
Contract 55107	Engineer of Choice Contract: [BBB]	0
CWO	Computer Work Orders: 01379024, 01418331, 01476619, 01509928, 01498437, 01457523, 01376156, 01353679, 01473385, 01353680, 01378008, 01471608, 01498253, 01500183, 01498792, 01511337, 01512583, 0497829, 01513598, 01494274, 01505497	NA
CWO Search	CWO search 12/1/2014-6/14/2016	NA
DAR01526703	EC 20576 and Level 3 Software Configuration Control	NA
DAR01526838	EC23796 Design Description does not include results of QF1501	NA
DAR01526839	SQA not properly addressed in EC 23092	NA
DAR01526967	HDTP Project SQA Classification	NA
DAR01527098	SQA Status in EC23914 QF0525 is open ended	NA
DAR01527103	SQA EC21498 Radio Fleet Software No QF1508 found	NA
DBD SYS-08	Design Bases Document For The Reactor Protection System	9
DBD SYS-35	Cooling Water System (CL)	13
DPR	Renewed Facility Operating License June 27, 2011	NA
EC00374	UPRATE / UPGRADE OF TURBINE BUILDING OVERHEAD CRANES (MOD 04PC01)	MOD
EC00530	ADD TARGET ROCK PLUNGER DEFECT INFO TO RCGVS TECH MAN. NX-21384-1 and TARGET ROCK LETTER NUMBER NID05069 AND PROBLEM REPORT PR-046	0
EC08754	EVALUATE THE RELAY & CABLE SPREADING COMPARTMENT FOR INTERNAL FLOODING	EVAL
EC11780	UNIT 1 HEATER DRAIN TANK PUMP DRIVE REPLACEMENT	MOD
EC13720	ALTERNATE SOURCE TERM LICENSING BASES	NA
EC16295	(PRI 80) D5/D6 FUEL RACK POSITION LVDT CONVERTER REPLACEMENTS	MOD
EC17584	(PRI 96.5) TORNADO MISSILE PROTECTION FOR CC SYSTEM FUNCTION AND ASSOCIATED CC SYSTEM PIPING FOR THE 122 SFP HX	MOD
EC18107	PARTIAL TURNOVER OF SR D5 FUEL RACK POS LVDT CONVERTERS	NA

NUCLEAR OVERSIGHT
AUDIT REPORT

Document Number	Title	Rev#
EC18108	PARTIAL TURNOVER OF D6 FUEL RACK POSITION LVDT CONVERTERS	NA
EC18109	D5 FUEL RACK POSITION LVDT CONVERTER REPLACEMENTS	NA
EC18391	(PRI 97.3) REPLACING TMODS 14665, 15510 AND 15102 WITH PERMANENT MOD	MOD
EC18840	SI TEST LINE VALVE FOR LLRT UNIT 1	MOD
EC19476	COMPLETE "AS BUILT" DRAWINGS AND AEL AFTER COMPLETION OF EC 16295	NA
EC19784	CR RECORDERS: RECORDER REPLACEMENT EC	MOD
EC19786	CR RECORDERS: NETWORK EC	MOD
EC19801	SUPPLEMENTAL COOLING FOR THE 11, 12, 21, AND 22 BATTERY ROOMS RECURRING TMOD	MOD-TMOD
EC20244	DOOR MODIFICATIONS AND UPGRADES	MOD-MMOD
EC20402	CREATE DC LOAD LIST CONTROLLED DOCUMENT	NA
EC20403	UNIT 2 HEATER DRAIN TANK PUMP DRIVE REPLACEMENT	NA
EC20494	SUBSTATION ELECTRICAL EQUIPMENT ENCLOSURE (EEE) AND RELAY UPGRADE PROJECT	MOD
EC20576	UNIT 2 GENERATOR AND EXCITER REPLACEMENT	NA
EC21254	UNIT 1 GENERATOR STEP-UP TRANSFORMER (GSU) REPLACEMENT	MOD
EC21264	LOSS OF DC CONTROL POWER COMMON ENCLOSURE ANALYSIS FOR NFPA 805	EVAL
EC21470	REVISE TIME DIAL SETTINGS OF BKR CT11-1 OVERCURRENT RELAY	SPT
EC21496	DOC ONLY CHANGE TO ALLOW THE CC HX INLET CL VALVES TO REMAIN IN THE OPEN POSITION WHILE IN STANDBY.	1
EC21498	REPLACE PLANT RADIO SYSTEM	NA
EC21576	NFPA 805 - STATION FIRE DETECTORS - NFPA 805	NA
EC21622	MODIFY UNIT 1 GENERATOR STEP-UP TRANSFORMER (1GT) FIRE PROTECTION	MOD
EC21667	REPLACE PLANT TELEPHONE SYSTEM (INSIDE PROTECTED AREA)	NA
EC21790	RCP SEAL REPLACEMENT - UNIT 1	NA
EC21838	VTM UPDATE - U2 - NX-30023-25, U1 - NX-30023-67 - BOP ANNUN - TOGGLE SWITCH ASSOCIATED WITH IEE-2013-034-00; RELATED WO# 476081, SEE NOTES	DOC
EC22019	TEMPORARY COOLING FOR MCC 2M2 - RECURRING TMOD	MOD-TMOD
EC22196	CALCULATION FOR DETERMINING MINIMUM COMPONENT COOLING PUMP FLOW RATE	DOC

NUCLEAR OVERSIGHT
AUDIT REPORT

Document Number	Title	Rev#
EC22220	VC SYSTEM VENT DOCUMENTS	MOD-WMOD
EC22254	MODIFY RECORDER SCREENS INSTALLED PER EC11751 TO ALIGN WITH THE DIGITAL RECORDER PROJECT (EC19784) AND H3 STANDARD.	MOD-ECN
EC22499	INSTRUMENT AIR COMPRESSOR REPLACEMENT	MOD
EC22582	REVISION OF QF-0525 IN SUPPORT OF EC19786	NA
EC22664	DOOR GENERIC MODIFICATION	MOD-GMOD
EC22742	REVISION OF UNCERTAINTY CALCS IN SUPPORT OF EC 19784 (CONTROL ROOM RECORDER REPLACEMENT)	NA
EC23010	UNIT 2 CYCLE 28 CORE RELOAD MODIFICATION	GMOD
EC23205	INSTALL GRAYBOOT CONNECTOR ON CL STRAINER POWER SUPPLY CABLE TO FACILITATE STRAINER COVER REMOVAL DURING MAINTENANCE	EQV
EC23207	REPLACE UNIT 2 AUTOMATIC VOLTAGE REGULATOR	MOD
EC23353	TUBE PLUGGING ON 21 AND 22 FCU, COMP MEASURE FOR OPR 1410533	MOD-TMOD
EC23402	TUBE PLUGGING ON 24 FCU, COMP MEASURE FOR OPR 1410533	MOD-TMOD
EC23555	FUKUSHIMA RESPONSE SPENT FUEL POOL INSTRUMENTATION	MOD
EC23556	FUKUSHIMA SATELLITE PHONE COMMUNICATIONS	MOD
EC23586	FRE-FA-31, NFPA 805 FIRE RISK EVALUATION - A TRAIN HOT SHUTDOWN PANEL & AIR COMPRESSOR/AUXILIARY FEEDWATER ROOM	EVAL
EC23587	FRE-FA-32, NFPA 805 FIRE RISK EVALUATION - B TRAIN HOT SHUTDOWN PANEL & AIR COMPRESSOR/AUXILIARY FEEDWATER ROOM	EVAL
EC23664	SCREENHOUSE & D5/D6 HEATUP CALCULATIONS	NA
EC23673	BODY-TO-BONNET LEAK REPAIR OF HD-17-1	MOD-TMOD
EC23729	INSTALL BLANK FLANGE FOR CD-34043	MOD-TMOD
EC23818	SLOW DOWN CLOSURE OF DDCLP JACKET HX CV	MOD-WMOD
EC23906	UNIT 1 STEAM GENERATOR NARROW RANGE LEVEL UPGRADE	MOD
EC24172	REVISE AOV CALCULATION 01110-C-021 TO REDUCE THE MAXIMUM ALLOWED AIR SUPPLY SETTING TO 25 PSIG AS LIMITED BY THE SOV.	DOC
EC24173	CHANGE THE LO ALARM U2 GENERATOR HYDROGEN PRESSURE ALARM FROM 55 PSIG TO 42 PSIG.	NA
EC24248	EVALUATION OF D1/D2 ROOM TEMPERATURES FOR SUMMER CONDITIONS WITH A ROOM TEMP LIMIT OF123.7F (125F-1.3F)	EVAL

NUCLEAR OVERSIGHT
AUDIT REPORT

Document Number	Title	Rev#
EC24294	REPLACE THE SI MINIMUM RECIRC LINE FLOW TRANSMITTERS AND METERS	MOD-WMOD
EC24300	UPGRADE VICTOREEN PREAMPS/DETECTORS	NA
EC24306	REPLACE U1 & U2 TRAIN A SERVICE BUILDING UPS SYSTEM	NA
EC24307	REPLACE U1 & U2 TRAIN B SERVICE BUILDING UPS SYSTEM	NA
EC24352	D1/D2 FAN BLADE PITCH POSITIONERS TMOD	MOD-TMOD
EC24377	UNIT 1 GL08-01 VOID LOCATION 1RH-13 VENT	NA
EC24422	OBSOLETE TIMER RELAY FOR AFW PUMPS - LUBE OIL	EQV
EC24681	NI INTERMEDIATE RANGE RESCALING OF TRIP SETPOINTS FOR 1R29 BASED ON EOC SHUTDOWN DATA FROM 1R28 - TP 1840 WCAP-17911-P REV. 0 - AUGUST 2014.	SPT
EC24692	INSTALL AMPHENOL CONNECTOR FOR COOLING WATER STRAINER MOTORS	EQV
EC24758	RIGGING EVALUATION FOR CV-31127 ACTUATOR	EVAL
EC24759	XCEL SUBSTATION ENGINEERING & DESIGN MODIFICATION TO LOAD TAP CHANGER (LTC) CONTROL CIRCUIT AND SETPOINT CHANGE TO LTC VOLTAGE SETTING (PLANT IMPACT)	DOC
EC24841	EVALUATION OF FAULT CURRENT FOR D1 FAST START	EVAL
EC24881	ADD NSC-PIP-M-SLR-92, [PLANT X] UNIT 1 PIPE RUPTURE ANALYSIS CHEMICAL AND VOLUME CONTROL SYSTEM, TO PASSPORT	0
EC24897	REVISE THE 11 AND 12 RCP VIBRATION ALARM SETPOINTS.	SPT
EC24915	RCP SHAFT VIBRATION ALERT AND DANGER SETPOINT CHANGE	SPT
EC25055	REPLACE CURRENT AC POWERED DOOR STRIKES TO DC POWERED STRIKES	EQV
EC25150	UNIT 1 AND UNIT 2 HYDROGEN PEROXIDE INJECTIONS. (RECURRING T-MOD)	MOD-TMOD
EC25229	FMEA AND DIGITAL SME REVIEW FOR 22499 IA COMPRESSOR REPLACEMENT & CR5 RELAY SEISMIC QUALIFICATION	MOD-ECN
EC25250	RECONFIGURE UNIT 2 RCP #3 SEAL LEAKOFF LINES TO RCDT	MOD-MMOD
EC25251	EVALUATION OF ADDITIONAL SVS ON SR BATTERIES	EVAL
EC25283	CHANGE NORMAL POSITION OF VALVES VC-16-4 AND VC-16-5 TO NORMALLY OPEN	MOD-WMOD
EC25294	FIRE DOOR 62 CABLE LATCH MODIFICATION	MOD-WMOD

NUCLEAR OVERSIGHT
AUDIT REPORT

Document Number	Title	Rev#
EC25387	REPLACE 6" 1503WE POWELL VALVES WITH EQUIVALENT VALVES TO ADDRESS PART OBSOLESENCE AND POWELL CONFIGURATION CONTROL ISSUES	NA
EC25405	12 RCP SEAL FACE REPLACEMENT WITH MAYER GROOVE	MOD
EC25498	U1 & U2 - R-10 PARTICULATE RADIATION MONITORNG	NA
EC25574	RCP - MOVING THE RCS BOUNDARY FROM THE BACKSEAT OF THE PUMP TO THE NEWLY INSTALLED MAYER SEAL.	EVAL
EC25757	COOLING TOWER OIL PRESSURE SWITCH AND VIBRATION SWITCH CT 122 FAN 4 LUBE OIL, CT 123 FAN 2 VIBE SW,CT124 FAN 7 LUBE OIL, CT 124 FAN 12 VIBE SW	MOD-TMOD
EC25772	SERVICE AIR COMPRESSORS (INSTRUMENT AND STATION AIR) BRASS COMPRESSION FITTING TO SS COMPRESSION FITTING	MOD-WMOD
EC25936	UNIT 2 FAN COIL UNIT FACE REPLACEMENT	MOD-MMOD
EC25955	GL08-01 U2 RHR RECIRCULATION (2R29)	MOD
EC25973	MMOD TO REMOVE EMERGENCY LIGHTS FROM DC SYSTEM	MOD-MMOD
EC25975	U2 CONDENSATE / FEEDWATER SYSTEM TIME DELAY RELAY MODIFICATION	MOD
EC25991	DIRECTING SUMP B OVERFLOW TO SUMP A	MOD-TMOD
EC26048	REVIEW OF EXCEL SCAFFOLDING	EVAL
EC26157	AUXILIARY BUILDING PLC REPLACEMENT	MOD
EC26309	21 RCP SEAL FACE REPLACEMENT WITH MAYER GROOVE	MOD
EC26498	FABRICATE REPLACEMENT CH-51 CLEVIS HANGER	NA
EC26505	SET POINT CHANGE - SET FP-107-1 RELIEF VALVE TO 50PSIG. PER VTM, NX-27524-1 PAGES 745 & 747, AIR PRESSURE MAX 45PSIG. RELIEF VALVE SHOULD BE SET 5PSI ABOVE MAX SYSTEM AIR PRESSURE.	DOC
EC26547	LA-16703 VENT T-MOD. A LOOP SEAL CONDITION EXISTS FOR LA-16703. VENT TOP SIDE OF LA-16703 BY INSTALLATION OF A JUMMPER.	MOD-TMOD
EC26588	GL08-01 U1 RHR RECIRCULATION (1R30)	NA
EC26599	SET POINT CHANGE - SET FP-107-1 RELIEF VALVE TO 50 PSIG.	SPT
EC26792	ASSESSMENT OF MARGIN BETWEEN HIGHEST PREDICTED 54 EFPY FLUENCE AND FLUENCE USED TO GENERATE P-T LIMITS	EVAL
EC26875	AMPACITY EVALUATION FOR D1-D2 CABLES DUE TO HIGHER AMBIENT TEMPERATURE.	EVAL
EC26946	COOLING TOWER FAN VIBRATION SWITCH TMOD	MOD-TMOD

NUCLEAR OVERSIGHT
AUDIT REPORT

Document Number	Title	Rev#
EC26992	INSTALL SHOP FABRICATED TWO PIECE PACKING GLAND FOLLOWER ON 2VC-7-11.	MOD-TMOD
EC27092	DISABLE NUISANCE ALARMS FOR D5/D6 EXHAUST GAS HIGH TEMP ANNUNCIATOR (CONTROL ROOM BLACK BOARD) UNTIL THE ALARMS ARE FIXED2TE-6400H AND 2TE-5900K	MOD-TMOD
ENG-ME-244	CC Heat Exchanger TCV Position Range	0
ENG-ME-820	CL Hydraulic Analysis – LOOP, LOCA, and SEISMIC RESPONSE	1
FG-E-04	Engineering Roles And Responsibilities	7
FG-E-CAL-01	Fleet Guidance on Calculations	1, 7
FG-E-DWG-01	EC Document Changes and Creation of Associated SharePoint Folders	8
FG-E-ECR-01	Fleet Guidance on Engineering change Requests Using Passport	1
FG-E-SE-03	50.59 Resource Manual	5
FG-R-LIC-11	License Amendment Requests	7
FL-BIT-SQA-002F	Software Product Manager Training / Qualification Exam	0
FL-ESP-DES-014M	Modification Design Mentoring Guide	7
FL-ESP-DES-015M	Modification Implementation Mentoring Guide	8
FL-ESP-GEN-001M	Prepare or Review Engineering Calculations Mentoring Guide	9
FL-ESP-GEN-002M	Prepare/Review 50.59 Screening Mentoring Guide	9
FL-ESP-GEN-003M	Engineering Evaluations Mentoring Guide	6
FL-ESP-GEN-007M	Prepare/Review Engineering Specification Mentoring Guide	8
FL-ESP-GEN-008M	Equivalency Evaluation Mentoring Guide	8
FL-ESP-GEN-010M	Engineering Change Prepare/Review Mentoring Guide	8
FL-ESP-GEN-014M	Setpoints Mentoring Guide	8
FL-ESP-ORT-029G	New Engineer Indoctrination Guide	3
FL-ESP-ORT-036G	NAD Engineering Indoctrination JFG	4
FL-ESP-PGM-069M	Software Quality Assurance (SQA) Lead	1
FL-ESP-TPD	Fleet Engineering Support Personnel Training Program Description	15
FP-BS-IFA-01	Interface Agreement Maintenance and Review	1
FP-DE-DSG-01	Conduct Of Design Engineering	1
FP-E-ABN-01	ABANDONED EQUIPMENT	5
FP-E-CAL-01	Calculations	14, 15
FP-E-CAP-01	ELECTROLYTIC CAPACITOR AGING MANAGEMENT	4
FP-E-CDBR-01	COMPONENT DESIGN BASIS REVIEW	1
FP-E-CLB-01	CURRENT LICENSING BASES	2
FP-E-CM-01	Margin Management	8

NUCLEAR OVERSIGHT
AUDIT REPORT

Document Number	Title	Rev#
FP-E-DBD-01	DESIGN BASIS DOCUMENT CONTROL	4
FP-E-DES-01	CONTRACTOR CONTROL AND STAKEHOLDER INVOLVEMENT	4
FP-E-DOC-01	Document-Only Engineering Change	14
FP-E-DRB-01	Design Review Board Process	10
FP-E-DSG-01	Conduct of Design Engineering	1
FP-E-DWG-01	ENGINEERING DRAWING CREATION AND REVISION	2
FP-E-DWG-02	CRITICAL DRAWING MARK-UPS	4
FP-E-DWG-03	CONSTRUCTION DRAWING CONTROL	7
FP-E-ECR-01	ENGINEERING CHANGE REQUEST	7
FP-E-ECR-01	Engineering Change Request	7
FP-E-EOC-01	Engineer of Choice (EOC) Process	1
FP-E-EOC-02	Engineer of Choice (EOC) Deliverable Review	0
FP-E-EQR-01	CONDUCT OF EQUIPMENT RELIABILITY ENGINEERING	0
FP-E-EQV-01	Equivalency Evaluations and Changes	12
FP-E-ER-01	EQUIPMENT RELIABILITY GOVERNANCE	0
FP-E-ERA-01	ENGINEERING RISK ASSESSMENT	1
FP-E-ERBC-01	EQUIPMENT RELIABILITY BUBBLE CHART	1
FP-E-EVL-01	Engineering Evaluations	7
FP-E-FRI-01	CERTIFICATION OF PERSONNEL TO PERFORM RECEIPT INSPECTION OF NEW FUEL	2
FP-E-ICES-01	ICES EQUIPMENT FAILURE REPORTING	2
FP-E-LCM-01	LIFE CYCLE MANAGEMENT PLAN DEVELOPMENT	6
FP-E-MOD-01	Modification Process Definitions	8
FP-E-MOD-02	Engineering Change Control	19
FP-E-MOD-03	Temporary Modifications	13
FP-E-MOD-04	Design Inputs	10
FP-E-MOD-05	Plant Modification Impact	13
FP-E-MOD-06	Design Description	7
FP-E-MOD-07	Design Verification and Technical Review	8
FP-E-MOD-08	Engineering Change Notices	10
FP-E-MOD-09	INSTALLATION AND TESTING INSTRUCTIONS	9
FP-E-MOD-10	Modification Turnover and Closeout	14
FP-E-MOD-11	Control of Design Interfaces	13
FP-E-MOD-12	GENERIC MODIFICATIONS	6
FP-E-MR-01	MAINTENANCE RULE PROCESS	6
FP-E-MR-02	MAINTENANCE RULE SCOPING	7
FP-E-MR-03	MAINTENANCE RULE MONITORING	3
FP-E-MR-04	MAINTENANCE RULE - (A)(1) PROCESS	3

NUCLEAR OVERSIGHT
AUDIT REPORT

Document Number	Title	Rev#
FP-E-MR-05	MAINTENANCE RULE EXPERT PANEL (MREP)	6
FP-E-MR-06	PERIODIC (A)(3) ASSESSMENT	3
FP-E-MR-07	MAINTENANCE RULE STRUCTURES MONITORING	2
FP-E-MR-09	MAINTENANCE RULE (A)(4) FIRE RISK ASSESSMENT RISK MANAGEMENT ACTIONS	2
FP-E-MSPI-01	MITIGATING SYSTEM PERFORMANCE INDEX (MSPI)	8
FP-E-NEIL-01	NUCLEAR ELECTRIC INSURANCE LIMITED (NEIL)	1
FP-E-P21-01	10 CFR PART 21 EVALUATIONS	1
FP-EP-EQP-01	Equipment Important to EP	10
FP-E-PHC-01	PLANT HEALTH COMMITTEE	19
FP-E-QRT-01	Quality Review Team (QRT)	6
FP-E-RI-01	RISK INTEGRATOR	0
FP-E-RTC-01	REVISION TRACKING AND CONTROL	10
FP-E-RTC-01	Revision Tracking and Control	10
FP-E-RTC-02	Equipment Classification	12
FP-E-SAR-01	USAR Changes	8
FP-E-SDP-01	SIGNIFICANCE DETERMINATION PROCESS EVALUATION	3
FP-E-SDY-01	DEVELOPMENT OF DESIGN STUDIES	4
FP-E-SE-02	COMPONENT CLASSIFICATION	13
FP-E-SE-03	10 CFR 50.59 and 72.48 Processes	9
FP-E-SE-04	CONDUCT OF SYSTEM ENGINEERING	20
FP-E-SE-05	SYSTEM ENGINEERING WALKDOWNS	1
FP-E-SE-06	SYSTEM HEALTH REPORTING	3
FP-E-SPEC-01	SPECIFICATION CONTROL	1
FP-E-SPT-01	Setpoint Change Control	6
FP-E-SPV-01	SINGLE POINT VULNERABILITY MITIGATION	0
FP-E-TRB-01	TECHNICAL REVIEW BOARD	1
FP-E-TS-01	TROUBLESHOOTING PROCESS	10
FP-E-VEN-01	Vendor Manual Control	8
FP-G-RM-01	Quality Assurance Records Control	24
FP-IT-CSP-10	Third Party Access Procedure	1
FP-IT-CSP-11	Cyber Security Incident Handling and Response Procedure	3
FP-IT-CSP-21	Cyber Security CDA Media Protection Procedure	2
FP-IT-CSP-25	CDA Cyber Security Management Procedure	2
FP-IT-SQA-01	Software Quality Assurance (SQA) Program	13
FP-IT-SQA-02	Software Review Board	8
FP-IT-SQA-03	Classifying Software Products	14
FP-IT-SQA-04	Creating, Maintaining, And Using The Master Software List	6

NUCLEAR OVERSIGHT
AUDIT REPORT

Document Number	Title	Rev#
FP-IT-SQA-05	Computer Work Order	11
FP-IT-SQA-06	The Software Planning Phase	10
FP-IT-SQA-07	The Software Requirements Phase	8
FP-IT-SQA-08	The Software Design Phase	7
FP-IT-SQA-09	The Software Coding Phase	6
FP-IT-SQA-10	The Software Testing Phase	8
FP-IT-SQA-11	Software Data Control	6
FP-IT-SQA-12	Impact Analysis	6
FP-IT-SQA-13	The Software Retirement Phase	4
FP-IT-SQA-14	Software Configuration Management	4
FP-IT-SQA-15	Software Error Reporting	7
FP-IT-SQA-16	Software Disaster Recovery And Contingency Plans	4
FP-IT-SQA-17	Software Access And Media Control	3
FP-IT-SQA-18	Software User Instructions And Training	6
FP-IT-SQA-19	Fleet Peer Group	1
FP-OP-REP-01	Event Reporting and Notification Process	0
FP-PA-SA-01	Focused Self-Assessment Planning, Conduct, and Reporting	19
FP-PA-SA-02	Focused Self-Assessment and Formal Benchmarking Scheduling	17
FP-PA-SA-03	Snapshot Evaluation	8
FP-PE-RLP-01	License Renewal Implementation	5
FP-R-EP-02	10 CFR 50.54(q) Review Process	7, 11
FP-R-LIC-07	Operating License Amendments	7
FP-S-FSIP-15	Development and Maintenance of Critical Target Sets	6
GAR01336417	DIC for EC 19786	NA
GAR01353906	EC 19784 Open Item Tracking GAR	NA
GAR01353910	EC 19786 Open Item Tracking	NA
GAR01379776	UPDATE CALCULATION SPC-EP-021	NA
GAR01379780	UPDATE CALCULATION SPC-EP-046 FOR EC19784	NA
GAR01380905	Impacted Calculations Processed After EC19784 Approval	NA
GAR01397786	Tracking of Interface Agreement Updates	NA
INPO 12-010	Temporary Configuration Changes	0
Interface Agreement	Quality Services Interface Agreement (Business Systems)	4
Interface Agreement	Quality Services Interface Agreement with Business Systems 11/30/2009	4
ITAR01353679	DAQSTANDARD Update per EC 19786	NA
ITAR01353680	PRINTWAVE Update per EC 19786	NA

NUCLEAR OVERSIGHT
AUDIT REPORT

Document Number	Title	Rev#
Job Aid	SQA Trifold 9/26/2013	NA
LM-0311 Reports	Qual Status Verification, Student (Various)	Various Personnel
LM-0616 Report	FL-ESP-DES-014M Modification Design	NA
LM-0616 Report	FL-ESP-GEN-001M Engineering Calculations	NA
LM-0616 Report	FL-ESP-GEN-002M 50.59 Screening	NA
LM-0616 Report	FL-ESP-GEN-003M 50.59 Evaluation	NA
LM-0616 Report	FL-ESP-GEN-010M Engineering Change Preparation and Review	NA
LM-0616 Report	FL-ESP-GEN-014M Setpoints	NA
LM-0616 Report	FL-ESP-GEN-020M Equipment Classification	NA
LM-0616 Report	FL-BIT-SOFTWAREPRODMGR Software Product Manager	NA
L-PI-14-058	Updated Safety Analysis Report (USAR) Revision 33, Technical Specification Bases Revisions, Commitment	33
L-PI-16-049	Updated Safety Analysis Report (USAR)	34
Master Software List (MSL) ID	13148, 13147, 13865, 13199, 13712	NA
MNGP E-Plan	Emergency Plan	52
MSL	Master Software List	6/13/2016
MSL	Automatic Voltage Regulator (AVR) Software)	NA
MTG	[Plant X] Software Review Board (Fatigue Pro Interface, ZPU-5000)	9/2/14
MTG	[Plant X] Software Review Board (Qualitrol, SEL Applications, Fatigue Pro Interface)	8/5/14
MTG	[Plant X] Software Review Board (Sullair Supervisor Controller)	2/12/15
MTG	[Plant X] Software Review Board (Insight Plan) 12/04/14 -12/18/14	NA
MTG	[Plant X] Software Review Board (Door 419 Electric Operator Controls)	6/4/2014
MTG	[Plant X] Software Review Board (Freescale, Sullair Supervisor Controller, URI, URI-DFI,Qualitrol 509ITM-100)	7/02/14
MTG	[Plant X] Software Review Board (MAPPro Interface, Sullair Supervisor Controller, NSmart Security System, URIURI-DFI, Freescale, GCM-X)	6/4/14
MTG	[Plant X] Software Review Board (ZPU-5000,Siemens MXL Fire Detection Panel Software, XLS Fire Finder, Security Management System, SFPLevel)	6/4/2014
MTG	[Plant X] Software Review Board (NRCDose72,Rosemount 5300 Transmitter Firmware, Rosemount 5300 RRM Software, Siemens GEN IV VFD Software, Siemens GEN IV VFD Tool Suite Software)	10/6/15
MTG	[Plant X] Software Review Board (WXin WRM2)	12/2/14

NUCLEAR OVERSIGHT
AUDIT REPORT

Document Number	Title	Rev#
MTG	[Plant X] Software Review Board (Power DB Lite, License Renewal Tracking Database)	1/6/15
MTG	[Plant X] Software Review Board (BN-3500 Panel Software, BN-System 1 Software, Turbine Building Crane Controls, ERCS MS WIN CLIENT)	2/3/15
MTG	[Plant X] Software Review Board (Trane Tracer Adapter)	3/18/16
MTG	[Plant X] Software Review Board (Qualitrol QNet4100, Cirrus Pro Detector, Cirrus Pro Window)	3/1/16
MTG	[Plant X] Software Review Board (EQMS)	1/18/16
MTG	[Plant X] Software Review Board (pcProx)	9/1/15
MTG	[Plant X] Software Review Board (PanoMap, MicroShield, Radiation Protection Notebook, Victoreen UDR Firmware, Generatortech)	2/2/16
MTG	[Plant X] Software Review Board (TSCBoard, ASCO NextGen Solenoid Valve)	1/8/16
MTG	[Plant X] Software Review Board (RVEST, SOV Manager, TSCBoard, Mileston, Qualitrol QNet4100)	1/5/16
NQA-1-1994	ASME NQA-1-1994 EDITION	NA
NUREG 0588	Interim Staff Position on Environmental Qualification of Safety-Related Electrical Equipment	NA
P-7500		NA
PCR01346066	F5 Appendix F EC19784 & EC 19786 (S)	NA
PI-ESP-GEN-001	Prepare or Review Engineering Calculation	0
PI-ESP-GEN-002	Prepare/Review 50.59 Screening	0
PI-ESP-GEN-003	Prepare/Review 50.59 Eval	0
PI-ESP-GEN-007	Prepare/Review Engineering Specification	0
PI-ESP-GEN-008	Prepare/Review Engineering EQV Change Evaluation	0
PI-ESP-GEN-010	Engineering Change Preparation/Review	0
PI-ESP-GEN-014	Setpoints	0
PI-ESP-GEN-020	Equipment Classification	0
1229	NMC Standard 10 CFR 50.59 Screening	6
1229	NMC Standard 10 CFR 50.59 Screening	1
1672	Equipment Important to EP	14
2261	EOP / SAMG Impact Assessment Checklist	0
PORC Mtg Minutes	3276 (5/13/13)	NA
QATR	Quality Assurance Topical Report	9
QATR C.2	Self Assessment	9
QF0501	50.59 Screening (Screening # 4903, EC 23207)	8
QF0502	50.59 Screening	8
QF0502	50.59 Evaluation (Evaluation# 1120, EC 23207)	5
QF0502	50.59 Evaluation	5

NUCLEAR OVERSIGHT
AUDIT REPORT

Document Number	Title	Rev#
QF0503	50.59 Screening (Screening # 4903, EC 23207)	NA
QF0503	50.59 Evaluation (Evaluation# 1120, EC 23207)	NA
QF0504	50.59 Screening No. 4339 – Classify CC HX CL Inlet Valves as Passive vs. Active	0
QF0505	50.59 Screening No. 5013 – EC 24172 Revise AOV Calculation 01110-C-021 to reduce the maximum allowed supply air pressure.	0
QF0505	50.59 Applicability Determination and Prescreening Number 0911 – Add calculation NSC-PIP-M-SLR-92 to Passport	0
QF0506	50.59 Screening No. 4773 – EC 24173 Change Unit 2 Generator Hydrogen Pressure to Lo Alarm	0
QF0506	Modification Control	9
QF0507	Modification Control EC 26498	NA
QF0507	Modification Package Index	8
QF0508	Modification Package Index	8
QF0508	SQAP EC20403	NA
QF0508	SQAP EC11780	NA
QF0509	SQAP EC20404	NA
QF0509	Modification Control	NA
QF0509	SQAP EC11780	NA
QF0510	SQAP EC20405	NA
QF0510	Modification Control	9
QF0510	SQAP EC11780	NA
QF0515A	Design Input Checklist	25
QF0515A	Design Input Checklist (Part A-Engineering Programs and Departmental Reviews)	25
QF0515B	Design Input Checklist (Part B-Design Considerations, Requirements, and Standards)	9
QF0516	Design Input Consultation Form	6
QF0516	Design Input Consultation Form EC24306	6
QF0516	Design Input Form EC 24306	6
QF0516A	Operations Department Modification Review Checklist	5
QF0516B	Maintenance Department Modification Review Checklist	6
QF0517-x series	ALARA Design Checklists	various
QF0518	EC 25975/Condensate/Feedwater System Time Delay Relay Modification	6
QF0525	Design Description	3
QF0526	Design Description Form: Condensate/Feedwater System Time Delay Relay Modification	NA
QF0527	Design Review Checklist	4
QF0533	Closeout Control Form	6

NUCLEAR OVERSIGHT
AUDIT REPORT

Document Number	Title	Rev#
QF0540	Temporary Modification Control Form	6
QF0542	Periodic review of Temporary Modification	1
QF0549	Calculation Signature Sheet	9
QF0574	DRM/DRB Effectiveness Scorecard	NA
QF1500	Computer Work Order (Proto-Flo Version 5.01)	13
QF1500	Computer Work Order (Combustible Loading Manager)	14
QF1500	Computer Work Order (Nuclear IQ version 1.2.7.1)	14
QF1500	Computer Work Order (Beacon-TSM 6.7.1)	11
QF1500	Computer Work Order	14
QF1500	Computer Work Order (Proto-Flo Version 5.01)	14
QF1500	Computer Work Order (Combustible Loading Manager)	14
QF1500	Computer Work Order (Nuclear IQ version 1.2.7.1)	14
QF1500	Computer Work Order (Beacon-TSM 6.7.1)	14
QF1501	Software Classification Determination (FLIIR Tools+)	16
QF1501	Software Classification Determination (Primavera SAP EPC Interface v2.0)	17
QF1501	Software Classification Determination (Fire Eye)	18
QF1501	Software Classification Determination (DocAssit)	18
QF1501	Software Classification Determination (VMWare Horizon Client)	16
QF1501	Software Classification Determination (Zeus)	16
QF1501	Software Classification Determination (2006)	16
QF1501	Software Classification Determination (CSGM 1701)	16
QF1501	Software Classification Determination (Turbine Bently Nevada 3500 Chassis 1	16
QF1501	Software Classification Determination (System 1 Server Suite)	16
QF1501	Software Classification Determination (Zeus)	14
QF1501	Software Classification Determination (MHPSA Electric Generator/ Exciter	14
QF1501	Software Classification Determination (EPP-IL SFPI/1.14)	14
QF1501	Software Classification Determination (Siemens GEN IV VFD Maintenance Software)	17
QF1501	Software Classification Determination (Siemens GEN IV Variable Frequency Drive Software)	17
QF1501	Software Classification Determination (Rosemount 5300 Maintenance Software)	17
QF1501	Software Classification Determination (Rosemount Guided Wave Radar Transmitter)	17
QF1501	Software Classification Determination (Aux Bldg PLC User Program)	18

NUCLEAR OVERSIGHT
AUDIT REPORT

Document Number	Title	Rev#
QF1501	Software Classification Determination (VTM Catalog 0)	7
QF1501	Software Classification Determination (Sullair)	16
QF1501	Software Classification Determination (Iridium Firmware HT10017)	13
QF1501	Software Classification Determination (MotorolaRadioSuite 7.13)	13
QF1501	Software Classification Determination (Sullair)	15
QF1501	Software Classification Determination	18
QF1501	Software Classification Determination SCD-14128, 14127,14026, 24306, 14197, EN-FLIRTools-NA-3-001, EN-PrimaveraInterf-2-3-001,EN-FireEye-na-4-001, en-DocAssist-na-4-001, en-HorizonClient-na-5-001, 13960, 12600, 13071, 14092, 14093, 14076, 14167, 14211, 14168, 13230, 14017, MotoRadioSuite-7-2-001	17
QF1501	Software Classification Determination SCD-14128, 14127, 14026, 24306, 14197, EN-FLIRTools-NA-3-001, EN-PrimaveraInterf-2-3-001,EN-FireEye-na-4-001, en-DocAssist-na-4-001, en-HorizonClient-na-5-001, 13960, 12600, 13071, 14092, 14093, 14076, 14167, 14211, 14168, 13230, 14017, MotoRadioSuite-7-2-001, SCD11429	17
QF1502	Software Requirements Specification (Proto-Flo Version 5.01)	5
QF1502	Software Requirements Specification (Beacon-TSM 6.7.1)	5
QF1502	Software Requirements Specification	5
QF1502	Software Requirements Specification (Proto-Flo Version 5.01)	NA
QF1502	Software Requirements Specification (Beacon-TSM 6.7.1)	NA
QF1504	Software Design Description (Proto-Flo Version 5.01)	5
QF1504	Software Design Description	5
QF1504	Software Design Description (Proto-Flo Version 5.01)	NA
QF1506	Software Test Plan (Proto-Flo Version 5.01)	7
QF1506	Software Test Plan (Combustible Loading Manager)	7
QF1506	Software Test Plan (Nuclear IQ version 1.2.7.1)	7
QF1506	Software Test Plan (Beacon-TSM 6.7.1)	7
QF1506	Software Test Plan EC24307	NA
QF1506	Software Test Plan	7
QF1506	Software Test Plan (Proto-Flo Version 5.01)	NA
QF1506	Software Test Plan (Combustible Loading Manager)	NA
QF1506	Software Test Plan (Nuclear IQ version 1.2.7.1)	NA

NUCLEAR OVERSIGHT
AUDIT REPORT

Document Number	Title	Rev#
QF1506	Software Test Plan (Beacon-TSM 6.7.1)	NA
QF1508	Software Quality Assurance Plan	14
QF1508	Software Quality Assurance Plan (Combustible Loading Manager [a.k.a Fire Protection Suite])	NA
QF1508	Software Quality Assurance Plan (Beacon-TSM 6.7.1)	NA
QF1508	Software Quality Assurance Plan (Combustible Loading Manager [a.k.a Fire Protection Suite])	14
QF1508	Software Quality Assurance Plan (Proto-Flo Version 5.01)	14
QF1508	Software Quality Assurance Plan (Combustible Loading Manager)	14
QF1508	Software Quality Assurance Plan (Nuclear IQ version 1.2.7.1)	14
QF1508	Software Quality Assurance Plan (Siemens Gen IV VFD)	14
QF1508	Software Quality Assurance Plan (Rosemount 5300 Transmitter)	14
QF1508	Software Quality Assurance Plan	14
QF1509	Software Quality Assurance Plan (Beacon-TSM 6.7.1)	12
QF1535	Software Quality Assurance Package Review	0
Reg Guide 1.89	Qualification of Class 1E Equipment for Nuclear Plants	3
RIS 2000-18	Guidance on Managing Quality Assurance Records in Electronic Media	0
RPP-SQA-SWO	PI Stop Work Order	NA
SAR01392707	Perform PI SQA Snapshot self assessment in 2015	NA
SCR 3744	10 CFR 50.59 Screening	0
SCR 4087	10 CFR 50.59 Screening	0
SCR 4088	10 CFR 50.59 Screening	0
SCR 4671	10 CFR 50.59 Screening	0
SRB Minutes	Software Review Board: Meeting Minutes 6/4/2014, 7/2/2014, 8/5/2014, 9/2/2014, 9/17/2014, 10/7/2014, 12/2/2014, 12/4/2014, 12/18/2014, 1/6/2015, 2/3/2015, 2/12/2015, 5/12/2014, 6/2/2015, 7/7/2015, 9/1/2015, 10/6/2015, 11/19/2015, 1/5/2016, 1/6/2016, 11/8/2016, 1/18/2016, 2/2/2016, 3/1/2016, 3/18/2016, 4/20/2016, 11/20/2013, 8/28//2015, 4/26/2016, 10/21/2015, 1/28/2015, 2/14/2016, 2/18/2015, 4/29/2015, 3/18/2015	NA
SWI ENG-20	DISPOSITION OF VENDOR INFORMATION	5
SWI ENG-3	Preparing Design Bases Documents	3
SWI ENG-4	Verifying Design Bases Documents	3
SWI O-4	Operations Records Management	NA
Tech Specs	[Plant X] Tech Specs	188

NUCLEAR OVERSIGHT
AUDIT REPORT

Document Number	Title	Rev#
USAR	12.02 Plant Structures and Shielding	32
USAR 1	Introduction & Summary Description	34
USAR 14	Safety Analyses	34
USAR 4	Reactor Coolant System	34
USAR 7	Plant Instrumentation and Control Systems	34
USAR Section 10	Plant Auxiliary Systems – Section 10.4.1 Cooling Water System	34
WO0465741	U1 CONTROL ROOM ICNET ETHERNET SWITCH REPLACEMENT - EC 19786	NA

Appendix E
Auditing of Nuclear Industry Suppliers

Background

The approach for auditing and qualifying nuclear industry suppliers has evolved significantly over the past 30 years. In 1989, the US domestic nuclear utilities merged CASE (Coordinated Agency for Supplier Evaluation) and NSQAC (Nuclear Supplier Quality Assurance Committee) to form the Nuclear Procurement Issues Committee (NUPIC) to coordinate the manner in which suppliers were audited. More recently renamed the Nuclear Procurement Issues Corporation (NUPIC), the organization developed a standardized audit checklist and implementation guidelines to assure that the audit packages produced by the various audit teams would provide a consistent approach. The audit packages from each utility were entered into a common database that was accessible to all NUPIC members. By sharing audit results among NUPIC members, the need for redundant audits by the individual utilities was eliminated, resulting in cost and time benefits for both the NUPIC members and the suppliers. Suppliers do not have access to the NUPIC database of audit results. The public does, however, have access to the NUPIC website.

Recognizing the benefits of the program, several suppliers applied for membership in NUPIC, but were denied. Consequently, in 1994 a small number of nuclear suppliers established a suppliers' group called the Nuclear Industry Assessment Committee (NIAC), now renamed Nuclear Industry Assessment Corporation. Their approach is similar to that of NUPIC, including the use of a standardized checklist and sharing audit results with those NIAC members that request the audit report.

The standardized NUPIC checklists are readily available to the public on the NUPIC website and are used extensively throughout the nuclear industry in various ways. Some suppliers even use the Audit Checklist to conduct their annual internal audit. NUPIC membership is constantly monitoring industry problems and issues, and their checklists are continually being updated to include new attributes to address emerging issues. Because of the changing nature of the checklists, copies are not included in this handbook.

Instead, readers are directed to the NUPIC website (nupic.com), where current copies of the following checklists are available:

- NUPIC Audit Checklist (75 pages)
- NUPIC Commercial Grade Item Survey Checklist (8 pages)
- Commercial Grade Calibration Services Checklist (22 pages)

Detailed implementation guidelines that describe how to complete each checklist attribute are also included on the website. In addition to the noted checklists, the website provides a valuable library of reference documents for any nuclear QA professional. The "Hot Links" folder is particularly informative.

NIAC's growth as an organization is clearly an indication of the value of the process. The standardized NIAC checklists are also periodically updated and revised, generally to remain consistent with the NUPIC checklists. Copies of the current NIAC checklists are not accessible to the public on the NIAC website (niac-usa.org). Clearly the NIAC process has value to the NIAC members and the suppliers that are audited. Interested parties should visit the NIAC website for information on how to join.

SUMMARY SHEET

SUPPLIER INFORMATION			
SUPPLIER NAME:		NUPIC SUPPLIER #:	
PRIMARY ADDRESS:			
CITY:	STATE:		ZIP CODE:
ADDITIONAL LOCATIONS:			
PRIMARY TELEPHONE #:		WEB ADDRESS:	
PRODUCT/SERVICE:			
ASME CODE STAMP, AUTHORIZATIONS, AND EXPIRATION DATES:			

QUALITY PROGRAM COMMITMENTS			
☐ 10 CFR 50 Appendix B	☐ ANSI/ASME NQA-1 (Yr.)	☐ ASME SECTION XI	☐ IEEE (specify)
☐ 10 CFR 21	☐ ANSI N45.2	☐ ASME NCA 3800	☐ SNT-TC-1A
☐ 10 CFR (other)	☐ ANSI (other)	☐ ASME NCA 4000	☐ CP-189
			☐ Other

SUPPLIER CONTACTS			
SENIOR COMPANY OFFICER:	TITLE:		PHONE:
SENIOR QA OFFICER:	TITLE:		PHONE:
	E-MAIL:		

AUDIT INFORMATION		
MEMBER AUDIT ID #:	NUPIC AUDIT ID #:	AUDIT DATES:

AUDIT TEAM INFORMATION				
AUDIT TEAM:	NAME/NUPIC MEMBER DESIGNATOR:	PHONE:	EMAIL:	CHECKLIST SECTIONS AUDITED:
TEAM LEADER				
TEAM MEMBER				
TEAM MEMBER				
TEAM MEMBER				
TEAM MEMBER				
TEAM MEMBER				
TECHNICAL SPECIALIST				
(Specify Discipline)				

AUDIT TEAM LEADER   DATE

_____ : _____

NUPIC REPRESENTATIVE   DATE

_____ : _____

SUMMARY SHEET

SUPPLIER QUALITY MANUAL: _____   REVISION: _____   DATE: _____

Audit Section	Section Description	E	F	Previous Audit Finding Reference	Section Status	Comments/Findings
1	Contract Review	✓	✓			
2	Design	✓				
3	Commercial Grade Dedication	✓				
4	Software Quality Assurance	✓	✓			
5	Procurement	✓	✓			
6	Fabrication/Assembly Activities, Material Control and Handling, Storage and Shipping		✓			
7	Special Processes		✓			
8	Tests, Inspections, and Calibration		✓			
9	Document Control/Adequacy	✓	✓			
10	Organization/Program	✓	✓			
11	Nonconforming Items/Part 21	✓	✓			
12	Internal Audit	✓				
13	Corrective Action	✓	✓			
14	Training/Certification	✓	✓			
15	Field Services	✓	✓			
16	Records	✓	✓			

SECTION STATUS KEY

S – SATISFACTORY   U – UNSATISFACTORY   N/A – NOT APPLICABLE (document basis)

E – Recommended for Engineering Service Suppliers   F – Recommended for Field Service Suppliers

NOTE: An audit section status identified as "U" only indicates that one or more attributes in this checklist section were found to be unacceptable and may not suggest that the entire section was found to be unsatisfactory.

SECTION 1 – CONTRACT REVIEW

METHOD OF VERIFICATION

1.1	Within the assessment/summary section of each checklist question, record the procedures/instructions/drawings including the revision/date used to verify implementation.
1.2	**Verify that measures are established and implemented for the translation of customer purchase order/contract technical and quality requirements into the supplier's control documents.**

Objective Evidence required for Figure 1:
- Customer PO/Contract **and** date
- Item/service description **and** part number
- Supplier control document **and** verification (Yes/No) of translation from customer PO/Contract
- Customer approval of exceptions (Yes/No)

Implementation Information:
Technical and quality requirements may include description, part numbers, tests/inspections, documentation, C of C, packaging/shipping, hold points, materials, etc.
Supplier control documents may include order review forms, travelers, shop work orders, work tracking documents, etc.

References:
Appendix B/ANSI N45.2 - (3/4)
ASME Section III
NQA-1 Supplement 3S-1

RESULTS: *SAT* ☐   *UNSAT* ☐ Describe Finding(s)   *N/A* ☐ Describe basis for N/A

ASSESSMENT/ SUMMARY:

a. *List* the Vendor Quality Manual reference and implementing procedure(s) established to provide the measures for translation of purchase order/contract technical and quality requirements into supplier's control documents:

Are procedural controls adequate and procedure revision current?
YES ☐ *or*
NO ☐ (Identify and provide input to the team member evaluating checklist Section 9.)

b. *Describe* implementation of the supplier's measures (who, what, how) for translating customer purchase order/contract requirements, including:
1. Correct translation of technical and quality requirements into the control documents
2. Documentation, customer notification, and customer approval of any exceptions to the purchase order/contract technical and quality requirements, including design changes

Are procedural controls adequately implemented?
YES ☐ *or*
NO ☐ (describe the inadequacy)

SECTION 1 – CONTRACT REVIEW

METHOD OF VERIFICATION

1.3   **Verify that measures are established and implemented for control of items returned from the customer for repair/rework.**

Implementation Information:
Returns may refer to previously purchased items that require repair/refurbishment due to age/use and are typically requested by the normal purchase order/contract process.
This question refers to items returned due to non-conformances at customer's receipt inspection, infantile failures, etc., and are typically requested by Return Material Authorization (RMA) or equivalent.

Checklist Interface:
Provide any related supplier nonconformance information to the audit team member evaluating checklist Section 11.

References:
Appendix B/ANSI N45.2 - (15/16)
ASME Section III
NQA-1 Supplement 15S-1

RESULTS: **SAT** ☐   **UNSAT** ☐ Describe Finding(s)   **N/A** ☐ Describe basis for N/A

ASSESSMENT/
SUMMARY:

a.   **List** the Vendor Quality Manual reference and implementing procedure(s) established to provide the measures for control of items returned from the customer for repair/rework:

Are procedural controls adequate and procedure revision current?
YES ☐ **or**
NO ☐ (Identify and provide input to the team member evaluating checklist Section 9.)

b.   **Describe** <u>implementation</u> of the supplier's measures (who, what, how) for return of items to be repaired/reworked:

Are procedural controls adequately implemented?
YES ☐ **or**
NO ☐ (describe the inadequacy)

SECTION 1 – CONTRACT REVIEW

METHOD OF VERIFICATION

1.4   **Verify that measures are established and implemented to ensure that final record packages, including Certificates of Compliance/Conformance, demonstrate that purchase order/contract technical and quality requirements were satisfied.**

Implementation Information:
Records must accurately describe the delivered products, including the "as-built" of the item or component, and should include documentation such as material certifications/test data, reports of inspections/examinations/tests, drawings, specifications, procedures, instructions, and non-conformances including the resolution.

References:
Appendix B/ANSI N45.2 - (6/7) (17/18)
ASME Section III
NQA-1 Supplement 17S-1

RESULTS: **SAT** ☐   **UNSAT** ☐ Describe Finding(s)   **N/A** ☐ Describe basis for N/A

ASSESSMENT/ SUMMARY:

a. *List* the Vendor Quality Manual reference and implementing procedure(s) established to provide measures to ensure that final record packages demonstrate that purchase order/contract technical and quality requirements were satisfied:

Are procedural controls adequate and procedure revision current?
YES ☐ or
NO ☐ (Identify and provide input to the team member evaluating checklist Section 9.)

b. *Describe* implementation of the supplier's measures (who, what, how) to ensure that final record packages demonstrate that purchase order/contract technical and quality requirements were satisfied:

Are procedural controls adequately implemented?
YES ☐ or
NO ☐ (describe the inadequacy)

SECTION 1 – CONTRACT REVIEW

(FIGURE 1)

CUSTOMER P.O. CONTRACT NUMBER and DATE	ITEM/SERVICE DESCRIPTION and PART NUMBER (as applicable)	SUPPLIER CONTROL DOCUMENTS (work orders, travelers, drawings, etc.) and CORRECT TRANSLATION TO SUPPLIER CONTROL DOCUMENTS (Yes/No)	CUSTOMER APPROVAL OF P.O. / CONTRACT EXCEPTIONS (Yes/No)
* 1.2	* 1.2	* 1.2	* 1.2

* Refers to applicable question

SECTION 2 – DESIGN

METHOD OF VERIFICATION

2.1	Within the assessment/summary section of each checklist question, record the procedures/instructions/drawings including the revision/date used to verify implementation.
2.2	**Verify that measures are established and implemented to control the translation of design requirements into design documents.**

Objective Evidence required for Figure 2:
- Member/Supplier Design Input **and** Bases
- Supplier Design Document
- Design Inputs Correctly Incorporated (Yes/No)

Implementation Information:
Design requirements (inputs) may be specified by the customer as technical and quality requirements in the purchase order/contract or may originate from the supplier. These include information such as design bases, regulatory requirements, codes, standards, EQ/seismic reports, etc.
Design bases is information which identifies the specific functions to be performed and specific values/ranges of values for controlling parameters, chosen as reference bounds for design.

Checklist Interface:
Identify any software used in design to the audit team members evaluating Checklist Section 3 (purchased commercially and dedicated), Section 4, and Section 5 (purchased safety-related). Identify any qualified / certified design specialists (i.e., ASME Code design personnel to ASME Section III) to the audit team member evaluating Checklist Section 14.

References:
Appendix B/ANSI N45.2 - (3/4)
ASME Section III
NQA-1 Supplement 3S-1

RESULTS: *SAT* ☐   *UNSAT* ☐ Describe Finding(s)   *N/A* ☐ Describe basis for N/A

ASSESSMENT/ SUMMARY:

a. **List** the Vendor Quality Manual reference and implementing procedure(s) established to provide the measures for translation of design requirements into design documents:

Are procedural controls adequate and procedure revision current?

YES ☐ *or*

NO ☐ (Identify and provide input to the team member evaluating checklist Section 9.)

b. **Describe** implementation of the supplier's measures (who, what, how) for translating design requirements into design documents:

Are procedural controls adequately implemented?

YES ☐ *or*

NO ☐ (describe the inadequacy)

SECTION 2 – DESIGN

METHOD OF VERIFICATION

2.3 **Verify that measures are established and implemented for the selection, and review for suitability of application, of materials, parts, equipment and processes that are essential to the safety-related function of the product.**

Implementation Information:
If safety-related components contain parts identified as non-safety-related, a documented evaluation process should exist to provide a basis for the non-safety-related classification. This evaluation process should consider the functional application of the part and a failure modes analysis to verify that the part failure would not prevent the parent component from performing its safety-related function.

References:
Appendix B/ANSI N45.2 - (3/4)
ASME Section III
NQA-1 Supplement 3S-1

RESULTS: *SAT* ☐   *UNSAT* ☐ Describe Finding(s)   *N/A* ☐ Describe basis for N/A

ASSESSMENT/
SUMMARY:

a. **List** the Vendor Quality Manual reference and implementing procedure(s) established to provide the measures for the selection, and review for suitability of application, of materials, parts, equipment and processes essential to the safety-related function:

Are procedural controls adequate and procedure revision current?
YES ☐ or
NO ☐ (Identify and provide input to the team member evaluating checklist Section 9.)

b. **Describe** implementation of the supplier's measures (who, what, how) for the selection, and review for suitability of application, of materials, parts, equipment and processes essential to the safety-related function:

• If the supplier's safety-related components have parts classified as non-safety-related, describe the measures in use which provide the basis for the non-safety-related classification.

Are procedural controls adequately implemented?
YES ☐ or
NO ☐ (describe the inadequacy)

SECTION 2 – DESIGN

METHOD OF VERIFICATION

2.4 **Verify that measures are established and implemented for the identification and control of design interfaces.**

Implementation Information:
Design activities may require interface between design groups within the same company, subcontracted design service suppliers, Code agencies such as ASME, and customer design organizations. These interfaces require establishment of procedures among participating design organizations (internal/external) for the review, approval, release, distribution, and revision of design documents.

Checklist Interface:
Identify any subcontracted design service suppliers to the audit team member evaluating Checklist Section 5.

References:
Appendix B/ANSI N45.2 - (3/4)
ASME Section III
NQA-1 Supplement 3S-1

RESULTS: *SAT* ☐   *UNSAT* ☐ Describe Finding(s)   *N/A* ☐ Describe basis for N/A

ASSESSMENT/
SUMMARY:

a. *List* the Vendor Quality Manual reference and implementing procedure(s) established to provide the measures for the identification and control of design interfaces:

Are procedural controls adequate and procedure revision current?

YES ☐ *or*

NO ☐ (Identify and provide input to the team member evaluating checklist Section 9.)

b. *Describe* implementation of the supplier's measures (who, what, how) for the identification and control of design interfaces:

Are procedural controls adequately implemented?

YES ☐ *or*

NO ☐ (describe the inadequacy)

SECTION 2 – DESIGN

METHOD OF VERIFICATION

2.5 **Verify that measures are established and implemented for the verification of design adequacy.**

Objective Evidence required for Figure 2:
- Method of Design Verification

References:
Appendix B/ANSI N45.2 - (3/4)
ASME Section III
NQA-1 Supplement 3S-1

RESULTS: **SAT** ☐   **UNSAT** ☐ Describe Finding(s)   **N/A** ☐ Describe basis for N/A

ASSESSMENT/
SUMMARY:

a. **List** the Vendor Quality Manual reference and implementing procedure(s) established to provide the measures for the verification of design adequacy:

Are procedural controls adequate and procedure revision current?
YES ☐ **or**

NO ☐ (Identify and provide input to the team member evaluating checklist Section 9.)

b. **Describe** <u>implementation</u> of the supplier's measures (who, what, how) for the verification of design adequacy:

1. Assure the verification method is identified (design review, alternate calculations or test) and that the verification is performed by individuals or groups other than those who performed the original design, but who may be from the same organization.

2. Verify that the design is supported by engineering data (i.e., calculations, performance test, etc.), including verification that design inputs are satisfied.

3. When the verification method used is qualification test, verify that a prototype unit is tested under the most adverse design conditions including design basis event service conditions.

Are procedural controls adequately implemented?
YES ☐ **or**

NO ☐ (describe the inadequacy)

SECTION 2 – DESIGN

METHOD OF VERIFICATION

2.6   Verify that measures are established and implemented to control design changes including changes for spare/replacement parts.

Objective Evidence required for Figure 2:
- Design Change Control **and** Revision **and/or** Date

References:
Appendix B/ANSI N45.2 - (3/4)
ASME Section III
NQA-1 Supplement 3S-1

RESULTS: *SAT* ☐   *UNSAT* ☐ Describe Finding(s)   *N/A* ☐ Describe basis for N/A

ASSESSMENT/ SUMMARY:

a.   *List* the Vendor Quality Manual reference and implementing procedure(s) established to control design changes including changes for spare/replacement parts:

Are procedural controls adequate and procedure revision current?
YES ☐ *or*
NO ☐ (Identify and provide input to the team member evaluating checklist Section 9.)

b.   *Describe* implementation of the supplier's measures (who, what, how) to control design changes including changes for spare/replacement parts:

1. Review revised design documents, (e.g., calculations, drawings, stress reports), to verify that design changes are made by the same organization as originally reviewed and approved, or by other knowledgeable, qualified and designated organizations.
2. Ensure design control measures are equal to those of the original design.
3. Ensure that design changes have been adequately evaluated to assure that the impact of the change or cumulative effect of multiple changes are carefully considered (i.e., material substitutions, performance, interchangeability, EQ/seismic, test and equipment qualification).

Are procedural controls adequately implemented?
YES ☐ *or*
NO ☐ (describe the inadequacy)

SECTION 2 – DESIGN

(FIGURE 2)

CUSTOMER/SUPPLIER DESIGN INPUT and BASES	SUPPLIER DESIGN DOCUMENT	DESIGN INPUTS CORRECTLY INCORPORATED (Yes/No)	METHOD OF DESIGN VERIFICATION	DESIGN CHANGE CONTROL and REV / DATE
* 2.2	* 2.2	* 2.2	* 2.2	* 2.2

* Refers to applicable question

SECTION 3 – COMMERCIAL GRADE DEDICATION

METHOD OF VERIFICATION

3.1	Within the assessment/summary section of each checklist question, record the procedures/instructions/drawings including the revision/date used to verify implementation.
3.2	**Verify that measures are established and implemented for the dedication of purchased Commercial Grade Items and services.**

Objective Evidence required for Figure 3A:
- Item Description, P/N, S/N, Model No., Software Name/ID, No., etc. (List items/services dedicated using Method 1 only or in combination with Methods 2, 3, 4.)
- Critical Characteristics **and** Method(s) of Dedication

Implementation Information:
This question applies to Commercial Grade Item's dedicated by the supplier for customer procurement as basic components, or for the supplier's use in safety-related parts/services (e.g., software, consumables, fasteners, elastomers etc.).

At a minimum, the process should include documented controls that define the dedication process including a documented technical evaluation that establishes requirements providing reasonable assurance the item/service will perform its intended safety function (or meet design requirements), identification of critical characteristics, and selection of acceptance method(s) for each critical characteristic identified.

If the design criteria for the commercial grade item are known by the dedicating entity, then the item may be dedicated to these criteria in lieu of defining a specific safety function. In this case, consideration of failure modes is not required and the item's design parameters and allowables become the critical characteristics and acceptance criteria. In this instance, the design requirements become the critical characteristics requiring verification.

For items that are seismically/environmentally qualified (e.g., relays, switches, nonmetallic items, etc.), appropriate critical characteristics should be verified, which ensures the seismic/environmental qualification of the item has been maintained.

Note 1: For suppliers who are unable to determine the items/materials safety function or end use (i.e., material suppliers, QSC Certificate holders, etc.), characteristics identified in the material specification, which are applicable to the finished product (i.e., chemical, physical, hydro, etc.), must be verified as critical characteristics.

References:
Appendix B/ANSI N45.2 - (3/4)
ASME Section III
NQA-1 Supplement 7S-1

RESULTS: *SAT* ☐   *UNSAT* ☐ Describe Finding(s)   *N/A* ☐ Describe basis for N/A

ASSESSMENT/
SUMMARY:

a. *List* the Vendor Quality Manual reference and implementing procedure(s) established to provide the measures for the dedication of purchased Commercial Grade items and services:

Are procedural controls adequate and procedure revision current?

YES ☐ *or*

NO ☐ (Identify and provide input to the team member evaluating checklist Section 9.)

SECTION 3 – COMMERCIAL GRADE DEDICATION

b. **Describe** implementation of the supplier's measures (who, what, how) for the dedication of purchased Commercial Grade items and services, including:

1. A documented technical evaluation, performed by the responsible engineering organization that establishes requirements that will provide reasonable assurance the item/service will perform its intended safety-related function (see **Note 1**). The Technical evaluation should include identification of safety-function, critical characteristics, and acceptance methods. Determination of the safety function for the item/service intended end use should include review of documents associated with the technical evaluation, such as:

   - Classification of the item
   - Item equivalency evaluations
   - Consideration of credible failure modes (See Implementation **Note 1**)

2. Measures for the selection of the acceptance method(s) of dedication, for each identified critical characteristic:

   - Method 1 – Inspection, and Test
   - Method 2 – Commercial Grade Item Surveys
   - Method 3 – Source Verification
   - Method 4 – Supplier/Performance history in conjunction with Methods 1, 2, or 3, above.

Are procedural controls adequately implemented?

YES ☐ *or*

NO ☐ (describe the inadequacy)

METHOD OF VERIFICATION

3.3 **Verify that measures are established and implemented for the acceptance of purchased commercial grade items and services by Method 1 dedication.**

Objective Evidence required for Figure 3A:
- Inspection/Test Procedure **and** Rev./Date
- Inspector/Tester Name/Stamp
- ID Number of M&TE used
- Results SAT or UNSAT (record NCR No. if UNSAT)

Implementation Information:
Special tests/inspections supporting Method 1 Dedication are different from receipt inspection. When used as the Dedication Method, tests/inspections selected must be appropriate to verify each critical characteristic **after receipt**.

Checklist Interface:
Identify the Inspector/Tester to the audit team member evaluating Checklist Section 14.
Identify the M&TE used to the audit team member evaluating Checklist Section 8.

References:
Appendix B/ANSI N45.2 - (10, 11/11, 12)
ASME Section III
NQA-1 Supplement 10S-1, 11S-1

RESULTS:　　　　**SAT** ☐　　　　**UNSAT** ☐ Describe Finding(s)　　*N/A* ☐ Describe basis for N/A

SECTION 3 – COMMERCIAL GRADE DEDICATION

ASSESSMENT/
SUMMARY:

a. ***List*** the Vendor Quality Manual reference and implementing procedure(s) established to provide the measures for the acceptance of purchased Commercial Grade items and services by Method 1 dedications:

Are procedural controls adequate and procedure revision current?

YES ☐ *or*

NO ☐ (Identify and provide input to the team member evaluating checklist Section 9.)

b. ***Describe*** implementation of the supplier's measures (who, what, how) for the acceptance of purchased Commercial Grade items and services by Method 1 dedications, including:

1. If the supplier's safety-related components have parts classified as non-safety-related, describe the measures in use which provide the basis for the non-safety-related classification.

2. Verify that the tests and inspections specified for the acceptance of commercial grade items incorporate and implement sampling plans that are controlled and their technical basis (homogeneity, item complexity, lot/batch control, heat traceability, supplier controls [survey], supplier performance, etc.) established and documented.

Are procedural controls adequately implemented?

YES ☐ *or*

NO ☐ (describe the inadequacy)

METHOD OF VERIFICATION

3.4 **Verify that measures are established and implemented for the acceptance of purchased commercial grade items and services by Method 2 and Method 3 dedication.**

Objective Evidence required for Figure 3B:
- Scope of Item/Service Requiring Dedication
- CGI Supplier Name **and** Location
- Commercial Grade Survey (Method 2) or Source Verification (Method 3) **and** Date(s) Performed
- Auditors (Method 2) Auditor **and/or** Inspectors (Method 3)
- Critical Characteristics (CCs) Verified **and** SAT **or** UNSAT
- CCs Verified Match Those Specified (Yes/No)

Implementation Information:
Surveys should be performed by personnel trained (qualified) in auditing and knowledgeable in operation of the item(s) being dedicated and critical characteristics being verified.
Source verifications should be performed by technically competent personnel, knowledgeable in operation of the item(s) being dedicated and critical characteristics being verified.

Checklist Interface:
Identify the Auditors or Inspectors (Source) to the audit team member evaluating Checklist Section 14.

References:
Appendix B/ANSI N45.2 - (10, 11/11, 12)
ASME Section III
NQA-1 Supplement 10S-1, 11S-1

RESULTS: ***SAT*** ☐   ***UNSAT*** ☐ Describe Finding(s)   ***N/A*** ☐ Describe basis for N/A

SECTION 3 – COMMERCIAL GRADE DEDICATION

**ASSESSMENT/
SUMMARY:**

a. *List* the Vendor Quality Manual reference and implementing procedure(s) established to provide the measures for the acceptance of purchased Commercial Grade items and services by Method 2 and Method 3 dedications:

Are procedural controls adequate and procedure revision current?

YES ☐ *or*

NO ☐ (Identify and provide input to the team member evaluating checklist Section 9.)

b. *Describe* implementation of the supplier's measures for the acceptance of purchased Commercial Grade items and services by Method 2 and Method 3 dedications, including:

1. Verify, as applicable, that the commercial grade survey or source verification used for the acceptance of commercial grade items:

    a. Is performed in accordance with a procedure describing the applicable commercial grade survey or source verification process.

    b. Is conducted by appropriately trained/qualified personnel.

    c. Documents the procedure/instruction/program controls in place that control the identified critical characteristics.

    d. Demonstrates that the identified critical characteristics are controlled.

    e. Identifies compensatory or corrective actions proposed/completed for critical characteristics found to be inadequately controlled.

Are procedural controls adequately implemented?

YES ☐ *or*

NO ☐ (describe the inadequacy)

SECTION 3 – COMMERCIAL GRADE DEDICATION

METHOD OF VERIFICATION

3.5 Verify the following measures have been established and implemented if the ILAC process is used in lieu of commercial grade survey for the verification of the critical characteristics for calibration and/or test laboratories.

Objective Evidence required for Figure 3C:
- CGI Supplier Name **and** Location
- Accrediting Body Name, Certificate Number **and** Expiration Date
- Scope Of Accreditation (Calibration or Testing Service)
- Dedication Technical Evaluation Completed **and** Satisfactory (Yes/No)
- Documented Review of Accreditation Completed **and** Satisfactory (Yes/No)
- Receipt Inspection of Accredited Calibrations Satisfactory (Yes/No)

Implementation Information:
The process for accepting accreditation to ISO/IEC 17025:2005 by an acceptable Accreditation Body (AB) must be proceduralized, including reference to the NRC APS SER and/or NEI 14-05A as applicable. If the NRC APS SER is utilized, acceptance of laboratory services is limited to domestic calibration laboratories that are accredited to by either NVLAP, A2LA, ACLASS, L-A-B, IAS, or PJLA. If NEI 14-05A is utilized, both calibration and test laboratories are acceptable provided the laboratory is accredited by an Accreditation Body that is a signatory to the ILAC MRA. This includes both domestic and international laboratories.

A technical evaluation must be documented that identifies the safety function and critical characteristics of the service.

<u>For implementation of the NRC APS SER</u>:
A documented evaluation must be performed by the supplier for the following requirements:
1. Sub-supplier has accreditation to ISO/IEC 17025:2005.
2. Accreditation is issued by NVLAP, A2LA, ACLASS, LAB, IAS, or PJLA.
3. Sub-supplier is a commercial grade, domestic (US) calibration laboratory.
4. The published scope of accreditation for the calibration laboratory covers the necessary measurement parameters, ranges, and uncertainties.
5. Receipt inspection is performed, which includes a review of the certification documentation supplied by the laboratory to verify the certification documentation includes the laboratory's name, location, Accreditation Body (AB) name and logo **(when required)**, certificate number, accreditation was current (not expired) at the time of calibration, certification indicates that the services were performed in accordance with the laboratory's accredited ISO/IEC 17025:2005 program and accredited scope, and a statement certifying that the purchase order requirements were met.

<u>For implementation of NEI 14-05A:</u>
A documented evaluation must be performed by the supplier for the following requirements:
1. The calibration or test laboratory holds accreditation by an Accreditation Body (AB) recognized by the ILAC MRA. The accreditation encompasses ISO/IEC 17025:2005.
2. For procurement of **calibration services**, the published scope of accreditation for the calibration laboratory covers the needed measurement parameters, ranges, and uncertainties.
3. For procurement of **testing services**, the published scope of accreditation for the test laboratory covers the needed testing services including test methodology and tolerances/uncertainty.
4. Receipt inspection is performed, which includes a review of the certification documentation supplied by the laboratory to verify the certification documentation includes the laboratory's name, location, Accreditation Body (AB) name and logo **(when required)**, certificate number, accreditation was current (not expired) at the time of calibration, certification indicates that the services were performed in accordance with the laboratory's accredited ISO/IEC 17025:2005 program and accredited scope, and a statement certifying that the purchase order requirements were met.

Note 1: Implementation of the requirements listed in either Implementation option (APS/NEI), respectively, is considered to be acceptable for use of the ILAC process to accept commercial grade calibration services.

SECTION 3 – COMMERCIAL GRADE DEDICATION

Checklist Interface:
Identify the use of the ILAC process to the audit team member evaluating Checklist Section 5.

References:
Appendix B/ANSI N45.2 - (3, 10, 11/ 4, 11, 12)
ASME Section III
NQA-1 Supplement 3S-1,10S-1, 11S-1

RESULTS: *SAT* ☐   *UNSAT* ☐ Describe Finding(s)   *N/A* ☐ Describe basis for N/A

ASSESSMENT/ SUMMARY:

a.   *List* the Vendor Quality Manual reference and implementing procedure(s) established to provide measures for use of the ILAC in lieu of commercial grade survey for the verification of the critical characteristics for calibration and/or test laboratories:

Are procedural controls adequate and procedure revision current?

YES ☐ or

NO ☐ (Identify and provide input to the team member evaluating checklist Section 9.)

b.   *Describe* implementation of the supplier's measures (who, what, how) for use of the ILAC process in lieu of commercial grade survey for the verification of the critical characteristics for calibration and/or test laboratories:

Are procedural controls adequately implemented?

YES ☐ or

NO ☐ (describe the inadequacy)

SECTION 3 – COMMERCIAL GRADE DEDICATION

(FIGURE 3A)

COMMERCIAL GRADE ITEMS / METHOD 1 ACCEPTANCE					
ITEM/SERVICE DESCRIPTION P/N, S/N, MODEL #, SOFTWARE NAME/ID #, ETC. (Note 1)	CRITICAL CHARACTERISTICS and METHOD(s) OF DEDICATION FOR EACH (Note 1)	INSPECTION/ TEST PROCEDURE and REV / DATE (Method 1 only)	INSPECTOR/ TESTER NAME / STAMP (Method 1 only)	ID # OF M&TE USED (Method 1 only)	RESULTS SAT or UNSAT (record NCR # if UNSAT) (Method 1 only)
* 3.2, 3.3, 3.4, 4.5	* 3.2, 3.3, 3.4, 4.5	* 3.2, 3.3, 3.4, 4.5	* 3.2, 3.3, 3.4, 4.5	* 3.2, 3.3, 3.4, 4.5	* 3.2, 3.3, 3.4, 4.5

* Refers to applicable question

Note 1: List items/services dedicated using Method 1 only or in combination with Methods 2, 3, 4.

SECTION 3 – COMMERCIAL GRADE DEDICATION

(FIGURE 3B)

SURVEYS / SOURCE VERIFICATION – METHODS 2 AND 3					
SCOPE OF ITEM/SERVICE REQUIRING DEDICATION (Note 1)	CGI SUPPLIER NAME and LOCATION	COMMERCIAL GRADE SURVEY (Method 2) or SOURCE VERIFICATION (Method 3) and DATE(s) PERFORMED	AUITORS (Method 2) and/or INSPECTORS (Method 3)	CRITICAL CHARACTERISTICS (CC) VERIFIED (Note 2)	DO CC(s) VERIFIED MATCH THOSE SPECIFIED IN TECHNICAL EVALUATION/ DEDICATION PLAN (Yes/No)
* 3.4, 4.5	* 3.4, 4.5	* 3.4, 4.5	* 3.4, 4.5	* 3.4, 4.5	* 3.4, 4.5

* Refers to applicable question

Note 1: List Items/Services being dedicated using Method 2 or 3.

Note 2: Critical characteristics, listed on this figure, should match those verified using Method 2 or 3, as listed on Figure 3A, when the item/service is being dedicated using Method 1 in combination with Methods 2 or 3.

SECTION 3 – COMMERCIAL GRADE DEDICATION

(FIGURE 3C)

ILAC ACCREDITATION ACCEPTANCE					
CGI SUPPLIER NAME and LOCATION	ACCREDITING BODY NAME CERTIFICATE # and EXPIRATION DATE	SCOPE OF ACCREDITATION (Calibration or Testing Service)	DEDICATION TECHNICAL EVALUATION COMPLETED and SATISFACTORY (Yes/No)	DOCUMENTED REVIEW OF ACCREDITATION COMPLETED and SATISFACTORY (Yes/No)	RECEIPT INSPECTION OF ACCREDITED CALIBRATIONS SATISFACTORY (Yes/No)
* 3.4, 4.5	* 3.4, 4.5	* 3.4, 4.5	* 3.4, 4.5	* 3.4, 4.5	* 3.4, 4.5

* Refers to applicable question

SECTION 4 – SOFTWARE

METHOD OF VERIFICATION

4.1	Within the assessment/summary section of each checklist question, record the procedures/instructions/drawings including the revision/date used to verify implementation.
4.2	**Verify documented measures (plans, policies, and procedures) are established and implemented to control the quality of software (including firmware).**

Objective Evidence required for Figure 4:
- Software Program (Name, Number, Revision **and/or** Date)

Implementation Information:
A "plan" for software quality is required at the start of software lifecycle for developed software or upon entry into the purchaser's organization for procured software. "Plans" may be unique to each project, may exist as a generic document (procedure), or may be incorporated into the overall QA program. "Plans" identify:
- The software product
- Responsible organizations, tasks, and responsibilities
- Documentation requirements
- Standards, conventions, techniques, methodologies applied to the development
- Review requirements
- Error reporting/corrective action methods

A software lifecycle includes activities such as requirements phase, design phase, implementation phase, testing phase, installation and checkout phase, operations and maintenance phase, and retirement phase. The number of phases, and emphasis placed on each, is dependent on nature and complexity of the software.

References:
Appendix B/ANSI N45.2 - (3/4)
ASME Section III
NQA-1-1994 Basic Requirements 3, 11 and 17, Supplement 3S-1, 11S-2, 17S-1 and Subpart 2.7

RESULTS: **SAT** ☐   **UNSAT** ☐ Describe Finding(s)   **N/A** ☐ Describe basis for N/A

**ASSESSMENT/
SUMMARY:**

a. **List** the Vendor Quality Manual reference and implementing procedure(s) established to control the development or procurement of safety-related software (including firmware):

Are procedural controls adequate and procedure revision current?

YES ☐ **or**

NO ☐ (Identify and provide input to the team member evaluating checklist Section 9.)

b. **Describe** implementation of the supplier's measures (who, what, how) for the development or procurement of safety-related software (including firmware):

- Verify that a "plan" exists for assuring software quality.
- Verify that lifecycle activities are identified and reviewed, as applicable to the nature and complexity of the software.

Are procedural controls adequately implemented?

YES ☐ **or**

NO ☐ (describe the inadequacy)

SECTION 4 – SOFTWARE

METHOD OF VERIFICATION

4.3   Verify that measures are established and implemented to assure that software acceptance testing (verification and validation) is planned and performed to demonstrate that software adequately and correctly performs all intended functions (i.e., specified software design requirements) and does not perform any unintended function.

Objective Evidence required for Figure 4:
• "Method of Acceptance" Testing **and** Date

Implementation Information:
Software verification, performed during development, ensures that results of a given lifecycle phase meet requirements of the previous phase/phases (i.e., design phase satisfies requirements phase, etc.). Software validation, performed at the conclusion of the implementation phase, ensures that the code satisfies the requirements by development and execution of test plans and test cases. To evaluate technical adequacy, test case results can be compared to alternative "Methods of Acceptance" such as:
• hand calculations
• other validated computer program
• experiments/tests
• standard problems with known solutions
• confirmed published data and correlations

Identify the software acceptance testing, listed on Figure 4, which was observed in progress versus reviewed in completed documentation.

References:
Appendix B/ANSI N45.2 - (4/5, 7/8)
ASME Section III
NQA-1-1994 Basic Requirement 11, Supplement 11S-2 and Subpart 2.7

RESULTS: *SAT* ☐   *UNSAT* ☐ Describe Finding(s)   *N/A* ☐ Describe basis for N/A

ASSESSMENT/   a.   *List* the Vendor Quality Manual reference and implementing procedure(s) established
SUMMARY: to control software acceptance testing:

Are procedural controls adequate and procedure revision current?
YES ☐ *or*
NO ☐ (Identify and provide input to the team member evaluating checklist Section 9.)

b.   *Describe* implementation of the supplier's measures (who, what, how) for software acceptance testing:

Are procedural controls adequately implemented?
YES ☐ *or*
NO ☐ (describe the inadequacy)

SECTION 4 – SOFTWARE

METHOD OF VERIFICATION

4.4 **Verify that measures are established and implemented to assure that software configuration is maintained and the changes to software are formally documented.**

Objective Evidence required for Figure 4:
- Software Program (Name, Number, Revision **and/or** Date)

Implementation Information:
Changes to software require formal documentation identifying:
- description of the change
- rationale for the change
- identification of affected baselines (e.g., Requirements documentation, Design documentation)

A configuration baseline defines completion of each major phase of software development. Approved changes added to the baseline define the current approved software configuration. Configuration management includes documentation of the approved configuration, the status of proposed changes to the configuration, and the status of approved changes to the configuration.

Note 1: Configuration management also applies to backups, maintenance, disaster recovery, and virus protection.

References:
Appendix B/ANSI N45.2 - (3/4)
ASME Section III
NQA-1-1994 Basic Requirement 3, Supplement 3S-1 and Subpart 2.7

RESULTS: **SAT** ☐   **UNSAT** ☐ Describe Finding(s)   **N/A** ☐ Describe basis for N/A

ASSESSMENT/SUMMARY:

a. **List** the Vendor Quality Manual reference and implementing procedure(s) established to control software changes and configuration:

Are procedural controls adequate and procedure revision current?
YES ☐ or
NO ☐ (Identify and provide input to the team member evaluating checklist Section 9.)

b. **Describe** implementation of the supplier's measures (who, what, how) for software change and configuration management including:
- Evaluation and approval of software changes by the organization responsible for the original software development.
- Software verification, to ensure the change is reflected in traceable software documentation, and software validation, as necessary.

Are procedural controls adequately implemented?
YES ☐ or
NO ☐ (describe the inadequacy)

SECTION 4 – SOFTWARE

METHOD OF VERIFICATION

4.5 **Verify measures are established and implemented for the procurement of software (safety-related or commercial grade).**

Objective Evidence required (as appropriate to the software classification):
- Commercial Grade: Figures 3A **and** 3B (as appropriate to the methods of Dedication)
- Safety-Related: Figures 5A **and** 5B

Implementation Information:
Safety-Related software procurement requires purchaser controls (i.e., acceptable supplier qualification, procurement practices and receipt inspection) to ensure that the software supplier is providing software that meets the technical and quality requirements specified in the purchase order. The purchaser's audit of the software supplier ensures that the software was developed and maintained in accordance with software quality assurance program requirements identified in this Checklist Section (4).

Procurement of commercial grade (commercial) software for use in safety-related applications requires Commercial Grade Item Dedication per Checklist Section 3. Dedication activities should establish configuration control and ensure, at a minimum, that application requirements are identified, test plans/test cases to validate software acceptability are performed, and user documentation is generated (input/output specifications, system limitations, etc.).

Procured software typically enters the purchaser's organization at the start of the lifecycle installation and checkout phase. This phase includes software verification and validation activities, which consist of testing for installation and integration and documentation of software approval for operational use. The purchaser's software quality plan should address applicable lifecycle activities (i.e., installation and checkout, operations and maintenance, retirement), once the software has entered the purchaser's organization.

Checklist Interface:
Safety-Related software procurement: Interface with, and identify the software supplier and software to, the auditor responsible for evaluating Checklist Section 5.
Commercial grade (commercial) software procurement: Interface with, and identify the software supplier and software to, the auditor responsible for evaluating Checklist Section 3.

References:
Appendix B/ANSI N45.2 - (3/4, 4/5, 7/8)
ASME Section III
NQA-1-1994 Basic Requirements 4, 7, 11, Supplements 4S-1, 7S-1, 11S-2 and Subpart 2.7

RESULTS: *SAT* ☐   *UNSAT* ☐ Describe Finding(s)   *N/A* ☐ Describe basis for N/A

**ASSESSMENT/
SUMMARY:**

a. **List** the Vendor Quality Manual reference and implementing procedure(s) established to control the procurement of software (safety-related or commercial grade):

Are procedural controls adequate and procedure revision current?

YES ☐ *or*

NO ☐ (Identify and provide input to the team member evaluating checklist Section 9.)

b. **Describe** implementation of the supplier's measures (who, what, how) for procurement of software (safety-related or commercial grade):

Are procedural controls adequately implemented?

YES ☐ *or*

NO ☐ (describe the inadequacy)

SECTION 4 – SOFTWARE

METHOD OF VERIFICATION

4.6   Verify that problem reporting measures are established and implemented to assure that software errors and failures from <u>both</u> internal and external sources are identified, documented, evaluated, resolved, and assessed for impact on past and present applications.

Objective Evidence required for Figure 4:
• Error Notice Date **and** Status (OPEN / CLOSED)

References:
Appendix B/ANSI N45.2 - (15/16)
ASME Section III
NQA-1-1994 Basic Requirement 16 and Subpart 2.7

RESULTS: *SAT* ☐   *UNSAT* ☐ Describe Finding(s)   *N/A* ☐ Describe basis for N/A

ASSESSMENT/   a.   *List* the Vendor Quality Manual reference and implementing procedure(s)
SUMMARY: established to control problem reporting:

Are procedural controls adequate and procedure revision current?
YES ☐ or
NO ☐ (Identify and provide input to the team member evaluating checklist Section 9.)

b.   *Describe* implementation of the supplier's measures (who, what, how) for control of problem reporting including:
• Methods of notification consistent with those identified in the problem reporting system.
• Problem classification with defined criteria based on impact of software output.
• Problems and their significance promptly reported to affected organizations.

Are procedural controls adequately implemented?
YES ☐ or
NO ☐ (describe the inadequacy)

SECTION 4 – SOFTWARE

METHOD OF VERIFICATION

4.7 **Verify measures are established and implemented to assure that software is adequately packaged, marked, stored, and shipped.**

References:
Appendix B/ANSI N45.2 - (13, 14/14, 15)
ASME Section III
NQA-1-1994 Basic Requirement 13 and Supplement 13S-1

RESULTS: *SAT* ☐   *UNSAT* ☐ Describe Finding(s)   *N/A* ☐ Describe basis for N/A

ASSESSMENT/
SUMMARY:

a.   *List* the Vendor Quality Manual reference and implementing procedure(s) established to control software packaging, marking, storage, and shipment:

Are procedural controls adequate and procedure revision current?

YES ☐ *or*

NO ☐ (Identify and provide input to the team member evaluating checklist Section 9.)

b.   *Describe* <u>implementation</u> of the supplier's measures (who, what, how) for control software packaging, marking, storage, and shipment:

•   Verify when duplicate copies are generated, that methods are in place to ensure exact duplication.

Are procedural controls adequately implemented?

YES ☐ *or*

NO ☐ (describe the inadequacy)

SECTION 4 – SOFTWARE

(FIGURE 4)

SOFTWARE PROGRAM (NAME, #, REV / DATE)	METHOD OF ACCETANCE TESTING and DATE	PROGRAM REPORT # DATE and STATUS (OPEN / CLOSED)
* 4.2, 4.4	* 4.2, 4.4	* 4.2, 4.4
* Refers to applicable question		

SECTION 5 – PROCUREMENT

METHOD OF VERIFICATION

5.1   Within the assessment/summary section of each checklist question, record the procedures/instructions/drawings including the revision/date used to verify implementation.

5.2   **Verify that measures are established and implemented for the control and release of procurement documents, including changes.**

Objective Evidence required for Figure 5A:
- ITEM DESCRIPTION NAME (PART NUMBER, SERIAL NUMBER, MODEL NUMBER, SOFTWARE NAME)
- SUPPLIER **and** LOCATION
- P.O. NUMBER **and** DATE

Implementation Information:
As applicable, supplier procurement processes should ensure the following requirements are identified in procurement documents and procurement document changes, for items and services:
- Scope of work
- Technical requirements (by reference to specific drawings, codes, specifications)
- Documented Quality Assurance program
- Right of access for source inspection/audit
- Document submittals for approval
- Deliverable records
- Reporting and approving nonconformance dispositions
- Records availability, retention and disposition
- Extending Technical and QA requirements to lower tier suppliers
- 10 CFR 21 applicability

Note 1: If the supplier utilizes NEI 14-05A, in lieu of commercial grade surveys, for acceptance of domestic and international commercial calibration and testing sub-supplier services from laboratories accredited to ISO/IEC 17025 that are a signatory to the ILAC MRA, procurement document requirements must include:
- The service must be provided in accordance with their accredited ISO/IEC 17025:2005 program and scope of accreditation.
- As-found calibration data must be reported in the certificate of calibration when calibrated items are found to be out-of-tolerance *(for calibration services only)*.
- The equipment/standards used to perform the calibration must be identified in the certificate of calibration *(for calibration services only)*.
- The customer must be notified of any condition that adversely impacts the laboratory's ability to maintain the scope of accreditation.
- Any additional technical and quality requirements, as necessary, based upon a review of the procured scope of services, which may include, but are not necessarily limited to, tolerances, accuracies, ranges, and industry standards.

Note 2: If the supplier utilizes the NRC APS SER, in lieu of commercial grade surveys, for acceptance of domestic commercial calibration sub-supplier services from laboratories accredited to ISO/IEC 17025 by NVLAP, A2LA, ACLASS, L-A-B, IAS, or PJLA, procurement document requirements must include:
- Requirement for reporting as-found calibration data when calibrated items are found to be out-of-tolerance.
- Requirement that calibration reports include identification of the laboratory equipment/standards used.
- Additional technical and administrative requirements, as necessary, to satisfy the supplier's QA program and technical requirements.

Note 3: Implementation of the requirements listed in either Note 1 or Note 2, respectively, is considered to be acceptable for use of ILAC process to accept commercial grade calibration services.

SECTION 5 – PROCUREMENT

Checklist Interface:
Identify any procurement, based on use of the ILAC process, to the audit team member evaluating Checklist Section 3.

References:
Appendix B/ANSI N45.2 - (4/5)
ASME Section III
NQA-1 Supplement 4S-1

RESULTS: **SAT** ☐   **UNSAT** ☐ Describe Finding(s)   **N/A** ☐ Describe basis for N/A

ASSESSMENT/ SUMMARY:

a. **List** the Vendor Quality Manual reference and implementing procedure(s) established to control and release procurement documents, including changes:

Are procedural controls adequate and procedure revision current?
YES ☐ **or**

NO ☐ (Identify and provide input to the team member evaluating checklist Section 9.)

b. **Describe** implementation of the supplier's measures (who, what, how) to control, release, and change procurement documents, including:

- Consistent inclusion of applicable requirements.
- Consistent inclusion of applicable requirements for accredited domestic and international commercial calibration and testing laboratory services.

Are procedural controls adequately implemented?
YES ☐ **or**

NO ☐ (describe the inadequacy)

METHOD OF VERIFICATION

5.3   **Verify that measures are established and implemented for the evaluation, selection and assessment of sub-suppliers including distributors, services (calibration, NDE, testing, heat treatment, etc.) and software.**

Objective Evidence required for Figure 5A:
- ITEM DESCRIPTION NAME (PART NUMBER, SERIAL NUMBER, MODEL NUMBER, SOFTWARE NAME)
- SUPPLIER **and** LOCATION
- P.O. NUMBER **and** DATE
- METHOD **and** DATE OF SUPPLIER EVALUATION
- SCOPE OF SUPPLIER APPROVAL

Implementation Information:
As applicable to sub-suppliers in use, the supplier's quality program must address audits of Appendix B sub-suppliers, commercial grade surveys of commercial grade sub-suppliers and, if applicable, the use of accreditation in lieu of commercial grade surveys for domestic and international commercial calibration and testing laboratory services:

SECTION 5 – PROCUREMENT

- Evaluation of the sub-supplier must be performed prior to award of the purchase order/contract, and periodically thereafter.
- Sub-suppliers must be "approved" for use as indicated by an approved/qualified suppliers list or equivalent.
- The sub-supplier scope of approval must encompass the items/services identified in the procurement documents.

Note 1: Content of CGI surveys is addressed in Checklist Question 3.4.

Note 2: Evaluation of suppliers using ILAC accreditation in lieu of commercial grade surveys, for acceptance of domestic and international commercial calibration and testing laboratory services is addressed in Checklist Question 3.5.

Checklist Interface:
Identify any evaluations, based on use of the ILAC process, to the audit team member evaluating Checklist Section 3.

References:
Appendix B/ANSI N45.2 - (7/8)
ASME Section III
NQA-1 Supplement 7S-1

RESULTS: **SAT** ☐   **UNSAT** ☐ Describe Finding(s)   **N/A** ☐ Describe basis for N/A

ASSESSMENT/
SUMMARY:

a. **List** the Vendor Quality Manual reference and implementing procedure(s) established for the evaluation, selection and assessment of sub-suppliers:

Are procedural controls adequate and procedure revision current?

YES ☐ *or*

NO ☐ (Identify and provide input to the team member evaluating checklist Section 9.)

b. **Describe** implementation of the supplier's measures (who, what, how) for the evaluation, selection and assessment of sub-suppliers:

Are procedural controls adequately implemented?

YES ☐ *or*

NO ☐ (describe the inadequacy)

SECTION 5 – PROCUREMENT

METHOD OF VERIFICATION

5.4   Verify that measures are established and implemented to ensure a comprehensive system of planned and periodic <u>external</u> audits (including 3rd party audits).

Objective Evidence required for Figure 5B:
- SUPPLIER NAME, LOCATION **and** DATE(S) PERFORMED
- EVALUATION METHOD (APPENDIX B AUDIT, SOURCE ACTIVITY)
- SCOPE OF SUPPLY
- AUDITORS
- NUMBER OF DEFICIENCIES (OPEN/ CLOSED)
- CORRECTIVE ACTION VERIFICATION METHOD **and** DATE

Implementation Information:
If 3rd party audits (NIAC, Consultant performed) are used as a basis for supplier qualification, the process must be addressed within the supplier's program/procedures. The evaluation of 3rd party audits must be documented and must address:
- Performance of the audit by qualified personnel.
- Performance of the evaluation by qualified personnel to ensure the user's program requirements are satisfied.
- Scope of the audit envelops the current scope of procurement.
- Applicable regulatory and/or commercial program requirements are adequately addressed in the audit scope.
- Sufficient objective evidence is available to support conclusions of the audit.

Checklist Interface:
Provide auditor names to the audit team member evaluating Checklist Section 14.

References:
Appendix B/ANSI N45.2 - (18/19)
ASME Section III
NQA-1 Supplement 18S-1

RESULTS: *SAT* ☐   *UNSAT* ☐ Describe Finding(s)   *N/A* ☐ Describe basis for N/A

ASSESSMENT/ SUMMARY: a.   *List* the Vendor Quality Manual reference and implementing procedure(s) established to ensure a comprehensive system of planned and periodic <u>external</u> audits (including 3rd party audits):

Are procedural controls adequate and procedure revision current?
YES ☐ *or*
NO ☐ (Identify and provide input to the team member evaluating checklist Section 9.)

SECTION 5 – PROCUREMENT

b. ***Describe*** <u>implementation</u> of the supplier's measures (who, what, how) to ensure a comprehensive system of planned and periodic <u>external</u> audits (including 3rd party audits):

1. Verify that the audits were conducted by qualified personnel and are of sufficient depth and scope to ensure adequacy and effectiveness of the sub-suppliers program.

2. Verify that checklists or procedures were used with sufficient objective evidence documented and that follow-up action is taken where needed.

Are procedural controls adequately implemented?

YES ☐ *or*

NO ☐ (describe the inadequacy)

METHOD OF VERIFICATION

5.5 **Verify that measures are established and implemented for acceptance of safety-related material from an ASME sub-supplier, <u>based on ASME Certification</u> (including materials supplied under provisions of NX2610).**

References:
Appendix B/ANSI N45.2 - (7/8)
IE Notice 86-21 including supplements
NQA-1 Supplement 7S-1

RESULTS: ***SAT*** ☐   ***UNSAT*** ☐ Describe Finding(s)   ***N/A*** ☐ Describe basis for N/A

ASSESSMENT/ SUMMARY:

a. ***List*** the Vendor Quality Manual reference and implementing procedure(s) established for acceptance of safety-related material from an ASME sub-supplier, based on ASME certification:

Are procedural controls adequate and procedure revision current?

YES ☐ *or*

NO ☐ (Identify and provide input to the team member evaluating checklist Section 9.)

b. ***Describe*** <u>implementation</u> of the supplier's measures (who, what, how) for acceptance of safety-related material from an ASME sub-supplier, based on ASME certification:

1. Verify that the certification is validated via surveillance, audit and/or independent test.

2. If validation of the certification is based on independent test, in lieu of auditing, and end use is not known, ensure the test encompasses all characteristics of the material specification (i.e., chemical, physical, hydro, etc.).

Are procedural controls adequately implemented?

YES ☐ *or*

NO ☐ (describe the inadequacy)

SECTION 5 – PROCUREMENT

(FIGURE 5A)

ITEM DESCRIPTION NAME (P/N, S/N, MODEL #, SOFTWARE NAME)	SUPPLIER and LOCATION	P.O. NUMBER and DATE	METHOD and DATE OF SUPPLIER EVALUATION	SCOPE OF SUPPLIER APPROVAL
* 4.5, 5.2, 5.3	* 4.5, 5.2, 5.3	* 4.5, 5.2, 5.3	* 4.5, 5.3, 5.4	* 4.5, 5.3, 5.4

* Refers to applicable question

SECTION 5 – PROCUREMENT

(FIGURE 5B AUDIT/SOURCE VERIFICATION)

SUPPLIER NAME, LOCATION **and** DATE(S) PERFORMED	EVALUATION METHOD (APPENDIX B AUDIT, SOURCE ACTIVITY)	SCOPE OF SUPPLY	AUDITORS	NUMBER OF DEFICIENCIES (OPEN / CLOSED)	CORRECTIVE ACTION VERIFICATION METHOD **and** DATE
* 3.4, 5.4	* 3.4, 5.4	* 3.4, 5.4	* 3.4, 5.4	* 3.4, 5.4	* 3.4, 5.4

* Refers to applicable question

SECTION 6 – FABRICATION/ASSEMBLY ACTIVITIES MATERIAL CONTROL, HANDLING, SHIPPING AND STORAGE

METHOD OF VERIFICATION	
6.1	Within the assessment/summary section of each checklist question, record the procedures/instructions/drawings including the revision/date used to verify implementation.
6.2	**Verify that measures are established and implemented for the control of fabrication/assembly activities.** **Objective Evidence required for Figure 6A:** • ITEM DESCRIPTION • WORK DOCUMENT • WORK ACTIVITY • WORK ACTIVITY PROCEDURE **Implementation Information:** Fabrication/assembly should be controlled by a shop work order/traveler type document identifying a controlled sequence of applicable work activities required for completion. Controls should include provision for rework. **Checklist Interface:** Provide any related supplier test/inspection activity information to the audit team member evaluating Checklist Section 8. **Note 1:** Assessment of software controls relating to the manufacturing processes is to be verified in Section 4. **References:** Appendix B Criteria VIII ANSI N45.2 Section 9 ASME Section III NQA-1 Supplement 9S-1

RESULTS: **SAT** ☐   **UNSAT** ☐ Describe Finding(s)   **N/A** ☐ Describe basis for N/A

ASSESSMENT/ SUMMARY:

a. *List* the Vendor Quality Manual reference and implementing procedure(s) which provide the measures for control of the fabrication/assembly activities:

Are procedural controls adequate and procedure revision current?

YES ☐ *or*

NO ☐ (Identify and provide input to the team member evaluating checklist Section 9.)

b. *Describe* implementation of the shop work order/traveler type document measures in use (who, what, how) including the applicable information/verifications it provides, such as:

• use of correct parts or materials;
• identification of each work activity;
• instructions, procedures and drawings to be used;
• hold/witness points;
• handling/cleanliness/environmental requirements

Are procedural controls adequately implemented?

YES ☐ *or*

NO ☐ (describe the inadequacy)

SECTION 6 – FABRICATION/ASSEMBLY ACTIVITIES MATERIAL CONTROL, HANDLING, SHIPPING AND STORAGE

METHOD OF VERIFICATION

6.3   **Verify that measures are established and implemented to assure the identification and traceability of items (i.e., materials, parts, weld filler material, etc.) is maintained throughout processing operations.**

Objective Evidence required for Figure 6B:
- ITEM DESCRIPTION
- METHOD OF IDENTIFICATION **and** TRACEABILITY
- INSPECTION STATUS

Implementation Information:
Item status and identification should be evident through fabrication/assembly/storage/etc. Indicators may be marked on items, attached to items, or identified in accompanying documents, as appropriate. Controls should include:
- Identification of items as to inspection/test status.
- Defined authority for application and removal of identification markings/status indicators.
- Item markings are clear and not detrimental. (For example, die stamps, if used, are low stress.)
- Subdivided items have satisfactory transfer of markings to each item.
- Defined shelf-life requirements.

Control of item traceability through fabrication/assembly should be provided by a documentation sequence such as serial number/part number to batch/lot/heat number to purchase order number to C of C, etc.

Note 1: Figure 6B, column 2, requires **Identification** and **Traceability**. As an example, a tag or stamp (identification) identifying heat number, serial number (traceability).

References:
Appendix B Criteria VIII, XIV
ANSI N45.2 Section 9, 15
ASME Section III
NQA-1 Basic Requirement 8, Supplement 7S-1

RESULTS: *SAT* ☐   *UNSAT* ☐ Describe Finding(s)   *N/A* ☐ Describe basis for N/A

ASSESSMENT/ SUMMARY:

a.   *List* the Vendor Quality Manual reference and implementing procedure(s) which provide the measures to assure the identification and traceability of items is maintained:

Are procedural controls adequate and procedure revision current?

YES ☐ *or*

NO ☐ (Identify and provide input to the team member evaluating checklist Section 9.)

b.   *Describe* <u>implementation</u> of the identification and traceability measures(s) in use (who, what, how):

Are procedural controls adequately implemented?

YES ☐ *or*

NO ☐ (describe the inadequacy)

SECTION 6 – FABRICATION/ASSEMBLY ACTIVITIES MATERIAL CONTROL, HANDLING, SHIPPING AND STORAGE

METHOD OF VERIFICATION

6.4   **Verify that measures are established and implemented for the control of storage and shipping activities.**

Objective Evidence required for Figure 6B:
- ITEM DESCRIPTION
- METHOD OF IDENTIFICATION **and** TRACEABILITY
- INSPECTION STATUS

Implementation Information:
The supplier's program and procedure controls should include typical storage and shipping activities, e.g., packaging practices to prevent damage during transit; marking of pertinent information on the container such as address, purchase order #, etc.; storage pending shipment; status of shipment such as identified on a traveler document, shipping log, etc.
As applicable to the product(s), specific controls should address:
- Handling
- Cleaning
- Preservation
- Foreign material controls
- Storing including access and environment
- Packaging
- Marking
- Documentation
- Shipment

Note 1: This question does not apply to software. Shipping of software is addressed in Item 4.7.

References:
Appendix B Criteria XIII
ANSI N45.2 Section 14
ASME Section III
NQA-1 Supplement 13S-1

RESULTS: *SAT* ☐   *UNSAT* ☐ Describe Finding(s)   *N/A* ☐ Describe basis for N/A

ASSESSMENT/ SUMMARY:

a.   *List* the Vendor Quality Manual reference and implementing procedure(s) which provide the measures for the control of storage and shipping activities:

Are procedural controls adequate and procedure revision current?
YES ☐ *or*
NO ☐ (Identify and provide input to the team member evaluating checklist Section 9.)

b.   *Describe* implementation of the supplier's measures (who, what, how) for the control of storage and shipping activities:

Are procedural controls adequately implemented?
YES ☐ *or*
NO ☐ (describe the inadequacy)

SECTION 6 – FABRICATION/ASSEMBLY ACTIVITIES MATERIAL CONTROL, HANDLING, SHIPPING AND STORAGE

(FIGURE 6A)

ITEM DESCRIPTION List description of part (Name, Part Number, P.O. number, etc.)	WORK DOCUMENT List Shop Work Order number, Traveler number, etc.	WORK ACTIVITY List activity (e.g., assembly, welding, packaging etc.)	WORK ACTIVITY PROCEDURE List the work activity procedure number **and** revision / date for the work activity observed.
* 6.2, 6.4	* 6.2, 6.4	* 6.2, 6.4	* 6.2, 6.4
* Refers to applicable question			

SECTION 6 – FABRICATION/ASSEMBLY ACTIVITIES MATERIAL CONTROL, HANDLING, SHIPPING AND STORAGE

(FIGURE 6B)

ITEM DESCRIPTION List description of part (Name, Part Number, P.O./Contract Number, etc.)	METHOD OF IDENTIFICATION and TRACEABILITY List the method used to identify the item (Heat Number, P.O./Contract number, etc.)	INSPECTION STATUS Indicate the status of the item (i.e., awaiting inspection, on hold, discrepant, rejected, etc.)
* 6.3, 6.4	* 6.3, 6.4	* 6.3, 6.4
* Refers to applicable question		

SECTION 7 – SPECIAL PROCESSES

METHOD OF VERIFICATION

7.1	Within the assessment/summary section of each checklist question, record the procedures/instructions/drawings including the revision/date used to verify implementation.

7.2	**Verify that measures are established and implemented to control welding.**

Objective Evidence required for Figure 7A:
- ITEM DESCRIPTION
- SPECIAL PROCESS
- PROCEDURE **and** REV / DATE
- QUALIFICATION (personnel, procedures, equipment)

Objective Evidence required for Figure 7B:
- WELDER NAME / STAMP
- CERTIFICATION TYPE (WELD PROCESS **and** POSITIONS)
- CODE QUALIFIED TO
- WELD PROCESS SPECIFICATION (WPS) **and** REV / DATE

Implementation Information:
Qualified personnel:
Nationally recognized standards have been developed for welding, such as ASME IX. The supplier's programmatic controls should follow the requirements and/or recommendations of those programs. Welder qualification is typically documented on a Procedure Qualification Record (PQR). Welders should be qualified for the weld process (e.g., GTAW, etc.), specific material, and position (e.g., overhead, etc.).
Qualified procedures:
There are two types of Procedure Qualification Records (PQR). One is for documenting the welder's qualification:
- The PQR is specific for different types of welding processes and requires maintaining proficiency (proficiency logs). One is for the technical approval of the welding parameters to the Code.
- Procedure Qualification Records contain essential and non-essential variables. It is mandatory that essential variables be followed. PQRs also contain and are not limited to Material (P) numbers, Filler Metal (F) numbers, Voltages and Polarity.

Welding procedures, usually denoted as Welding Procedure Specifications (WPS), are required for each type of welding process being used. WPSs are developed from a Procedure Qualification Record.
Qualified equipment:
Welding equipment requirements and any specific calibration requirements are usually referenced in the controlling procedure. The equipment must meet the parameters required by the procedure.

References:
Appendix B/ANSI N45.2 - (9/10)
ASME Section III
NQA-1 Supplement 9S-1

RESULTS: *SAT* ☐   *UNSAT* ☐ Describe Finding(s)   *N/A* ☐ Describe basis for N/A

ASSESSMENT/
SUMMARY: a. *List* the Vendor Quality Manual reference and implementing procedure(s) which provide the measures for control of welding:

Are procedural controls adequate and procedure revision current?

YES ☐ *or*

NO ☐ (Identify and provide input to the team member evaluating checklist Section 9.)

SECTION 7 – SPECIAL PROCESSES

b. ***Describe*** implementation of the supplier's measures (who, what, how) to control welding including the use of:

- qualified personnel;
- qualified procedures;
- qualified equipment.

Are procedural controls adequately implemented?

YES ☐ *or*

NO ☐ (describe the inadequacy)

METHOD OF VERIFICATION

7.3 **Verify that measures are established and implemented to control Non-Destructive Examination (NDE).**

Note: NDE disciplines include Ultrasonic Testing (UT), Magnetic Particle Testing (MT), Liquid Penetrant Testing (PT), Radiographic Testing (RT), Eddy Current Testing (ET), and Leak Testing (LT). PT, UT and RT may be automated processes, as opposed to being manually performed.

Objective Evidence required for Figure 7A:
- ITEM DESCRIPTION
- SPECIAL PROCESS
- PROCEDURE **and** REV / DATE
- QUALIFICATION (personnel, procedures, equipment)

Implementation Information:
Qualified personnel:
Nationally recognized standards have been developed for NDE, such as SNT-TC-1A and CP-189. The supplier's programmatic controls should follow the requirements and/or recommendations of those programs. Personnel are usually qualified to a "written practice," which identifies education, training and experience requirements for certification.
Qualified procedures:
NDE procedures should contain the requirements outlined in the referenced standards (e.g., ASTM standards for Nondestructive Testing).
Qualified equipment:
NDE equipment requirements and any specific calibration requirements are usually referenced in the controlling procedure.

Checklist Interface:
Identify any M&TE used to the audit team member evaluating Checklist Section 8.

References:
Appendix B/ANSI N45.2 - (9/10, 10/11)
ASME Section III
NQA-1 Supplement 9S-1, 10S-1

RESULTS: **SAT** ☐   **UNSAT** ☐ Describe Finding(s)   **N/A** ☐ Describe basis for N/A

SECTION 7 – SPECIAL PROCESSES

ASSESSMENT/
SUMMARY:

a. *List* the Vendor Quality Manual reference and implementing procedure(s) which provide the measures for control of Nondestructive Examination (NDE):

Are procedural controls adequate and procedure revision current?

YES ☐ *or*

NO ☐ (Identify and provide input to the team member evaluating checklist Section 9.)

b. *Describe* implementation of the supplier's measures (who, what, how) to control NDE including the use of:

- qualified personnel;
- qualified procedures;
- qualified equipment.

Are procedural controls adequately implemented?

YES ☐ *or*

NO ☐ (describe the inadequacy)

METHOD OF VERIFICATION

7.4 **Verify that measures are established and implemented to control other special processes (e.g., heat treating, soldering, painting, etc.).**

Objective Evidence required for Figure 7A:
- ITEM DESCRIPTION
- SPECIAL PROCESS
- PROCEDURE and REV./DATE
- QUALIFICATION (personnel, procedures, equipment)

Implementation Information:
Qualified personnel:
Personnel qualification requirements for heat treatment, soldering, and painting are usually based on the supplier's experience but may have a basis in a standard (ASTM, SSPC, IPC, etc.). Any requirements for personnel qualification should be identified in the controlling procedure.

Qualified procedures:
As applicable, procedures should contain the requirements outlined in any referenced standards (e.g., ASTM standards for heat treating / coatings, SSPC standards for coatings, IPC standards for soldering, etc.).
Qualified equipment:
Equipment requirements and any specific calibration requirements are usually referenced in the controlling procedure.

Checklist Interface:
Identify any M&TE used to the audit team member evaluating Checklist Section 8.

References:
Appendix B/ANSI N45.2 - (9/10)
ASME Section III
NQA-1 Supplement 9S-1

RESULTS: *SAT* ☐   *UNSAT* ☐ Describe Finding(s)   *N/A* ☐ Describe basis for N/A

SECTION 7 – SPECIAL PROCESSES

ASSESSMENT/
SUMMARY:

a. *List* the Vendor Quality Manual reference and implementing procedure(s) which provide the measures for control of other special processes (e.g., heat treating, soldering, painting, etc.):

Are procedural controls adequate and procedure revision current?

YES ☐ *or*

NO ☐ (Identify and provide input to the team member evaluating checklist Section 9.)

b. *Describe* implementation of the supplier's measures (who, what, how) to control other special processes (e.g., heat treating, soldering, painting, etc.) including the use of:

*   qualified personnel;
*   qualified procedures;
*   qualified equipment.

Are procedural controls adequately implemented?

YES ☐ *or*

NO ☐ (describe the inadequacy)

SECTION 7 – SPECIAL PROCESSES

(FIGURE 7A)

ITEM DESCRIPTION (NAME, P/N, S/N, MODEL #)	SPECIAL PROCESS	PROCEDURE and REV / DATE	QUALIFICATION		
			PERSONNEL and LEVEL	PROCEDURE	EQUIPMENT
* 7.2	* 7.2	* 7.2	* 7.2	* 7.2	* 7.2
* Refers to applicable question					

SECTION 7 – SPECIAL PROCESSES

(FIGURE 7B WELDER/WELD-OPERATOR)

WELDER (NAME / STAMP)	CERT. TYPE (PROCESS & POSITIONS)	CODE QUALIFIED TO	WELD PROCESS SPECIFICATION (WPS) and REV / DATE	MAINTENANCE OF QUALIFICATION
* 7.2	* 7.2	* 7.2	* 7.2	* 7.2

* Refers to applicable question

SECTION 8 – TESTS, INSPECTIONS, AND CALIBRATION

METHOD OF VERIFICATION

8.1 Within the assessment/summary section of each checklist question, record the procedures/instructions/drawings including the revision/date used to verify implementation.

8.2 **Verify that adequate measures are established and implemented for the inspection (receipt, in-process, and final) and testing of materials, components and parts.**

Objective Evidence required for Figure 8:
- ITEM DECRIPTION (NAME, P/N, S/N, ETC.)
- TEST/INSPECTION ACTIVITY TYPE **and** DATE
- TEST/INSPECTION DOCUMENT TITLE/NUMBER **and** REV./DATE
- INSPECTOR/TESTER NAMES/STAMP
- ID NUMBERS OF M&TE USED **and** CALIBRATION CURRENT (Yes / No)
- SAT OR UNSAT **and** NCR NO. IF UNSAT

Implementation Information:
Inspection/testing activities and resultant documentation must provide applicable information that verifies conformance to specified requirements/demonstrates acceptability for service of materials, components and parts.
The Test/Inspection to be performed must be clearly identified in a shop work order/traveler type document (e.g., in-process, final) and/or administrative procedure that must identify/provide the procedures, specifications, work instructions, drawings, etc., which control performance of the test/inspection.
Documentation should identify:
- Procedures, specifications, work instructions, drawings, etc., which control performance of the test/inspection, including revision;
- Hold or witness points;
- Test/inspection prerequisites identified and met;
- Characteristics to be inspected;
- Appropriate inspection equipment, tools, gages, and instrumentation (correct type, range, and accuracy);
- Acceptance criteria (from applicable design documents);
- Test/inspection personnel;
- Results (approved by responsible authority);
- Action taken relative to any non-conformances/deficiencies identified.

Identify Inspection/testing activities, listed on Figure 8, which were observed in progress versus reviewed in completed documentation.

Checklist Interface:
Provide inspection/test personnel names to the audit team member evaluating Checklist Section 14.

References:
Appendix B/ANSI N45.2 - (7/8, 10/11, 11/12)
ASME Section III
NQA-1 Supplement 7S-1, 10S-1, 11S-1

RESULTS: *SAT* ☐ *UNSAT* ☐ Describe Finding(s) *N/A* ☐ Describe basis for N/A

SECTION 8 – TESTS, INSPECTIONS, AND CALIBRATION

ASSESSMENT/
SUMMARY:

a. *List* the Vendor Quality Manual reference and implementing procedure(s) which provide the measures for the inspection (receipt, in-process, and final) and testing of materials, components and parts:

Are procedural controls adequate and procedure revision current?

YES ☐ *or*

NO ☐ (Identify and provide input to the team member evaluating checklist Section 9.)

b. *Describe* implementation of the inspection and test measures in use (who, what, how) including the applicable information/verifications they provide:

Are procedural controls adequately implemented?

YES ☐ *or*

NO ☐ (describe the inadequacy)

METHOD OF VERIFICATION

8.3 **Verify that measures are established and implemented to assure that purchased material, items, equipment, software, services (including engineering services, studies, and evaluations) conform to the procurement documents (i.e., receipt inspection, source inspection, post installation testing).**

Objective Evidence required for Figure 8:
- ITEM DESCRIPTION (NAME, P/N, S/N, ETC.)
- TEST/INSPECTION ACTIVITY TYPE **and** DATE
- TEST/INSPECTION DOCUMENT TITLE/NUMBER **and** REV / DATE
- INSPECTOR/TESTER NAMES/STAMP
- IDN UMBER OF M&TE USED **and** CALIBRATION CURRENT (Yes / No)
- SATE OR UNSAT **and** NCR NO. IF UNSAT

Implementation Information:
Appendix B and ANSI N45.2 (references below) address the requirement to establish and implement measures to assure that purchased items and services conform to procurement documents. Relative to inspection activities, the measures specifically identified include source inspection and receiving inspection. NQA-1 (reference below) adds post installation testing.
While most material, items, equipment, software are adaptable to inspection/test, some services (e.g., engineering, auditing, inspection services, etc.) do not provide measureable attributes such as dimensions, configuration, etc. verifiable by inspection/test. In these instances, assurance methods may include review of associated documentation (e.g., certifications), technical evaluation of data, and oversight of the service activity.

Checklist Interface:
Provide inspection/test personnel names to the audit team member evaluating Checklist Section 14.

References:
Appendix B/ANSI N45.2 - (7/8)
ASME Section III
NQA-1 Supplement 7S-1

RESULTS: *SAT* ☐   *UNSAT* ☐ Describe Finding(s)   *N/A* ☐ Describe basis for N/A

SECTION 8 – TESTS, INSPECTIONS, AND CALIBRATION

**ASSESSMENT/
SUMMARY:**

a. *List* the Vendor Quality Manual reference and implementing procedure(s) which provide the measures for the inspection (receipt, in-process, and final) and testing of materials, components and parts:

Are procedural controls adequate and procedure revision current?

YES ☐ *or*

NO ☐ (Identify and provide input to the team member evaluating checklist Section 9.)

b. *Describe* implementation of the inspection and test measures in use (who, what, how) including the applicable information/verifications they provide:

Are procedural controls adequately implemented?

YES ☐ *or*

NO ☐ (describe the inadequacy)

METHOD OF VERIFICATION

8.4 **Assess the adequacy of inspection/testing processes (such as those used during receipt/in-process/final inspection and/or testing) for identifying suspect/counterfeit/fraudulent material, items or components that may not be equivalent to those ordered.**

Implementation Information:
Appendix B, ANSI N45.2, NQA-1 (references below) address the requirement to establish and implement measures to assure that purchased items and services conform to procurement documents. With the global economy, opportunities for the introduction of suspect/counterfeit/fraudulent material, items or components into the supply chain have increased. As such, specific measures for the detection of suspect/counterfeit/fraudulent material, items or components should be an integral part of ensuring that purchased items and services conform to procurement documents, commensurate with the complexity of the items/services provided.
Suspect/counterfeit/fraudulent indications may include:
- Altered manufacturer's name, logo, serial number, manufacturing date
- Items differing in configuration, dimensions, fit, finish, color, or other attributes from that expected
- Markings on items or documentation are missing, unusual, altered, or inconsistent with that expected
- Markings or documentation from country other than that of the sub-supplier
- Items, sold as new, exhibiting evidence of prior use
- Performance inconsistent with specifications, certification, or test data furnished
- Documentation that appears altered, incomplete, or lacks expected traceability, UL or manufacturer's markings

References:
Appendix B/ANSI N45.2 - (7/8, 10/11, 11/12)
ASME Section III
NQA-1 Supplement 7S-1, 10S-1, 11S-1

RESULTS: *SAT* ☐   *UNSAT* ☐ Describe Finding(s)   *N/A* ☐ Describe basis for N/A

SECTION 8 – TESTS, INSPECTIONS, AND CALIBRATION

ASSESSMENT/
SUMMARY:

a. *List* the Vendor Quality Manual reference and implementing procedure(s) which provide the measures for identifying suspect/counterfeit/fraudulent material, items or components that may not be equivalent to those ordered:

Are procedural controls adequate and procedure revision current?

YES ☐ *or*

NO ☐ (Identify and provide input to the team member evaluating checklist Section 9.)

b. *Describe* implementation of the supplier's measures (who, what, how) for identifying suspect/counterfeit/fraudulent material, items or components that may not be equivalent to those ordered:

- Assess whether responsible personnel are aware of suspect/counterfeit/ fraudulent indications.

- Assess if measures established are commensurate with the complexity of the items/services provided.

Are procedural controls adequately implemented?

YES ☐ *or*

NO ☐ (describe the inadequacy)

METHOD OF VERIFICATION
8.5 **Verify that measures are established and implemented for the use of sampling plans, in lieu of 100% inspection, during receipt/in-process/final inspection.** **Note 1:** Sampling plans used for commercial grade dedication are addressed in Checklist Section 3.   **Implementation Information:**   Sampling used to verify acceptability of multiple identical items requires procedure controls based on recognized industry standard sampling practices. The procedures that implement the receipt/in-process/final inspection activities should identify the sampling criteria and associated standard, or reference a procedure, which identifies the sampling criteria and associated standard.   **References:**   Appendix B/ANSI N45.2 - (10/11)   ASME Section III

RESULTS: *SAT* ☐   *UNSAT* ☐ Describe Finding(s)   *N/A* ☐ Describe basis for N/A

ASSESSMENT/
SUMMARY:

a. *List* the Vendor Quality Manual reference and implementing procedure(s) which provide the measures for sampling during inspection (receipt, in-process, and final) of materials, components and parts:

Are procedural controls adequate and procedure revision current?

YES ☐ *or*

NO ☐ (Identify and provide input to the team member evaluating checklist Section 9.)

SECTION 8 – TESTS, INSPECTIONS, AND CALIBRATION

b. **Describe** implementation of the supplier's measures (who, what, how) for sampling during inspection (receipt, in-process, and final) of materials, components and parts:

Are procedural controls adequately implemented?

YES ☐ *or*

NO ☐ (describe the inadequacy)

METHOD OF VERIFICATION

8.6 **Verify that measures are established and implemented for the control of measuring and test equipment (M&TE).**

Objective Evidence required for Figure 8:
- ID NUMBER OF M&TE USED **and** CALIBRATION CURRENT (Yes / No)

Implementation Information:
Appendix B, ANSI, and NQA-1 references below require control, periodic calibration, and adjustment (as necessary) of M&TE to maintain accuracy. Controls include:
- Labeling/identification of M&TE to ensure the device and calibration status are readily identifiable;
- Calibration of M&TE and standards at periodic (recall) intervals;
- Adequacy of standards to assure accuracy, stability, range, and resolution required for their intended use;
- Traceability of reference (primary) and working (secondary) standards used to the National Institute of Standards and Technology (NIST), other recognized standards, or natural law;
- Documentation of As Found/As Left information;
- Maintenance of Calibration History – dates calibrated, by whom/supplier, results, due date, primary standard, and P.O. No. (if applicable);
- Control of M&TE found to be "out-of tolerance", "out of calibration", and/or past due for calibration, including evaluation of past use affected M&TE and customer notification where appropriate;
- Calibration performed by the supplier in an environment that is controlled to the extent necessary to assure required accuracy.

Checklist Interface:
M&TE data from Sections 3 and 7 to be obtained from the responsible auditor(s) for those sections. Identify any sub-suppliers providing calibration services to the audit team member(s) evaluating Checklist Sections 3 and 5.

Note 1: If required by P.O./Contract, standards must have nominal accuracy of four times the nominal accuracy of the measuring and test equipment being calibrated. If a 4:1 ratio is not possible, a documented (and authorized) basis of acceptance must be provided.

References:
Appendix B/Ansi N45.2 – (12/13)
ASME Section III
NQA-1 Supplement 12S-1

RESULTS: **SAT** ☐ **UNSAT** ☐ Describe Finding(s) **N/A** ☐ Describe basis for N/A

SECTION 8 – TESTS, INSPECTIONS, AND CALIBRATION

**ASSESSMENT/
SUMMARY:**

a. ***List*** the Vendor Quality Manual reference and implementing procedure(s) which provide the measures for the control of measuring and test equipment (M&TE):

Are procedural controls adequate and procedure revision current?

YES ☐ *or*

NO ☐ (Identify and provide input to the team member evaluating checklist Section 9.)

b. ***Describe*** implementation of the supplier's measures (who, what, how) for the control of measuring and test equipment (MT&E):

Are procedural controls adequately implemented?

YES ☐ *or*

NO ☐ (describe the inadequacy)

SECTION 8 – TESTS, INSPECTIONS, AND CALIBRATION

(FIGURE 8)

ITEM DESCRIPTION (NAME, P/N, S/N, ETC.)	TEST/INSPECTION ACTIVITY TYPE and DATE	TEST/INSPECTION PROCEDURE (TITLE/NUMBER) and REV / DATE	INSPECTOR/ TESTER (NAME/ STAMP)	ID NUMBER OF M&TE and CALIBRATION CURRENT (Yes / No)	SAT OR UNSAT and NCR NO. IF UNSAT
* 8.2, 8.3	* 8.2, 8.3	* 8.2, 8.3	* 8.2, 8.3	* 8.2, 8.3	* 8.2, 8.3

* Refers to applicable question

SECTION 9 – DOCUMENT CONTROL/ADEQUACY

METHOD OF VERIFICATION

9.1	Within the assessment/summary section of each checklist question, record the procedures/instructions/drawings including the revision/date used to verify implementation.
9.2	**Verify that measures are established and implemented to control the preparation, review/approval, and issue of documents (i.e., procedures, instructions, drawings, work orders, etc.) including changes.**

Implementation Information:
Measures to control the issue of documents include the following:
- Documented review for adequacy;
- Approved for release by authorized personnel;
- Adequate controls if maintained electronically.

Objective evidence can be obtained by comparing the supplier's master procedure listing to a sample of controlled documents from workstations, verifying that required documents are available at the work stations, are the latest reviewed/approved revision, and are legible. In addition, audit team members will provide reference to documents (with revisions) that were found while auditing their assigned checklist sections and will verify the document and revision numbers they reviewed are current as compared to the supplier's master procedure listing.

Documents may also be available in electronic form at work stations. If provided electronically at work stations, also verify there is sufficient control to prevent unauthorized changes to the electronic documents (read only).

Query other audit team members regarding the verification of document and revision numbers they reviewed. Checklist questions in Section 1-8 and 10-16 require the following determination:

Are procedures listed the current revision?

YES or NO (Provide information to the audit team member evaluating checklist Section 9.)

References:
Appendix B/ANSI N45.2 - (5, 6/6, 7)
ASME Section III
NQA-1 Supplement 6S-1

RESULTS: **SAT** ☐   **UNSAT** ☐ Describe Finding(s)   **N/A** ☐ Describe basis for N/A

ASSESSMENT/SUM MARY:

a. **List** the Vendor Quality Manual reference and implementing procedure(s) established to provide measures to control the preparation, review/approval, and issue of documents (i.e., procedures, instructions, drawings, work orders, etc.) including changes:

Are procedural controls adequate and procedure revision current?

YES ☐ *or*

NO ☐ (Identify and provide input to the team member evaluating checklist Section 9.)

b. **Describe** implementation of the supplier's measures (who, what, how) to control the preparation, review/approval, and issue of documents (i.e., procedures, instructions, drawings, work orders, etc.) including changes:

Are procedural controls adequately implemented?

YES ☐ *or*

NO ☐ (describe the inadequacy)

SECTION 10 – ORGANIZATION/PROGRAM

METHOD OF VERIFICATION
10.1 Within the assessment/summary section of each checklist question, record the procedures/instructions/drawings including the revision/date used to verify implementation.
10.2 **Verify that adequate measures are established and implemented for management, direction, and execution of the Quality Assurance Program.** **Implementation Information:** The supplier's Quality Assurance Program must: • Define the organizational structure (typically by an organizational chart depicting reporting relationships between management, production, engineering, quality positions, etc.); • Define individual responsibilities (An individual/organization responsible for defining/measuring the overall effectiveness of the QA Program must be designated, e.g., QA Manager/QA Department); • Provide quality organizational authority, independence, and freedom to identify problems, recommend solutions, control non-conformances (The organization chart and defined responsibilities for Quality personnel should clearly indicate sufficient independence from production and direct access to management levels having authority to ensure appropriate actions are taken); • Assure that management regularly reviews the effectiveness of the QA program (typically an annual review presented by the QA Manager to senior management including such items as non-conformances, corrective actions, internal audit results, customer returns, etc. An effective management review process would result in additional corrective actions for areas found to be unsatisfactory as a result of the review.) **References:** Appendix B/ANSI N45.2 - (1-3) ASME Section III NQA-1 Supplement 1S-1

RESULTS: *SAT* ☐   *UNSAT* ☐ Describe Finding(s)   *N/A* ☐ Describe basis for N/A

ASSESSMENT/ SUMMARY:

a. *List* the Vendor Quality Manual reference and implementing procedure(s) which provide the measures for management, direction, and execution of the Quality Assurance Program:

Are procedural controls adequate and procedure revision current?
YES ☐ *or*
NO ☐ (Identify and provide input to the team member evaluating checklist Section 9.)

b. *Describe* implementation of the supplier's measures for management, direction, and execution of the Quality Assurance Program (who, what, how) including:
• Designation of an individual/organization responsible for defining/measuring the overall effectiveness of the QA Program;
• Adequacy of the authority, independence and organizational freedom of personnel performing verification activities;
• Regular supplier management review of the status and effectiveness of the Quality Assurance Program including corrective actions for areas found to be unsatisfactory as a result of the review.

Are procedural controls adequately implemented?
YES ☐ *or*
NO ☐ (describe the inadequacy)

SECTION 11 – NONCONFORMING ITEMS/PART 21

METHOD OF VERIFICATION

11.1	Within the assessment/summary section of each checklist question, record the procedures/instructions/drawings including the revision/date used to verify implementation.

11.2   **Verify that measures are established and implemented to control items which do not conform to requirements:**

Implementation Information:
Nonconforming items must be clearly recognizable as nonconforming by marking/tagging of the item or segregation in a clearly marked (as nonconforming) container, area, etc. Nonconforming items must be identified on nonconformance documents and assigned a unique identification number which is logged and tracked. This process, in conjunction with marking, tagging, segregation, controls further processing, delivery and installation of items until disposition is completed.

References:
Appendix B/ANSI N45.2 - (15/16)
ASME Section III
NQA-1 Supplement 15S-1

RESULTS: **SAT** ☐   **UNSAT** ☐ Describe Finding(s)   **N/A** ☐ Describe basis for N/A

ASSESSMENT/   a.   **List** the Vendor Quality Manual reference and implementing procedure(s)
SUMMARY: established to provide the measures for control of items which do not conform to
                             requirements:

Are procedural controls adequate and procedure revision current?
YES ☐ *or*
NO ☐ (Identify and provide input to the team member evaluating checklist Section 9.)

b.   **Describe** implementation of the supplier's measures (who, what, how) for control of items which do not conform to requirements:

Are procedural controls adequately implemented?
YES ☐ *or*
NO ☐ (describe the inadequacy)

SECTION 11 – NONCONFORMING ITEMS/PART 21

METHOD OF VERIFICATION

11.3 **Verify that measures are established and implemented to disposition items which do not conform to requirements:**

Objective Evidence Required:
Document NCR Numbers reviewed under the Assessment/Summary.

Implementation Information:
Review a sample of Nonconformance documents. Select sample from:
- Actual nonconforming items observed during the audit by the audit team. Verify that these items are entered into the nonconformance process. (This will verify that a nonconformance which occurred was entered into the QA program);
- References in quality documentation being reviewed by the audit team to a nonconforming condition and resulting nonconformance report number;
- Select additional sample as needed from the supplier's nonconformance records (logs or electronic database files).

The selected disposition, such as use-as-is, reject, repair, rework, must be identified and documented, typically on the "nonconformance" document.
- Authority and responsibility for personnel performing the review/disposition must be defined.
- Documented justification must be provided verifying the acceptability of the nonconforming items which are dispositioned as repair or use-as-is.

Note 1: Customer approval of use-as-is and repair dispositions is necessary when required by customer purchase order.
- Procedures or instructions for repair and rework must be provided.
- Repaired and reworked items must be re-inspected.

A clear connection between the nonconformance process and the Part 21 procedure must exist such that a mechanism exists to identify and elevate conditions requiring 10 CFR 21 evaluation.
- The nonconformance process should clearly interface and direct users to the 10 CFR 21 evaluation process such that conditions adverse to quality are evaluated for 10 CFR 21 reportability.

Note 2: If the supplier uses a Material Review Committee or similar organization, review a sample of the meeting minutes of this organization to verify follow through on any commitments from the meeting pertaining to significant conditions adverse to quality.

References:
Appendix B/ANSI N45.2 - (15/16)
ASME Section III
NQA-1 Supplement 15S-1 (paragraph 4.1)

RESULTS: *SAT* ☐   *UNSAT* ☐ Describe Finding(s)   *N/A* ☐ Describe basis for N/A

ASSESSMENT/   a. *List* the Vendor Quality Manual reference and implementing procedure(s)
SUMMARY: established to disposition items which do not conform to requirements:

                        Are procedural controls adequate and procedure revision current?
                        YES ☐ *or*
                        NO ☐ (Identify and provide input to the team member evaluating checklist Section 9.)

SECTION 11 – NONCONFORMING ITEMS/PART 21

b. **Describe** implementation of the supplier's measures (who, what, how) to disposition items which do not conform to requirements including:

- Documented disposition by authorized personnel.
- Justification for repair and use-as-is dispositions including customer notification when required.
- Identification of procedures/instructions for rework.
- Re-inspection of repaired/reworked items.
- Evaluation for 10 CFR 21 reportability.

Are procedural controls adequately implemented?

YES ☐ **or**

NO ☐ (describe the inadequacy)

METHOD OF VERIFICATION

11.4   **Verify that measures are established and implemented to address posting, evaluation, notification, and reporting requirements of 10 CFR 21.**

Objective Evidence Required:
- Document NCR/CAR Numbers associated with 10 CFR 21 evaluations reviewed in the Assessment/Summary.
- Document any NRC inspections performed since the previous NUPIC audit which identify noncompliance to 10 CFR 21 requirements.

Implementation Information:
Posting:
Appropriate documents are required to be posted per 10 CFR 21.6(a) **OR** (b):
10 CFR 21.6(a)
- 10 CFR 21 regulations, and
- Section 206 of the Energy Reorganization Act of 1974, and
- Procedures adopted pursuant to the 10 CFR 21 regulations.
10 CFR 21.6(b)
- Section 206 of the Energy Reorganization Act of 1974, and
- Notice describing regulations/procedures.

Evaluation:
Procedures are required to provide criteria (10 CFR 21.21 (a)) for evaluation/determination, within 60 days of discovery of the deviation, if a defect or failure to comply exists under 10 CFR 21.3; or an Interim Report submitted within 60 days of discovery of the deviation.
Obtain a sample of Nonconformance Reports (Checklist Section 11) and Corrective Action Reports (Checklist Section 13) which have been screened for reportability and determined to be potentially reportable, requiring 10 CFR 21 evaluation.
Review a sample of 10 CFR 21 evaluations performed to verify procedure implementation for conditions determined to be potentially reportable.

Notification:
Procedures are required to establish notification timeframes consistent with 10 CFR 21.21(a), (b) and (d):
- Purchaser/affected licensee within 5 working days of the determination of inability to perform the evaluation?
- Director or responsible officer within 5 working days after evaluation completion?
- Initial NRC notification by facsimile or telephone within 2 days of informing the responsible officer of a defect or failure to comply?
- Written NRC notification within 30 days of informing the responsible officer of a defect or failure to comply?

SECTION 11 – NONCONFORMING ITEMS/PART 21

Reporting:
10 CFR 21 notifications must include (10 CFR 21.21(d)):
- Name/address of individual providing the report,
- Identification of facility/activity/basic component failing to comply or containing a defect,
- Identification of constructor/supplier,
- Nature of defect/failure to comply and safety hazard,
- Date information was obtained,
- Number and location of components in use/supplied/being supplied,
- Corrective actions, responsible entity, and time to complete,
- Advice related to the defect/failure to comply.

Review any NRC inspections performed since the previous NUPIC audit which identify noncompliance to 10 CFR 21 requirements (10 CFR 21.41). Verify that any NRC inspection issues, related to 10 CFR 21 compliance, were corrected. If no NRC inspections of 10 CFR 21 requirements were performed, state this.

References:
10 CFR 21.3, 10 CFR 21.6, 10 CFR 21.21, 10 CFR 21.41

RESULTS: *SAT* ☐   *UNSAT* ☐ Describe Finding(s)   *N/A* ☐ Describe basis for N/A

**ASSESSMENT/
SUMMARY:**

a. *List* the Vendor Quality Manual reference and implementing procedure(s) established to address posting, evaluation, notification, and reporting requirements of 10 CFR 21:

Are procedural controls adequate and procedure revision current?
YES ☐ *or*
NO ☐ (Identify and provide input to the team member evaluating checklist Section 9.)

b. *Describe* implementation of the supplier's measures (who, what, how) to address posting, evaluation, notification, and reporting requirements of 10 CFR 21 including:
- Posted documents per 10 CFR 21.6 (a) or 10 CFR 21.6 (b).
- Evaluation/Notification timeframes per 10 CFR 21.21 (a), (b) and (d).
- Reporting content per 10 CFR 21.21 (d).

Are procedural controls adequately implemented?
YES ☐ *or*
NO ☐ (describe the inadequacy)

SECTION 12 – INTERNAL AUDITS

METHOD OF VERIFICATION

12.1 Within the assessment/summary section of each checklist question, record the procedures/instructions/drawings including the revision/date used to verify implementation.

12.2 **Verify that measures are established and implemented to ensure a comprehensive system of planned and periodic <u>internal</u> audits.**

Objective Evidence required for Figure 12:
- AUDIT SCOPE **and** DATE
- AUDITOR(S)
- NUMBER OF DEFICIENCIES **and** STATUS (OPEN/CLOSED)
- CORRECTIVE ACTION VERIFICATION METHOD (document review, follow-up audit, surveillance, etc.)

Checklist Interface:
Identify any corrective actions resulting from the audits to the audit team member evaluating Checklist Section 13.
Identify the Auditors to the audit team member evaluating Checklist Section 14.

Implementation Information:
The supplier's current audit schedule and a sample of audits conducted since the last NUPIC audit will identify objective evidence for Figure 12. The audit planning/scheduling process should ensure that the audits are comprehensive (i.e., cover all aspects of the quality program) and that the frequency of the audits is defined, tracked, and met.
The audit must be performed by individual(s) that are independent from the suppliers QA Program implementation/administration (have not performed internal program audits, supplier audits, or inspections under the suppliers program). This audit verifies that the activities directly performed by the suppliers QA staff are implemented as required.
In the context of performing an audit of the suppliers QA Program implementation, an auditor independence concern would only occur if the auditor had been responsible for or performed activities that are the responsibility of the QA staff during the scope period. (e.g., Subsequent audits of the design program could be led by the same ATL, provided this individual has not performed any line functions/responsibilities in the design area since the last audit.)
Audit results (conclusions) must be clearly documented, including a statement of "effectiveness." Checklists and/or procedures must contain adequate objective evidence to support the conclusions.
Audit results must be reviewed by responsible management in area(s) audited and the overall "effectiveness" of the QA program communicated to upper management.
The process should include follow-up on issues from previous audits and verification of continued corrective action effectiveness, as documented in the audits reviewed.

References:
Appendix B/ANSI N45.2 - (18/19)
ASME Section III
NQA-1 Supplement 18S-1

RESULTS: *SAT* ☐   *UNSAT* ☐ Describe Finding(s)   *N/A* ☐ Describe basis for N/A

ASSESSMENT/   a. *List* the Vendor Quality Manual reference and implementing procedure(s) established
SUMMARY: to ensure a comprehensive system of planned and periodic <u>internal</u> audits:

Are procedural controls adequate and procedure revision current?
YES ☐ or
NO ☐ (Identify and provide input to the team member evaluating checklist Section 9.)

SECTION 12 – INTERNAL AUDITS

b. ***Describe*** implementation of the supplier's measures (who, what, how) to ensure a comprehensive system of planned and periodic internal audits including:

- Planning/scheduling
- Auditor independence
- Adequate objective evidence to support the conclusions
- Management review of audit results
- Evaluation of corrective action effectiveness from previous audits

Are procedural controls adequately implemented?

YES ☐ *or*

NO ☐ (describe the inadequacy)

METHOD OF VERIFICATION

12.3 **Assess the overall effectiveness of the internal audit process by review of previous internal audits and comparison of the results/issues identified in these audits with those identified by this NUPIC audit.**

Implementation Information:
The supplier QA program implementation should encourage self-identification and effective resolution of quality issues. If effectively implemented, it would be expected that the NUPIC audit would not identify any significant QA program implementation issues, process gaps, or recurrence of issues previously identified by the supplier.
For non-significant issues, some variations in quantity and subject of audit issues identified may occur, dependent on scopes, team sizes, performance timeframes, objective evidence selected, etc. However, the NUPIC results should generally validate the supplier's previous results, e.g., if NUPIC is identifying issues, the previous supplier audits would be expected to also be identifying and correcting issues.

References:
Appendix B/ANSI N45.2 - (18/19)
ASME Section III
NQA-1 Basic Requirement 18S-1

RESULTS: ***SAT*** ☐   ***UNSAT*** ☐ Describe Finding(s)   ***N/A*** ☐ Describe basis for N/A

ASSESSMENT/ SUMMARY: a. ***Describe*** the comparison of previous supplier internal audit results/issues with those identified by this NUPIC audit:

Has the internal audit process been effective, overall?

YES ☐ *or*

NO ☐ (describe the inadequacy)

SECTION 12 – INTERNAL AUDITS

(FIGURE 12)

AUDIT SCOPE and DATE(s)	AUDITOR(s)	NUMBER OF DEFICIENCIES and STATUS (OPEN / CLOSED)	CORRECTIVE ACTION VERIFICATION METHOD (document review follow-up audit, surveillance, etc.)
* 12.2	* 12.2	* 12.2	* 12.2

* Refers to applicable question

SECTION 13 – CORRECTIVE ACTION

METHOD OF VERIFICATION

13.1   Within the assessment/summary section of each checklist question, record the procedures/instructions/drawings including the revision/date used to verify implementation.

13.2   **Verify that measures are established and implemented to assure that conditions adverse to quality are promptly identified and corrected.**

Objective Evidence Required:
- Document CAR Numbers reviewed under the Assessment/Summary.

Implementation Information:
Review a sample of corrective action documents selected from sources such as:
- Actual conditions adverse to quality identified during the audit by the NUPIC audit team. Verify that these conditions are entered into the supplier corrective action process. (This will verify that a condition discovered was entered into the supplier's corrective action program.)
- References in quality documentation, such as audits, to conditions adverse to quality and resulting corrective action report numbers.
- Select additional sample as needed from the supplier's corrective action program records (logs or electronic database files).

Note:
The supplier's program should define "significant" conditions adverse to quality.
If the supplier uses a Corrective Action Review Board or similar organization, review a sample of the meeting minutes of this organization to verify follow through on any commitments from the meeting pertaining to significant conditions adverse to quality.

As a minimum, measures to control conditions adverse to quality must include the following:
- Identification and description of the condition adverse to quality;
- Determination of the cause and actions taken to prevent recurrence and notification to appropriate levels of management for significant conditions adverse to quality;
- Review and approval by responsible authority (programmatically defined) on the adequacy of the corrective action;
- A clear connection between the corrective action process and the Part 21 procedure such that a mechanism exists to identify and elevate conditions requiring 10 CFR 21 evaluation;
- Follow-up actions verifying that the corrective actions are scheduled and/or have taken place.

References:
Appendix B/ANSI N45.2 - (16/17)
ASME Section III
NQA-1 Basic Requirement 16

RESULTS: *SAT* ☐   *UNSAT* ☐ Describe Finding(s)   *N/A* ☐ Describe basis for N/A

ASSESSMENT/ SUMMARY:

a.   *List* the Vendor Quality Manual reference and implementing procedure(s) established to provide measures to assure that conditions adverse to quality are promptly identified and corrected:

Are procedural controls adequate and procedure revision current?

YES ☐ *or*

NO ☐ (Identify and provide input to the team member evaluating checklist Section 9.)

SECTION 13 – CORRECTIVE ACTION

b. **Describe** implementation of the supplier's measures (who, what, how) to assure that conditions adverse to quality are promptly identified and corrected:

Are procedural controls adequately implemented?

YES ☐ **or**

NO ☐ (describe the inadequacy)

METHOD OF VERIFICATION

13.3 **Verify that deficiencies identified/reported by customers, to the supplier, (e.g., receipt inspection rejections, source verification rejections, return material authorizations, site nonconformances, etc.) are adequately evaluated and entered into the supplier's nonconformance or corrective action program, as applicable.**

Objective Evidence Required:
- Document NCR **and/or** CAR Numbers reviewed under the Assessment/Summary.

References:
Appendix B/ANSI N45.2 - (16/17)
ASME Section III
NQA-1 Basic Requirement 16

RESULTS: **SAT** ☐   **UNSAT** ☐ Describe Finding(s)   **N/A** ☐ Describe basis for N/A

ASSESSMENT/ SUMMARY:

a. **List** the Vendor Quality Manual reference and implementing procedure(s) established to provide measures to assure that deficiencies identified/reported by customers, to the supplier, are entered into the supplier's nonconformance or corrective action program, as applicable, and adequately evaluated:

Are procedural controls adequate and procedure revision current?

YES ☐ **or**

NO ☐ (Identify and provide input to the team member evaluating checklist Section 9.)

b. **Describe** implementation of the supplier's measures (who, what, how) to assure that deficiencies identified/reported by customers, to the supplier, are adequately evaluated and entered into the supplier's nonconformance or corrective action program, as applicable:

Are procedural controls adequately implemented?

YES ☐ **or**

NO ☐ (describe the inadequacy)

SECTION 13 – CORRECTIVE ACTION

METHOD OF VERIFICATION

13.4   **Verify the overall effectiveness of the corrective action process.**

Objective Evidence Required:
- Document CAR Numbers reviewed under the Assessment/Summary.

Implementation Information:
- Evaluate the adequacy of actions taken to prevent recurrence for any <u>significant</u> conditions adverse to quality.
- Review the adequacy of corrective actions taken as a result of the issues identified during previous supplier internal audits (if applicable) to determine if there were any repeat issues.
- Review the adequacy of corrective actions taken as a result of the issues identified during the last NUPIC audit (if applicable) to determine if there are any repeat issues.

Checklist Interface:
Adequacy of corrective actions taken, as a result of the issues identified during the last NUPIC audit, will be provided by audit team members assigned to the checklist sections which identified the previous issues.

References:
Appendix B/ANSI N45.2 - (16/17)
ASME Section III
NQA-1 Basic Requirement 16

RESULTS: *SAT* ☐   *UNSAT* ☐ Describe Finding(s)   *N/A* ☐ Describe basis for N/A

ASSESSMENT/   a.   *Describe* the adequacy of the corrective action process in preventing
SUMMARY: recurrence of previously identified issues:

Has the corrective action process been effective, overall?

YES ☐ *or*

NO ☐ (describe the inadequacy)

SECTION 14 – TRAINING/CERTIFICATION

METHOD OF VERIFICATION

14.1	Within the assessment/summary section of each checklist question, record the procedures/instructions/drawings including the revision/date used to verify implementation.

14.2 **Verify that measures are established and implemented to ensure quality program indoctrination and training of personnel who perform activities affecting quality.**

Objective Evidence required for Figure 14:
- NAME **and** JOB TITLE
- INDOCTRINATION **and** TRAINING COMPLETED (Yes / No)

Implementation Information:
Any individuals performing functions described in the Quality Program require quality program indoctrination and training. Obtain a sample of personnel from those observed, interviewed, or whose quality related work was reviewed, during the audit and verify they received quality program indoctrination and training.

References:
Appendix B/ANSI N45.2 - (2/2)
ASME Section III
NQA-1 Supplement 2S-4

RESULTS: *SAT* ☐   *UNSAT* ☐ Describe Finding(s)   *N/A* ☐ Describe basis for N/A

ASSESSMENT/
SUMMARY:

a. *List* the Vendor Quality Manual reference and implementing procedure(s) established to ensure quality program indoctrination and training of personnel who perform activities affecting quality:

Are procedural controls adequate and procedure revision current?

YES ☐ *or*

NO ☐ (Identify and provide input to the team member evaluating checklist Section 9.)

b. *Describe* implementation of the supplier's measures (who, what, how) to ensure quality program indoctrination and training of personnel who perform activities affecting quality:

Are procedural controls adequately implemented?

YES ☐ *or*

NO ☐ (describe the inadequacy)

SECTION 14 – TRAINING/CERTIFICATION

METHOD OF VERIFICATION

14.3   Verify that inspection/test personnel, auditors, calibration, repair personnel and similar specialists (i.e., ASME Code design personnel to ASME Section III) are qualified and have certifications on file.

Objective Evidence required for Figure 14:
- NAME and JOB TITLE
- INDOCTRINATION and TRAINING COMPLETED (Yes/No)
- QUALIFICATION / CERTIFICATION TYPE and LEVEL

Implementation Information:
Obtain a sample of personnel from Checklist Sections 2 (Design), 3 (Commercial Grade Dedication), 5 (Procurement), 8 (Tests/Inspections/Calibrations), and 12 (Internal Audits) and verify these personnel were properly qualified and/or certified for the activities they performed by review of supporting documents on file (qualification, certification and training records).

Note:
Special process personnel Qualification / Certification is addressed in Checklist Section 7.

References:
Appendix B/ANSI N45.2 - (2, 9, 10, 11, 18/2, 10, 11, 12, 19)
ASME Section III
NQA-1 Supplement 2S-1, 2S-2, 2S-3

RESULTS: *SAT* ☐   *UNSAT* ☐ Describe Finding(s)   *N/A* ☐ Describe basis for N/A

ASSESSMENT/ SUMMARY:

a.   *List* the Vendor Quality Manual reference and implementing procedure(s) established to ensure that inspection/test personnel, auditors, calibration, repair personnel and similar specialists are qualified and have certifications on file:

Are procedural controls adequate and procedure revision current?
YES ☐ *or*
NO ☐ (Identify and provide input to the team member evaluating checklist Section 9.)

b.   *Describe* implementation of the supplier's measures (who, what, how) to ensure that inspection/test personnel, auditors, calibration, repair personnel and similar specialists are qualified and have certifications on file:

Are procedural controls adequately implemented?
YES ☐ *or*
NO ☐ (describe the inadequacy)

SECTION 14 – TRAINING/CERTIFICATION

(FIGURE 14 PERSONNEL INDOCTRINATION/TRAINING/QUALIFICATION)

NAME and JOB TITLE	INDOCTRINATION and TRAINING COMPLETED (Yes / No)	QUALIFICATION / CERTIFICATION TYPE and LEVEL
* 14.2, 14.3	* 14.2, 14.3	* 14.2, 14.3
* Refers to applicable question		

SECTION 15 – FIELD SERVICES

METHOD OF VERIFICATION
15.1   Within the assessment/summary section of each checklist question, record the procedures/instructions/drawings including the revision/date used to verify implementation.
15.2   **Verify that measures are established and implemented to control field services.** **Implementation Information:** Each checklist section must be evaluated to determine if Field Services should be addressed. If applicable, each checklist section assessment should clearly address the adequacy of controls for this area as it applies to Field Services. If the supplier controls Field Services under the same quality program which is implemented for the control of in-house activities, examples of the adequacy and implementation of the controls must be documented in each applicable section of the checklist. If the supplier has a separate quality program for Field Services, examples of the adequacy and implementation of the controls prescribed by the separate quality program should be evaluated and addressed in the applicable sections of the checklist in addition to the other (in-house) quality program requirements. **Checklist Interface:** Query the audit team members regarding applicability of field services to their assigned checklist sections. **References:** Appendix B/ANSI N45.2 - 2/2 ASME Section III NQA-1 Basic Requirement 2

RESULTS: *SAT* ☐   *UNSAT* ☐ Describe Finding(s)   *N/A* ☐ Describe basis for N/A

ASSESSMENT/ SUMMARY:

a.   *List* the Vendor Quality Manual reference and implementing procedure(s) established to control field services:

Are procedural controls adequate and procedure revision current?

YES ☐ *or*

NO ☐ (Identify and provide input to the team member evaluating checklist Section 9.)

b.   *Describe* implementation of the supplier's measures (who, what, how) to control field services:

- Verify the controls for these services have been evaluated in the appropriate sections of the checklist and list the checklist sections determined to be applicable.

Are procedural controls adequately implemented?

YES ☐ *or*

NO ☐ (describe the inadequacy)

SECTION 16 – RECORDS

METHOD OF VERIFICATION

16.1   Within the assessment/summary section of each checklist question, record the procedures/instructions/drawings including the revision/date used to verify implementation.

16.2   **Verify that adequate measures are established and implemented to ensure that all QA records not transferred to the member are maintained in facilities that provide storage, retention requirements and protection against environmental effects, damage and loss.**

Implementation Information:
Record storage standards recognize differing extent of storage requirements, dependent on single or dual storage. Record storage must provide protections to ensure that records are legible, identifiable, and retrievable. These protections should include environmental hazards (fire, moisture, sunlight, etc.) and controlled access.
Methods of obtaining objective evidence include:
- Query the audit team regarding the condition of any quality records which they have reviewed.
- Request the supplier to demonstrate ability to retrieve quality records from storage.
- Tour the records storage facility and sample records in storage.

10 CFR 21.51, "Reporting of Defects And Noncompliance – Maintenance and Inspection of Records," provides specific retention requirements for associated records:
- Evaluation of deviations and failures to comply retained a minimum of 5 years after the date of the evaluation.
- Notifications sent to purchasers and affected licensees for a minimum of 5 years after the date of the notification.
- Record of purchases of basic components retained for 10 years after the delivery of the basic component or service associated with a basic component.
For 10 CFR 52 licensed plants, "Early Site Permits; Standard Design Certifications; and Combined Licenses for Nuclear Power Plants," 10 CFR 21.51 requires:
- Notifications sent to purchasers and affected licensees for a minimum of 5 years after the date of notification.
- Record of purchases purchasers for 15 years after delivery of design which is the subject of the design certification rule or service associated with the design. This pertains to applicants for standard design certification, typically NSSS suppliers (e.g., Westinghouse, AREVA, GE) and Engineering-Procurement-Construction contractors (e.g., Shaw).

Checklist Interface:
Query the audit team regarding the condition of any quality records which they have reviewed.

References:
Appendix B/ANSI N45.2 - (17/18)
10 CFR 21.51
10 CFR 52
ASME Section III
NQA-1 Supplement 17S-1, 6S-1

RESULTS: *SAT* ☐   *UNSAT* ☐ Describe Finding(s)   *N/A* ☐ Describe basis for N/A

ASSESSMENT/   a.   *List* the Vendor Quality Manual reference and implementing procedure(s)
SUMMARY: established to ensure that all QA records not transferred to the member are
                             maintained in facilities that provide storage, retention requirements and protection
                             against environmental effects, damage and loss:

                             Are procedural controls adequate and procedure revision current?
                             YES ☐ *or*
                             NO ☐ (Identify and provide input to the team member evaluating checklist
                             Section 9.)

SECTION 16 – RECORDS

b. ***Describe*** <u>implementation</u> of the supplier's measures (who, what, how) to ensure that all QA records not transferred to the member are maintained in facilities that provide storage, retention requirements and protection against environmental effects, damage and loss including:

- Records are legible, identifiable, and retrievable.
- Records are retained and maintained per 10 CFR 21.51 including those for 10 CFR 52 licensed plants.

Are procedural controls adequately implemented?

YES ☐ *or*

NO ☐ (describe the inadequacy)

Appendix F
Blank Forms

AUDIT CHECKLIST

REPORT NO.	DATE OF AUDIT	ORGANIZATION AUDITED	CHECKLIST PAGE 1 OF ____	REV. ____

ACTIVITY AUDITED: _____   AUDITORS: _____   AUDIT TEAM LEADER: _____

REFERENCE DOCUMENTS: _____   AUDIT TEAM LEADER: _____
(initial / date)

NO.	REF DOC.	DESCRIPTION	OBJECTIVE EVIDENCE	S	U	N/A
1						
2						
3						
4						

Comments:

AUDIT CHECKLIST

REPORT NO.	DATE OF AUDIT	ORGANIZATION AUDITED	CHECKLIST PAGE 2 OF ___
___	___	___	REV. ___

NO.	REF DOC	DESCRIPTION	OBJECTIVE EVIDENCE	S	U	N/A
5						
6						
7						
8						

Comments:

	AUDIT FINDING REPORT	AFR No.: _____ AUDIT No.:_____

ACTIVITY: _____ CLIENT:

ORGANIZATION: _____ REPLY DUE DATE: _____

STATEMENT OF REQUIREMENTS:

FINDINGS: Contrary to the above requirements:

Finding
Classification: **Major**   **Minor**

RECOMMENDED CORRECTIVE ACTION: It is recommended

You are requested to further investigate the finding(s) to identify the cause and effect of the condition(s) in order to determine the extent of corrective action required. The results of the review are to be considered in your reply.

AUDITOR   DATE

CORRECTIVE ACTION RESPONSE: (Attach additional sheets as necessary)	Requires Evaluation for 10 CFR 21 Reportability Yes ☐ No ☐

A. Action taken/proposed to correct findings:

     Proposed Completion Date:

B. Cause of Condition:

C. Corrective Action to prevent recurrence:

D. Date for Completion of Proposed Corrective Action(s): _____

AUDITEE SIGNATURE   TITLE   DATE

EVALUATION OF RESPONSE	**VERIFICATION OF IMPLEMENTATION**
Accept [ ] Reject [ ]	Accept [ ] Reject [ ] Not Required [ ]
SIGNATURE/TITLE DATE	SIGNATURE/TITLE DATE

ATTENDANCE SHEET

AUDIT NO.:_____

PRE AUDIT CONFERENCE		DATE:
NAME (Please Print)	TITLE	ORGANIZATION

POST AUDIT CONFERENCE		DATE:
NAME (Please Print)	TITLE	ORGANIZATION

	AUDIT OBSERVATION REPORT	AOR No.: _____ AUDIT No.: _____

ACTIVITY: _____ CLIENT: _____

ORGANIZATION: _____

STATEMENT OF REQUIREMENTS:

OBSERVATION

Classification: **Major** ☐ **Minor** ☐ Response Due Date:

AUDITOR   DATE

OBSERVATION RESPONSE Major Observations only

SIGNATURE   TITLE   DATE

<table>
<tr><td align="center">AUDIT NOTIFICATION
AND
AUDIT PLAN</td><td align="center">AUDIT NO.:
#####</td></tr>
</table>

NOTIFICATION OF AUDIT

DATE:

TO:	**LOCATION:**
FROM:	**LOCATION:**

DATE OF AUDIT:	**CC:**

An audit has been scheduled to be performed as indicated below. If there is a problem concerning the plan, or a conflict with the schedule, please contact the team leader. Any changes to the plan or date of audit must be confirmed in writing.

AUDIT TEAM LEADER / TELEPHONE NO.:	**TENTATIVE SCHEDULE:**
AUDIT TEAM:	**PRE AUDIT:**
	POST AUDIT:

AUDIT PLAN

ORGANIZATION / ACTIVITY TO BE AUDITED:

PURPOSE / SCOPE:

PROGRAM REQUIREMENTS / APPLICABLE PROCEDURES:

Quality Program:

Departmental Procedures:

Project Procedures:

Other:

CHECKLIST REFERENCE:	**PREVIOUS AUDIT:**
	Audit No: Date:
AUDIT TEAM LEADER SIGNATURE	Findings: Yes: [ ] No: [ ]

AUDIT ID	CODE*	AUDITEE	DESCRIPTION	AUDITOR	SCHED. DATE	ACTUAL/NOTES

	Auditor - Annual Evaluation		Name: _____ Sheet ___ of ___
Audit Participation 　　No. 　　Date			
Review of Codes, Standards & Procedures			
Training/Seminars 　　Title 　　Date			
Status 　　Cert Extended to 　　Re-cert Required 　　Cert Revoked			
Evaluated By Title, Date			
Audit Participation 　　No. 　　Date			
Review of Codes, Standards & Procedures			
Training/Seminars 　　Title 　　Date			
Status 　　Cert Extended to 　　Re-cert Required 　　Cert Revoked			
Evaluated By Title, Date			
Audit Participation 　　No. 　　Date			
Review of Codes, Standards & Procedures			
Training/Seminars 　　Title 　　Date			
Status 　　Cert Extended to 　　Re-cert Required 　　Cert Revoked			
Evaluated By Title, Date			

Auditor Participation Record

Sheet _____ of _____

Name: _____

Auditee & Location	Audit Type	Audit Report No. & Lead Auditor	Dates	Classification (Auditor/Lead)

Introductions:
   Audit Team Leader:
   Audit Team:
   Audited Organization Management:
   Other Attending Personnel:

Safety Moment:

Audit Scope:
   Standard Audit Plan (   )

Audit Schedule:
   Entrance Meeting (   )
   Audit Conduct (   )
   Exit Meeting Date: (   ) Time: (   )

Purpose of Audit:
   Verify compliance with applicable QA Program and other requirements
   Identify declining performance in programs, processes or behaviors
   Identify noteworthy gaps to industry performance and between stations
   Identify safety culture concerns

Activities Audited:

Auditee Contacts:

Audit Team Location: [room(s), phone #s]

In-process Audit Debrief Arrangements:
   Location:
   Frequency:
   Time:
   Participants:

Questions?

Use of this form as a procedural aid does not require retention as a quality record.

NUCLEAR OVERSIGHT
AUDIT EXIT MEETING OUTLINE

Topic	Speaker	Time (nominal)

Audit Title:

Safety Moment: — 1 minutes

Introductions: — 3 minutes

Team Lead:
NOS Auditors:

Audit Scope: — Tony Brion — 1 minute

This audit verifies the implementation and effectiveness of the .....

The scope also includes confirming compliance with the following ...

Audit Results:

Key Take-Aways — Team Lead, Auditors — 12 minutes

Nuclear Oversight (NOS) concludes that [Plant x] is effectively [or is not effective in] implementing the requirements for ... based upon ... .

The following issues were identified.

- Topic for Discussion I:
- Topic for Discussion II:
- etc.

Technical Specialist Insights (if audit included TS) — 2 minutes

Site/Line Management perspective or questions — 3 minutes

Site Management

Fleet Management

Site Executive Leadership

Wrap-up — Team Lead

Please fill out Feedback Form and return to Tony Brion

Use of this form as a procedural aid does not require retention as a quality record.

NOTE: STANDARD AUDIT PLAN   APPLIES TO THIS AUDIT

AUDIT TITLE	AUDIT NUMBER

SCOPE	REQUIREMENTS

AUDIT SCHEDULE	
AUDIT START	AUDIT FINISH

ACTIVITIES TO BE AUDITED	

ORGANIZATIONS TO BE NOTIFIED	

AUDIT PERSONNEL	

APPLICABLE DOCUMENTS	

Prepared by: (ATL) (print/sign/date)	
Approved by: (Audit Supervisor) (print/sign/date)	

NUCLEAR OVERSIGHT
AUDIT REPORT

Audit Title
(Audit Number)

Location(s):

Entrance Date: **Exit Date:**

Audit Scope:

Summary of Results:

Report Details:

Findings / IRMAs / Discussion Items:

Picture of Excellence / Nuclear Performance Model:

Approved by: (print/sign)   **Date:**

Reviewed by: (print/sign)   **Date:**

QA Program Elements:

Criterion	Title	Results
I	Organization	
II	Quality Assurance Program	

Regulatory Elements:

Source	Requirement	Results

Audit Personnel:

Supporting Information:

Corrective Action Documents:

CAP #	Description	Level

Personnel Contacted: (attended entrance; contacted; attended exit)

Name	Entrance	Audit Contact	Exit	Department

Documents Reviewed:

Document Number	Title	Rev#

	AUDIT FEEDBACK FORM **Part 3 – Post Audit Exit Meeting**

Audit Date(s):

Audit Topic: **Report Number:**

For any needed follow up, please record your name (optional):
The rating scale is as follows:
1 = Weak Area, needs improvement
2 = Sometimes met expectations
3 = Met expectations
4 = Sometimes exceeded expectations
5 = Strong area, good practice
NA = Not applicable or not observed

Post Audit Exit Meeting or Briefing:	**Rating:**					
	1	2	3	4	5	NA
Did NOS clearly communicate the audit findings and recommendations?						
Did NOS keep the meeting brief and to the point?						
Please provide additional comments/specifics:						

NUCLEAR OVERSIGHT AUDITOR
CERTIFICATION OF QUALIFICATION

☐ **Initial Qualification**
(Complete all sections)

☐ **Annual Renewal**
(Complete Section 1 only)

Section 1: Annual Supervisor Certification Letter

Qualifying Auditor Name: _____ **ID Number:**_____

This is to certify that _____ has met the education, experience, training and proficiency demonstration requirements and is fully qualified to perform the following functions/roles for calendar year _____:

☐ **Internal Audit Team Leader**
(Supervisor update NOS Qual Tracking Matrix)

☐ **Supplier Audit Certified Lead Auditor**
(Supervisor update NOS Qual Tracking Matrix)

[Basis for Initial qualification summarized on worksheet, page 2. Basis for annual renewal included on attached form, "Audit Participation Record."]

_____ _____
Approved (Responsible Supervisor or Manager)   **Date**
(Print/Sign)

☐ **Add LMS Item** ☐ **Terminate LMS Item** ☐ **Suspend LMS Item** ☐ **NA**

_____ _____
LMS Entry Complete   **Date**
(Print/Sign)

Qualification Basis Worksheet for Initial Certification
Audit Team Leader/Supplier Audit Team Leader

Candidate Name _____

Section 2: Education and Experience

List nuclear plant line experience	Discipline	Years in Discipline

List Audit/Assessment, Supplier Audit/Assessment experience	Experience	Years

List college degrees in engineering, physical sciences, or mathematics:

Describe Military, Department of Energy, or commercial nuclear industry experience in engineering, manufacturing, construction, operation, maintenance, quality assurance, or quality assurance auditing:

List certifications of competency in engineering science or quality assurance specialties issued and approved, by a State Agency or National Professional or Technical Society:

Section 3: Communication Skills

	Yes	No
Does the candidate have the capability to communicate effectively, both in writing and orally?		

Comments:

Section 4: Completion of Training

Training Component	Date Completed
Completion of NOS Training plan, including pre-requisites (attach any applicable approved exemptions)	

Section 5: Audit Participation

	Yes	No
Has the candidate participated in at least one independent audit or supplier audit within the year preceding the date of qualification?		

Date and subject of most recent independent audit, or supplier audit participation:

Section 6: Examination

Candidate is required to pass examination(s) that evaluate their comprehension of and ability to apply:

Qualification Basis Worksheet for Initial Certification
Audit Team Leader/Supplier Audit Team Leader

• Knowledge and understanding of nuclear-related codes, standards, regulations, and regulatory guides, as applicable. • General structure of quality assurance programs as a whole and applicable elements. • Audit techniques of examining, questioning, evaluating, and reporting; methods of identifying and following up on corrective action items; and closing out audit findings. • Audit planning		
Written Examination Passed?	Yes	No
Date/Details:		
Oral Examination Passed?	Yes	No
Date/Details:		

Completed by _____ **Date** _____
    (Print/Sign)

Retention: Lifetime
Retain in: Individual Training File
Form retained in accordance with record retention schedule identified in Procedure XXX

SOLUTION KEY TO QUESTIONS 1–94

1	c	33	a	65	d
2	a	34	c	66	d
3	a	35	b	67	b
4	c	36	a	68	c
5	d	37	b	69	b
6	b	38	d	70	b
7	d	39	b	71	c
8	a	40	d	72	b
9	c	41	d	73	c
10	d	42	d	74	a
11	b	43	b	75	b
12	c	44	d	76	c
13	a	45	a	77	a
14	c	46	d	78	c
15	d	47	d	79	d
16	a	48	a	80	c
17	d	49	c	81	b
18	c	50	d	82	c
19	d	51	a	83	c
20	a	52	c	84	d
21	b	53	c	85	c
22	d	54	c	86	a
23	a	55	c	87	d
24	c	56	a	88	b
25	d	57	d	89	b
26	c	58	d	90	a
27	b	59	b	91	a
28	b	60	b	92	d
29	a	61	b	93	a
30	a	62	a	94	d
31	b	63	b		
32	d	64	a		

SOLUTION KEY TO ADDITIONAL
QUESTIONS 1–46: LEAD AUDITOR EXAM

1	a		26	e
2a	a		27	t
	b		28	c
2b	a		29	b
	b		30	a
3	d		31	c
4	f		32	b
5	c		33	b
6	t		34	d
7	e		35	a
8	d		36	d
9	f		37	a
10	b			b
11	c			c
12	d		38	b
13	a		39	c
14	a		40	a
15	d		41	d
16	a		42	d
17	c		43	a
18	a		44a	a
19	t			b
20	c		44b	a
21	d			b
22	b		45	c
23	a		46	e
24	d			
25	a			
	b			
	c			

About the Authors

Nuclear Quality Assurance Auditor Training Handbook Third Edition 2021

Karen M. Douglas

Karen M. Douglas is a Longenecker & Associates nuclear engineer with more than 25 years of experience contributing to Department of Energy (DOE) and National Nuclear Security Administration (NNSA) programs, including the NNSA Office of Secure Transportation, where she served as a nuclear quality assurance (QA) specialist and nuclear safety specialist. Karen managed strategic partnerships programs for more than five years, serving interagency and corporate sponsors including the Nuclear Navy, Air Force, Nuclear Regulatory Commission (NRC), and Kodak. For several years Karen offered Los Alamos National Laboratory (LANL) QA and materials engineering support to the NNSA Pit Project Office. She chaired the DOE/EM Site Technology Group for four years, matching environmental cleanup projects with technologies from DOE and NNSA national laboratories. Karen first contributed to DOE programs by serving as an NQA-1 lead nuclear QA auditor for the WIPP and UMTRA sites and authored the initial DOE nonweapons QA program approved in 1993. She initiated her professional career as a metallurgist and materials program manager for the General Electric Nuclear Energy Division and subsequently served as a QA manager for Raychem Corporation, attaining the ASME NQA-1 Lead Nuclear Quality Assurance Auditor qualification and ASQ Certified Quality Auditor and Certified Quality Engineer credentials. She is a senior member of ASQ and currently serves as chair of both the ASQ Energy & Environmental Division, and the ASQ Nuclear Committee. Karen earned a Bachelor of Science in Biomedical and Nuclear Engineering from the University of New Mexico and a Master of Science in Materials Science and Engineering from Stanford University.

Thomas (Tom) F. Ehrhorn

Tom Ehrhorn began his quality career by designing and implementing a software QA program for US Air Force B-52 and KC-135 simulators. After retiring from the Air Force and a short stint as a contractor, Tom returned to the quality profession as an on-site engineer for various simulators, where his responsibilities included overseeing the simulator contractors' quality programs. Tom then became a QA specialist providing quality services to one of the national labs. He did various software development and software quality jobs until he transitioned to a corporate QA department as a quality engineer. In this role, Tom was responsible for establishing an NQA-1 compliant software quality program and developing numerous procedures for that program. He also developed a software configuration management database, allowing the various divisions of the company to track their software and associated configuration items. As part of the QA department, Tom was also responsible for both internal and supplier audits. He has presented software QA papers at various conferences, beginning with a paper titled "Software Quality Assurance for Aircrew Training Devices," which he presented at the 1984 Interservice/Industry Training Equipment Conference in Washington, DC. Tom has since presented at various other industry conferences and at ASQ's World Conference on Quality and Improvement (WCQI). He holds ASQ Certified Quality Auditor and Certified Software Quality Engineer credentials. At the time of his retirement from AREVA, he was also a certified NQA-1 lead auditor. He has participated in ASQE's body of knowledge and test development workshops for both the software quality engineer and quality auditor certifications. Tom is a member of the Energy and Environment, Audit, and Software Divisions of ASQ. He served as a member of the Software Division leadership team as well as that of his section. He is a senior member of ASQ and has been a member for 25 years. He is currently treasurer of the Albuquerque section.

James Hill

James Hill is an information technology program manager with Xcel Energy. His nuclear career started as a hands-on machinist mate and radiation-chemistry specialist in the US Nuclear Navy Submarine Service. After his military service he worked in various individual and management functions in the commercial nuclear industry, including plant and corporate management roles in engineering, quality, performance improvement, and project management. His current focus is to support Xcel's nuclear fleet operation improvement through the use of innovative IT applications and infrastructure. He has an electrical engineering degree from the University of Illinois, an MBA from Cardinal Stritch University, is a licensed professional engineer in Minnesota and Wisconsin, and has held a senior reactor operator license, issued by the NRC. He is a senior member of the ASQ. James's ASQ certifications include Manager of Quality/Organizational Excellence and Quality Auditor. He is a certified project management professional, and is ITIL Foundation certified. He has served with the Midwest-based Performance Excellence Network as an evaluation team leader, judge, and chief judge in assessing applications from organizations that apply the Baldrige Performance Excellence program to improve their performance. He is also a certified master evaluator with the American Health Care Association National Quality Award Program, which uses the same Baldrige performance criteria. He has consulted and contracted with International Atomic Energy Association working groups for nuclear knowledge management guides and is currently participating in the Electric Power Research Institute's Plant Modernization effort, focused on identifying and using technology to lower operating costs for commercial nuclear plant operation.

Norman (Norm) P. Moreau

Norm Moreau is the CEO and chief instructor of Theseus Professional Services, where he has provided consulting services and implementation support, performed assessments, and trained on all nuclear QA-related subjects. He has worked directly for NRC and international licensees, DOE facilities and laboratories; and at all level within the nuclear industry supply chain. He began his QA journey in 1986 working as a quality engineer at the Fort St. Vrain Nuclear Generating Station in Colorado. He became an NQA-1 lead auditor in 1989. He expanded his auditing experience by becoming a lead auditor for a registrar for ISO 9001 ISO 14001, ISO 13485, and OHSAS 18001. In addition to being a practicing lead auditor, Norm has been training lead auditors since the mid-1990s. His NQA-1 Lead Auditor course has made it possible for many students to become successful lead auditors. He has taught students at all levels of the nuclear supply chain in the United States and abroad. Learners include regulators and utilities as well. In 2008 he started sharing his knowledge and experience with candidate lead auditors directly for the ASME Learning and Development organization. Norm has been an active participant of the ASME NQA-1 Standards Committee since 1992 to remain current with nuclear industry practices and to influence the content of this standard. He is also a member of the NQA Main Committee and a former co-vice chair and chair of the Executive Committee. In 2008 he was elected to lead the newly formed Subcommittee on Software Quality Assurance (SQA). He also has served as a vice-chair of engineering and procurement practices and as a member of the subcommittees on SQA, international activities, engineering and procurement process, and work practices. In 2021 he was awarded the NQA Outstanding Service Award. Norm holds a Bachelor of Science in Mechanical Engineering and a Master of Science Administration in Software Engineering Administration. He is a licensed professional engineer, ASME fellow and life member, ASQ senior member, and holds ASQ Certified Quality Auditor and Certified Software Quality Engineer credentials.

Charles (Chuck) H. Moseley Jr.

Chuck H. Moseley Jr. has over 45 years of progressively responsible technical and management experience in the nuclear industry and has worked extensively with DOE and in the commercial nuclear power sector. He is highly skilled in the development and review of safety programs, most notably in the areas of programmatic QA and operational QA and quality control. He has provided DOE headquarters assistance in developing QA orders and guidance documents, as well as NNSA programmatic initiatives for implementation across the complex. He is a nationally recognized expert in nuclear standards and has received the ANS Standards Award for lifetime achievement. He retired from Oak Ridge (Y12) as the quality programs manager and has provided assessments, surveys, training, and consulting services to DOE and the commercial industry. He assists utilities and suppliers evaluate and develop ASME NQA-1-compliant programs and performs due diligence of companies for DOE. He has a BS in Engineering from the United States Military Academy, an MS in Nuclear/Civil Engineering from Princeton University, an Executive

MBA from the University of North Carolina, Chapel Hill, and a Master's Certificate from the Southeastern Baptist Theological Seminary.

Stephen (Steve) Prevette

Steve Prevette is an advocate of Dr. Deming's management methods and applies statistical process control to performance metrics. He is an ASQ fellow and an ASQ certified quality engineer. Steve is an employee of Fluor Corporation's "Government Group" and supports nuclear sites in Ontario, Ohio, South Carolina, and Idaho with statistical performance analyses. This includes development and oversight of statistical process control-based contractor assurance and other performance metrics at Canadian Nuclear Laboratories and Savannah River National Laboratory. He has been active with ASQ since 1996. Steve is a past chair of Section 614 (Richland, WA) and has maintained ties with the section since moving to South Carolina in 2009, acting as its current webmaster. Steve started his career as a US Navy Nuclear Submarine Service officer. At the end of the Cold War, he left the Navy and was hired by Westinghouse Hanford as a tank farms maintenance supervisor. Steve was transferred to the desk job of running performance indicators in June 1993 and has fulfilled that function for various DOE contractors ever since. He taught evening courses at the former City University campus in Richland and developed courses as an adjunct instructor for Aiken Technical College's Nuclear Quality Assurance program. He currently teaches data analysis and software project courses for the Information Technology Department at Southern Illinois University at Carbondale.

Dr. Abhijit Sengupta

Dr. Abhijit Sengupta's areas of specialization include light water-pressurized and boiling-water reactors engineering inspections following both ASME Sections II (Materials), III (Construction), V (NDE), IX (Welding), and XI (In-Service Inspection), and 10 CFR 50, 52, and 50.55a. He has extensively used 10 CFR 50 Appendices A and B. Abhijit's experience extends across primary water stress corrosion cracking mitigation, flaw crack growth analysis in dissimilar metal welds in reactor pressure vessels, license renewals, heat exchangers, steam generators, and emergency nuclear plant response, among other areas. He has authored several engineering publications and was awarded ASQ's highest honor with two others in 2018, becoming an ASQ fellow. He is a certified Six Sigma Black Belt and holds ASQ Certified Quality Auditor, Reliability Engineer, and Quality Engineer credentials. Abhijit is also associated with ASME quality standard NQA-1, ASM, and ASQ committees. He currently serves as newsletter editor for ASQ's Energy & Environmental Division.

Disclaimer: This write-up is provided for information and educational purposes only, and the views expressed are those of Dr. Abhijit Sengupta and not necessarily those of the US Government.

ASQ'S
QUALITY RESOURCES

ASQ MEMBERS
MAKE A DIFFERENCE

Every day around the globe, quality professionals help to make the world a better place. Let ASQ membership make a professional difference for you.

Seeking new career resources?
Visit **careers.asq.org** for your next opportunity.

Want to raise your professional credibility?
Find your pathway to the right quality certification at **asq.org/cert**.

Need peer support?
Join the **myASQ.org** online community to seek solutions and celebrate your quality projects!

How can we help you make a difference?
Contact Customer Care:
help@asq.org
livechat on asq.org

ASQ
Excellence Through Quality®